Mathematics
for Key Stage Three

Hundreds of practice questions and worked examples
covering the Key Stage Three Maths curriculum.

Book Three

Contents

Ratio, Proportion and Rates of Change

Algebra

Section 12 — Graphs and Equations

Geometry and Measures

Section 13 — Angles and Shapes

Section 14 — Constructions

Section 15 — Perimeter, Area and Volume

Section 16 — Transformations

Section 17 — Geometric Relationships

Probability

Section 18 — Probability

Statistics

Section 19 — Statistics

Throughout the book, the more challenging questions are marked like this:

Editors:

Katherine Craig, Shaun Harrogate, Ceara Hayden, Sam Pilgrim, Sophie Scott, Caley Simpson,
Ben Train, Charlotte Whiteley, Dawn Wright

Contributors:

Mark Moody, Jan Walker

Reviewers:

Mona Allen, Alastair Duncombe

Proofreaders:

Rob Harrison, Simon Little and David Ryan

Published by CGP

ISBN: 978 1 78294 160 6

Clipart from Corel®

Printed by Elanders Ltd, Newcastle upon Tyne.

Based on the classic CGP style created by Richard Parsons.

Section 1 — Numbers and Arithmetic

1.1 Place Value and Ordering Decimals

Place Value in Decimals

Both <u>decimals</u> and <u>integers</u> can be split up into columns.
Decimals have columns after the <u>decimal point</u>, called <u>decimal places</u>.

Decimals are a way of showing parts of a whole number.

```
        tens                hundredths
hundreds  |  units            /        thousandths
   \      |   |   tenths     /        /
    7  2  0 . 1     3     6
     \         \    |           \
        decimal point
```

> **Example 1**   **What is the value of each of the digits in 0.732?**
>
> | | Words: | Decimals: | Fractions: |
> |---|---|---|---|
> | The 0 is in the units column. | Zero units | 0 | 0 |
> | The 7 is in the tenths column. | Seven tenths | 0.7 | $\frac{7}{10}$ |
> | The 3 is in the hundredths column. | Three hundredths | 0.03 | $\frac{3}{100}$ |
> | The 2 is in the thousandths column. | Two thousandths | 0.002 | $\frac{2}{1000}$ |

Exercise 1

1   Write the value of the digits in each of the following columns **in words**.

    i) hundreds column   **ii)** units column   **iii)** thousandths column

    a) 732.191   **b)** 896.382   **c)** 960.583   **d)** 200.317   **e)** 921.935

    f) 795.628   **g)** 263.372   **h)** 241.467   **i)** 193.719   **j)** 852.673

    k) 568.389   **l)** 324.061   **m)** 622.381   **n)** 821.556   **o)** 823.584

2   Write down the value of the underlined digit in each of these numbers as a **fraction**.

    a) 231.1<u>3</u>   **b)** 3.<u>4</u>22   **c)** 28.<u>2</u>7   **d)** 15.49<u>4</u>   **e)** 11.21<u>7</u>

    f) 2.0<u>9</u>1   **g)** 714.1<u>8</u>9   **h)** 4.<u>4</u>33   **i)** 521.<u>9</u>   **j)** 102.93<u>1</u>

    k) 50.1<u>7</u>   **l)** 1.2<u>1</u>8   **m)** 412.<u>4</u>54   **n)** 1.4<u>9</u>3   **o)** 5.77<u>5</u>

3 Write down the following values as decimal numbers.

a) two tenths   **b)** three hundredths   **c)** four thousands

d) twelve thousandths   **e)** ninety-two hundredths   **f)** seventy-one hundredths

4 Write down the following values as decimal numbers.

a) $\dfrac{7}{10}$ **b)** $\dfrac{3}{100}$ **c)** $\dfrac{8}{100}$ **d)** $\dfrac{1}{1000}$ **e)** $\dfrac{5}{10}$

f) $1\dfrac{3}{100}$ **g)** $7\dfrac{9}{10}$ **h)** $12\dfrac{1}{100}$ **i)** $7\dfrac{3}{1000}$ **j)** $19\dfrac{6}{10}$

5 A gram (g) is one thousandth of a kilogram (kg). Use this fact to write:

a) 3 g in kg   **b)** 12 g in kg   **c)** 135 g in kg   **d)** 520 g in kg

e) 1345 g in kg   **f)** 0.007 kg in g   **g)** 0.255 kg in g   **h)** 0.14 kg in g

i) 1.772 kg in g   **j)** 0.5 kg in g   **k)** 9218 g in kg   **l)** 1.27 kg in g

6 A centimetre (cm) is one hundredth of a metre (m).
A millimetre (mm) is one tenth of a centimetre.
Use these facts to write 1.635 m in millimetres.

Investigate — Different Number Systems

We use the decimal system, which has a base of 10. There are other number systems — for example the binary system, which uses a base of 2.

The binary number system uses a series of 0s and 1s to write different numbers.

	16	8	4	2	1
1					1
2				1	0
3				1	1
4			1	0	0
5			1	0	1

This table shows that:

3 is made up of one 2 and one 1: 2 + 1 = 3.
5 is made up of one 4 and one 1: 4 + 1 = 5.

a) Copy the table and add more rows to write larger numbers in binary form.
How high can you go?

b) Invent your own number system, using 0s and 1s, but using numbers other than 1, 2, 4, 8, 16, etc.
Use it to try to write out the numbers from 1 to 10.

Ordering Decimals

You can use the place value of digits to put decimals in
order of size — digits further to the left have a higher place value.

Example 2 — Sort the decimals 2.07, 2.1, 2.071 and 2.7
into size order, starting with the smallest.

1. Arrange the numbers in columns and fill in any gaps with 0s.

2. Compare the numbers in each column, one column at a time.
   Start with the very left-hand column and work right.

3. If the numbers in a column are the same, move on
   to the next column until you find a larger number.

4. Write the numbers out in the correct order.

```
2 . 0 7 0
2 . 1 0 0
2 . 0 7 1
2 . 7 0 0
```

2.07, 2.071, 2.1, 2.7

Example 3 — Sort the decimals −1.03, −1.3, −0.13 and −3.1
into size order, starting with the smallest.

1. Arrange the numbers in columns and fill in any gaps with 0s.

2. Compare the numbers in each column, one column at a time.
   Start with the very left-hand column and work right.

3. With negative numbers, the larger the digit,
   the lower the number is (i.e. −2 is less than −1).

4. Write the numbers out in the correct order.

```
− 1 . 0 3
− 1 . 3 0
− 0 . 1 3
− 3 . 1 0
```

−3.1, −1.3, −1.03, −0.13

Exercise 2

1 Write down the smaller amount from each of these pairs.

   a) 0.105 m, 0.15 m   **b)** 15.6 g, 15.07 g   **c)** 14.199 cm, 14.99 cm

   d) 11.21 kg, 11.201 kg   **e)** 0.98 ms, 0.975 ms   **f)** 9.774 ml, 9.78 ml

2 Sort these lists of numbers into size order, starting with the smallest.

   a) −7.04, −6.04, −7.14, −6.004, −7.19   **b)** −0.102, −0.149, −0.092, −0.028, −0.0961

   c) 0.901, 0.905, 0.912, 0.9, 0.9023   **d)** 1.276, 1.0276, 1.4726, 1.467, 1.4276

   e) 3.0009, 3.09, 3.001, 3.002, 3.9   **f)** −2.119, −2.089, −3.01, −3.119, −2.09

3 Sort these lists of decimals and fractions into size order, starting with the smallest.

a) $\dfrac{8}{10}$, 0.81, 0.018, $\dfrac{8}{1000}$, $\dfrac{1}{1000}$

b) 0.002, 0.2, 0.21, $\dfrac{21}{1000}$, $\dfrac{12}{1000}$

c) $\dfrac{9}{10}$, $\dfrac{999}{1000}$, 0.94, 0.098, $\dfrac{9}{100}$

d) −0.31, −0.003, −0.013, −$\dfrac{33}{1000}$, −$\dfrac{3}{10}$

e) −$\dfrac{243}{1000}$, −0.24, −0.21, −$\dfrac{2}{10}$, −0.022

f) $\dfrac{16}{100}$, $\dfrac{6}{10}$, 0.006, 0.61, $\dfrac{166}{1000}$

4 Copy out the number lines and label them with the decimals in each list.

a) ~~0.95,~~ 0.59, 0.09, 0.45, ~~0.9~~

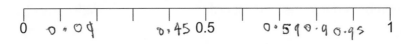

0   0·09   0·45 0.5   0·59 0·9 0·95   1

b) ~~−2.05~~, ~~−1.15~~, −1.51, ~~−1.25~~, ~~−1.02~~

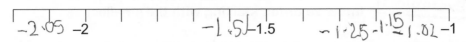

−2·05 −2   −1·5 −1.5   ~−1·25 −1·15 1·02 −1

c) 0.875, 0.125, 0.25, 0.6, 0.45

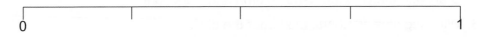

0   1

d) −1.035, −1.019, −1.0075, −1.0205, −1.015

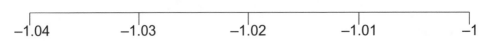

−1.04   −1.03   −1.02   −1.01   −1

5 Write down a decimal that is between:

a) 0.6 and 0.61   0·605

b) 0.784 and 0.785

c) 0.99 and 1

d) 0.08 and 0.081

e) 0.0049 and 0.005

f) −0.001 and −0.0011

g) −$\dfrac{8}{10}$ and −$\dfrac{9}{10}$ −$\dfrac{85}{100}$

h) $\dfrac{3}{100}$ and $\dfrac{3}{1000}$

i) $\dfrac{19}{100}$ and $\dfrac{2}{10}$

j) $\dfrac{81}{100}$ and $\dfrac{9}{10}$

k) −$\dfrac{9}{10}$ and −$\dfrac{99}{100}$

l) −$\dfrac{12}{100}$ and −$\dfrac{126}{1000}$

1.2 Multiplying and Dividing with Decimals

Multiplying and Dividing by 0.1, 0.01 and 0.001

When you <u>multiply</u> by a number less than one, it gets **smaller**.
When you <u>divide</u> by a number less than one, it gets **bigger**.

Multiplying by a tenth (0.1), a hundredth (0.01) or a thousandth (0.001) is exactly the same as **dividing** by 10, 100 or 1000.

Dividing by a tenth (0.1), a hundredth (0.01) or a thousandth (0.001) is exactly the same as **multiplying** by 10, 100 or 1000.

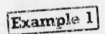

a) Divide 0.89 by 0.001.

1. Dividing by 0.001 is the same as multiplying by 1000.

2. To multiply by 1000, move each digit three places to the left, leaving the decimal point where it is.

3. Fill up the places to the left of the decimal point with zeros, and get rid of the zero at the start.

$$0.89 \div 0.001 = \mathbf{890}$$

b) Multiply 7.2 by 0.01.

1. Multiplying by 0.01 is the same as dividing by 100.

2. To divide by 100, move each digit two places to the right, leaving the decimal point where it is.

3. Fill in the gaps with zeros.

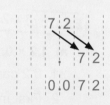

$$7.2 \times 0.01 = \mathbf{0.072}$$

Exercise 1

Don't use a calculator for this exercise.

1 Work out the answers to these multiplications.

    a) 18 × 0.1   **b)** 26 × 0.1   **c)** 23 × 0.1   **d)** 90 × 0.01

    e) 139 × 0.01   **f)** 732 × 0.01   **g)** 2217 × 0.001   **h)** 931 × 0.001

2 Work out the answers to these divisions.

    a) 14 ÷ 0.1   **b)** 12 ÷ 0.1   **c)** 164 ÷ 0.1   **d)** 48 ÷ 0.01

    e) 2011 ÷ 0.01   **f)** 921 ÷ 0.01   **g)** 191 ÷ 0.001   **h)** 47 ÷ 0.001

3 Answer these multiplication questions.

    a) 6.6 × 0.1   **b)** 28.55 × 0.1   **c)** 152.8 × 0.1   **d)** 21.02 × 0.01

    e) 3.381 × 0.01   **f)** 73.2 × 0.01   **g)** 56.21 × 0.001   **h)** 106.2 × 0.001

4 Work out the answers to these divisions.

    a) 220.2 ÷ 0.1   **b)** 16.3 ÷ 0.1   **c)** 10.02 ÷ 0.1   **d)** 1.829 ÷ 0.01

    e) 53.89 ÷ 0.01   **f)** 0.823 ÷ 0.01   **g)** 110.03 ÷ 0.001   **h)** 12.487 ÷ 0.001

5 Shaun buys 47 sweets costing £0.10 each. How much does Shaun spend altogether?

6 A paperclip weighs 0.001 kg. How much would 283 paperclips weigh?

7 Claire divides 7 litres of water between some cups. Each cup holds 0.1 litres of water. How many cups does Claire fill?

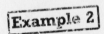

Example 2   **Work out:**

    a) 1.2 × 0.2.

      1. 0.2 can be split up into 2 × 0.1.

      2. First multiply 1.2 by 2.   1.2 × 2 = 2.4

      3. Then multiply your answer by 0.1 to get your final answer.
         Multiplying by 0.1 is the same as dividing by 10.   2.4 ÷ 10 = **0.24**

    b) 2.4 ÷ 0.03.

      1. 0.03 can be split up into 3 × 0.01.

      2. First divide 2.4 by 3.   2.4 ÷ 3 = 0.8

      3. Then divide your answer by 0.01 to get your final answer.
         Dividing by 0.01 is the same as multiplying by 100.   0.8 × 100 = **80**

8 Work out the answers to these multiplications.

a) 1.4 × 0.2 *0⸱28*
   2⸱8
b) 1.1 × 0.7
c) 2.5 × 0.6
d) 1.6 × 0.03

e) 2.2 × 0.04
f) 1.2 × 0.08
g) 1.8 × 0.005
h) 1.2 × 0.009

9 Work out the answers to these divisions.

a) 1.4 ÷ 0.2
b) 1.2 ÷ 0.3
c) 6.4 ÷ 0.8
d) 4.8 ÷ 0.06

e) 2.7 ÷ 0.09
f) 4.9 ÷ 0.07
g) 3.5 ÷ 0.005
h) 2.8 ÷ 0.007

10 A block of cheese weighs 0.8 kg. How much would 1.5 blocks of cheese weigh?

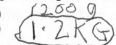
800 g   *800*   *1200 g*
+400   *(1·2 KG)*

11 A lab technician needs to split a 0.6 litre solution into 0.002 litre samples. How many samples will there be?

12 Work out the missing numbers in each of these calculations.

420
a) ..... ÷ 0.002 = 2100
b) ..... × 0.3 = 0.93
c) ..... ÷ 0.09 = 90

d) ..... ÷ 0.6 = 11
e) 0.03 × ..... = 0.051
f) 0.6 × ..... = 2.52

g) ..... ÷ 0.05 = 110
h) ..... ÷ 0.007 = 900
i) 0.8 × ..... = 0.96

13 Peter has 14.4 kg of chocolate bars. Each chocolate bar weighs 0.12 kg. How many chocolate bars does Peter have?

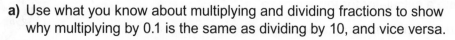

Investigate — Decimals as Fractions

0.1 can be written as $\frac{1}{10}$ (i.e. a tenth).

a) Use what you know about multiplying and dividing fractions to show why multiplying by 0.1 is the same as dividing by 10, and vice versa.

b) Do the same for 0.01 $\left(\frac{1}{100}\right)$ and 0.001 $\left(\frac{1}{1000}\right)$.

c) Does this work with other decimals?
   Investigate with decimals such as 0.2, 0.25 and 0.002.

d) Can you use your findings to find ways of multiplying and dividing by decimals less than 1 without using a calculator?

Written Multiplication

Example 3   Calculate **13.7 × 1.8.**

1. Ignore the decimal points and work out 137 × 18.
   Write one number above the other and make sure the
   columns line up. It's best to put the larger integer at the top.

   $$\begin{array}{r} 1\,3\,7 \\ \times\ \ 1\,8 \\ \hline \end{array}$$

2. Start by working out 137 × 8.
   Multiply each digit in 137 by 8, working from right to left.
   If the answer is 10 or more, carry the tens digit.

   E.g. 7 × 8 = 56, so write the 6 in the units column and
   carry the 5. Then 3 × 8 = 24, plus the carried 5 gives 29...

   $$\begin{array}{r} 1\,3\,7 \\ \times\ \ 1\,8 \\ \hline 1\,0\,{}_2 9\,{}_5 6 \end{array}$$

3. Work out 137 × 10 on the next row.
   You can do this by putting a 0 in the right hand column and
   multiplying each digit in 137 by 1.
   Work from right to left.

   $$\begin{array}{r} 1\,3\,7 \\ \times\ \ 1\,8 \\ \hline 1\,0\,{}_2 9\,{}_5 6 \\ 1\,3\,7\,0 \end{array}$$

4. Add the two rows together to get your answer.

   $$\begin{array}{r} 1\,3\,7 \\ \times\ \ 1\,8 \\ \hline 1\,0\,{}_2 9\,{}_5 6 \\ +\,1\,3\,7\,0 \\ \hline 2\,4\,{}_1 6\,6 \end{array}$$

5. Write the decimal point back in.
   The number of decimal places in the
   answer must be the same as the total
   number of decimal places in the question.

   13.7 × 1.8

   Two decimal places

   13.7 × 1.8 = **24.66**

Exercise 2

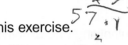

Don't use a calculator for this exercise.

1   Work out the answers to these questions:

   a) 7 × 8.3   **b)** 9.4 × 9   **c)** 2.2 × 2   **d)** 1.7 × 8

   e) 0.2 × 8   **f)** 3 × 3.5   **g)** 5.8 × 4   **h)** 9 × 9.5

   i) 3 × 7.9   **j)** 5 × 2.7   **k)** 8 × 7.2   **l)** 9.9 × 5

   m) 1.9 × 5   **n)** 4.2 × 9   **o)** 6 × 3.8   **p)** 2.7 × 9

2 Work out the answers to these multiplication questions.

a) 0.91 × 9   b) 3.21 × 8   c) 2 × 86.6   d) 14.3 × 6

e) 63.1 × 5   f) 4 × 3.21   g) 14.9 × 5   h) 7.94 × 8

i) 4.82 × 3   j) 8.72 × 9   k) 8 × 76.6   l) 94.9 × 9

3 Answer the following questions.

a) 1.2 × 31   b) 7.6 × 15   c) 5.5 × 24   d) 6.1 × 86

e) 1.5 × 74   f) 4.8 × 41   g) 21 × 3.2   h) 6.4 × 39

i) 7.5 × 33   j) 22 × 6.7   k) 9.2 × 77   l) 78 × 4.8

4 Answer the following questions.

a) 24.7 × 24   b) 83.2 × 20   c) 17.4 × 15   d) 29 × 24.1

e) 42.8 × 52   f) 15.6 × 42   g) 40.8 × 17   h) 15.2 × 48

i) 53 × 5.32   j) 66 × 2.73   k) 7.29 × 72   l) 8.28 × 35

5 Work out the answers the following questions.

a) 0.9 × 0.3   b) 0.8 × 0.6   c) 0.75 × 0.4   d) 0.6 × 0.23

e) 4.2 × 8.9   f) 2.8 × 1.4   g) 6.6 × 7.9   h) 1.9 × 9.1

i) 11.2 × 4.1   j) 2.52 × 5.2   k) 4.21 × 1.5   l) 2.5 × 1.52

m) 2.4 × 5.87   n) 1.2 × 5.28   o) 0.16 × 6.2   p) 2.63 × 1.3

6 Here are 8 numbers: 0.1   0.3   0.4   0.8   4   6   7   9
Fill in the gaps using these numbers to make the calculations correct.

a) ..... × ..... = 2.4   b) ..... × ..... = 0.9   c) ..... × ..... = 1.2   d) ..... × ..... = 5.6

7 It costs £3.99 for 1 kg of cheese.
To the nearest pence, work out how much it will cost to buy cheese that weighs:

a) 1.21 kg   b) 9.72 kg   c) 12.83 kg   d) 16.01 kg

e) 8.07 kg   f) 0.08 kg   g) 60.01 kg   h) 28.91 kg

Written Division

Example 4 **Work out 95.62 ÷ 7 without a calculator.**

1. Set out the division as usual. Include the decimal point in both the question and the answer.

$$7\overline{)9\ 5.6\ 2}$$

2. Carry the division out exactly like you would with a whole number, using either short or long division.

$$7\overline{)9\ ^25.6\ 2}\quad \begin{array}{r} 1\ \ .\end{array}$$

$$7\overline{)9\ ^25.\!^46\ 2}\quad \begin{array}{r} 1\ 3.\end{array}$$

$$7\overline{)9\ ^25.\!^46\ ^42}\quad \begin{array}{r} 1\ 3.6\end{array}$$

$$7\overline{)9\ ^25.\!^46\ ^42}\quad \begin{array}{r} \mathbf{1\ 3.6\ 6}\end{array}$$

Example 5 **Work out 5.78 ÷ 1.7 without a calculator.**

1. If you have to divide by a decimal, you can make the calculation simpler by multiplying **both** numbers by 10. This makes the number you're dividing by an integer.

$$5.78 \times 10 = 57.8$$
$$1.7 \times 10 = 17$$

2. Set out the division as usual. Include the decimal point in both the question and the answer.

$$17\overline{)5\ 7\!^1\!8}\quad \begin{array}{r} ^03\ .4\end{array}$$

3. Carry the division out exactly like you would with a whole number, using either short or long division.

$$\begin{array}{r} 0\ \mathbf{3.4} \\ 17\overline{)5\ 7.8} \\ \underline{5\ 1}\ \downarrow \\ 6\ 8 \\ \underline{6\ 8} \\ 0 \end{array}$$

Exercise 3

Don't use a calculator for this exercise.

1 Complete the following divisions.

    a) 7.8 ÷ 6   **b)** 22.4 ÷ 7   **c)** 44.8 ÷ 7   **d)** 74.7 ÷ 9

    e) 97.5 ÷ 5   **f)** 76.8 ÷ 8   **g)** 60.8 ÷ 4   **h)** 44.8 ÷ 8

2 Work out the answers to the following divisions.

    a) 72.16 ÷ 8   **b)** 28.08 ÷ 9   **c)** 39.45 ÷ 5   **d)** 85.32 ÷ 6

    e) 79.31 ÷ 7   **f)** 97.28 ÷ 4   **g)** 96.16 ÷ 8   **h)** 77.44 ÷ 4

3 Work out the answers to the following divisions.

    a) 39.9 ÷ 1.9   **b)** 80.3 ÷ 1.1   **c)** 88.4 ÷ 2.6   **d)** 72.6 ÷ 3.3

    e) 67.2 ÷ 4.2   **f)** 49.4 ÷ 2.6   **g)** 79.2 ÷ 6.6   **h)** 57.6 ÷ 1.8

4 Work out the answers to the following divisions.

    a) 5.76 ÷ 1.8   **b)** 5.85 ÷ 4.5   **c)** 4.62 ÷ 2.2   **d)** 8.28 ÷ 3.6

    e) 2.47 ÷ 1.3   **f)** 4.35 ÷ 1.5   **g)** 9.92 ÷ 3.1   **h)** 7.56 ÷ 2.1

5 Work out the answers to the following divisions.

    a) 0.544 ÷ 0.16   **b)** 0.396 ÷ 0.22   **c)** 0.912 ÷ 0.12   **d)** 0.451 ÷ 0.11

    e) 0.504 ÷ 0.36   **f)** 0.819 ÷ 0.21   **g)** 0.598 ÷ 0.26   **h)** 0.572 ÷ 0.13

6 Janet makes 6 cakes using 4.8 kg of cake mixture.
If each cake weighs the same amount, how much does one cake weigh?

7 Pick-and-mix costs £2.40 for 300 g.
How much pick-and-mix can you buy for £1?

8 Work out the answers to the following divisions.

    a) 41.86 ÷ 4.6   **b)** 20.25 ÷ 2.5   **c)** 14.31 ÷ 2.7   **d)** 60.68 ÷ 8.2

    e) 31.11 ÷ 5.1   **f)** 24.14 ÷ 3.4   **g)** 52.64 ÷ 5.6   **h)** 67.68 ÷ 7.2

9 It costs £14.40 to buy 4.5 m² of fabric. How much does it cost per m²?

10 Frank takes 8.7 seconds to run 62.64 metres.
What is his average speed in metres per second?

11 It costs £1.35 for a ticket to ride on a merry-go-round.
In one afternoon, the merry-go-round sells £91.80 worth of tickets.
How many tickets is this?

1.3 Calculations with Negative Numbers

Adding and Subtracting Negative Numbers

Adding a <u>negative</u> number is the same as subtracting a <u>positive</u> number.

Subtracting a negative number is the same as adding a positive number.

Look at the signs next to each other in a calculation to work out what you need to do:

+ next to –	means subtract
– next to –	means add

Example 1 **Work out the answers to the following calculations.**

a) 7 + (–4)

1. There is a + and a – sign next to each other.   7 + (–4)
2. So replace them with one – sign.   7 – 4
3. Work out the answer.   7 – 4 = **3**

b) 2 – (–7)

1. There are two – signs next to each other.   2 – (–7)
2. So replace them with one + sign.   2 + 7
3. Work out the answer.   2 + 7 = **9**

Exercise 1

Don't use a calculator for this exercise.

1 Work out the answers to the following questions.

a) –17 + 11   b) –43 + 24   c) –72 + 14   d) 16 – 20

e) 49 – 56   f) –11 – 9   g) –16 – 11   h) –25 – 12

2 Answer these questions.

a) 13 – (–7)   b) (–11) – (–49)   c) 63 + (–15)   d) 38 + (–19)

e) (–22) + (–43)   f) (–89) – (–17)   g) (–40) + (–27)   h) 15 – (–83)

3 Work out the answers to the following questions.

a) (–19) – (–12) + (–5)   b) (–8) – (–35) – (–54)   c) 45 + (–23) – (–11)

d) 54 – (–12) + (–39)   e) (–52) + (–33) – (–80)   f) (–11) + (–71) + (–14)

4 Fill in the missing numbers in the following calculations.

a) $(-11) - \ldots = -4$

b) $\ldots + (-9) = -7$

c) $(-11) - \ldots = -24$

d) $\ldots + (-12) = -31$

e) $\ldots + (-22) = -14$

f) $\ldots - (-15) = 7$

g) $22 + \ldots - (-6) = -5$

h) $14 - (-6) + \ldots = 6$

i) $\ldots + (-11) - (-12) = -4$

Investigate — Infinity and Beyond

The set of integers (whole numbers) is infinite — it goes on forever in both directions, positive and negative. Infinity is shown by this symbol:

∞ = positive infinity $-\infty$ = negative infinity

a) An infinite set is a set of numbers that can carry on infinitely. Compare the integers with the corresponding multiples of 10. (i.e. compare 1, 2, 3, ... with 10, 20, 30, ...) Do you think both of these sets will carry on to infinity? Will both sets be the same size?

b) How about the infinite set of decimals? Will this infinite set be the same size as the set of integers? Investigate — use the internet to help you.

Multiplying and Dividing Negative Numbers

A <u>multiplication</u> or <u>division</u> with one <u>positive</u> and one <u>negative</u> number will have a negative (–ve) answer.

If both numbers are negative, the answer will be positive (+ve).

+ and – means a negative answer	– and – means a positive answer

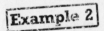 **Example 2** Work out the answers to the following calculations.

a) $4 \times (-6)$

1. Ignore the signs and work out the answer to the number bit.

$4 \times 6 = 24$

2. Work out the sign. A positive and a negative number give a negative answer.

$4 \times (-6) = -24$

b) $(-49) \div (-7)$

1. Ignore the signs and work out the answer to the number bit.

$49 \div 7 = 7$

2. Work out the sign. Two negative numbers give a positive answer.

$(-49) \div (-7) = 7$

Exercise 2

Don't use a calculator for this exercise.

1 Answer these questions.

    a) $10 \times (-4)$ **b)** $(-8) \times (-7)$ **c)** $(-11) \times 7$ **d)** $(-10) \times (-14)$

    e) $(-22) \times 3$ **f)** $(-11) \times 14$ **g)** $88 \times (-4)$ **h)** $32 \times (-4)$

2 Answer these questions.

    a) $(-54) \div (-9)$ **b)** $(-72) \div (-8)$ **c)** $(-50) \div 2$ **d)** $48 \div (-8)$

    e) $333 \div (-3)$ **f)** $(-112) \div (-7)$ **g)** $(-98) \div 14$ **h)** $110 \div (-11)$

3 Answer these questions.

    a) $(-108) \div 6$ **b)** $(-99) \div (-11)$ **c)** $(-100) \times (-5)$ **d)** $(-17) \times (-8)$

    e) $84 \div (-4)$ **f)** $(-13) \times (-10)$ **g)** $(-98) \div 7$ **h)** $24 \times (-6)$

    i) $13 \times (-11)$ **j)** $(-108) \div 9$ **k)** $(-35) \times 3$ **l)** $12 \times (-15)$

4 For each of these calculations, replace the star with the correct number.

    a) $12 \times \bigstar = -12$ **b)** $\bigstar \times 11 = -99$ **c)** $(-15) \times (-8) = \bigstar$

    d) $(-14) \times \bigstar = -56$ **e)** $(-9) \times \bigstar = 81$ **f)** $\bigstar \times (-40) = -2800$

    g) $(-6) \times \bigstar = -114$ **h)** $6 \times \bigstar = -120$ **i)** $(-28) \times \bigstar = 308$

5 For each of these calculations, replace the star with the correct number.

    a) $\bigstar \div 6 = -6$ **b)** $\bigstar \div (-7) = 11$ **c)** $(-40) \div (-5) = \bigstar$

    d) $(-90) \div \bigstar = 3$ **e)** $(-65) \div \bigstar = -5$ **f)** $\bigstar \div 14 = -2$

    g) $\bigstar \div (-6) = 12$ **h)** $(-99) \div \bigstar = 3$ **i)** $(-108) \div \bigstar = -54$

6 Answer these questions.

    a) $9 \times (-8) \div 2$ **b)** $(-11) \times (-8) \div 4$

    c) $(-8) \times 9 \div (-3)$ **d)** $(-144) \div (-12) \times (-7)$

    e) $81 \div (-3) \times (-7)$ **f)** $96 \div (-6) \times 5$

    g) $11 \times (-12) \div (-2)$ **h)** $(-10) \times (-9) \div (-3)$

1.4 Calculators, BODMAS and Checking

BODMAS and Calculations

Operations in a calculation are things like addition, subtraction, multiplication and division. The order you do these things in is really important.

BODMAS tells you the order you should do things in a calculation:

BRACKETS ←——————————— Work out things in **brackets** first.

OTHER ←——————————— Then do other things like **powers** and **roots**.

DIVISION
MULTIPLICATION ←——————————— **Divide/Multiply** groups of numbers working from left to right.

ADDITION
SUBTRACTION ←——————————— **Add/Subtract** groups of numbers working from left to right.

To find the reciprocal of a number, you need to find 1 divided by that number.
To find the reciprocal of a calculation, make sure you put the calculation in brackets first, then divide 1 by the entire calculation.

For example, the reciprocal of $2^2 - 1$ would be $1 \div (2^2 - 1)$.

For calculations expressed as fractions, work out the top line and the bottom line separately (by putting each line in brackets) before doing the calculation.

Example 1 | **Find the reciprocal of $6 + 2^2 \times 9 - 32$.**

1. To find the reciprocal, put the calculation in brackets first, then divide 1 by the brackets.

$1 \div (6 + 2^2 \times 9 - 32)$

2. BODMAS tells us that the calculation in brackets needs to be done first. Then inside the brackets, the **power** comes first.

$2^2 = 4$
$1 \div (6 + 4 \times 9 - 32)$

3. The **multiplication** needs to be done next.

$4 \times 9 = 36$
$1 \div (6 + 36 - 32)$

4. Working from left to right, the **addition** needs to be done next, followed by the **subtraction**.

$6 + 36 = 42$
$42 - 32 = 10$

5. Finally, do the division to find the reciprocal.

$1 \div 10 = 0.1$

Example 2 Work out $\dfrac{12 \times 4 - 3}{25 \div 5}$ using your calculator.

1. You need to divide the top line by the bottom line. $12 \times 4 - 3 \div 25 \div 5$

2. The top line needs to be worked out separately from the bottom line, so you'll need to put brackets around each part. $(12 \times 4 - 3) \div (25 \div 5)$
   $= 9$

Exercise 1

1 Use BODMAS to answer these questions without a calculator.

(handwritten: $9 1$, $\times 3$, 27^3)

   a) $40 - 11 \times 2$

   b) $12 + 16 \div 4$

   c) $(44 + 12) \div (23 - 15)$

   d) $(30 + 34) \div (21 - 19)^4$

   e) $24 + 11 - 2^4 + 8$

   f) $62 + 8 + \sqrt{25} - 17$

   g) 4×9^2

   h) $10^2 \div 5$

   i) $(5 + 6)^2$

   j) $(30 - 24)^3$

   k) $(8 + 2 \times 4)^2$

   l) $(12 - 9)^4 + 11^2$

(handwritten: $3^4 + 11^2$ 38^7 $273 + 121$)

2 Write each fraction as a division with brackets as you would enter them on a calculator. Then, use your calculator to work out the answer.

   a) $\dfrac{12 + 13}{7 - 2}$

   b) $\dfrac{2 \times 8 + 2}{3 \times 3}$

   c) $\dfrac{12 \times 11 - 2}{76 - 66}$

   d) $\dfrac{17 - 3 + 22}{3 \times 2}$

   e) $\dfrac{5 \times 3 + 17}{16 \div 2}$

   f) $\dfrac{8 \times 2 + 64}{43 - 38}$

   g) $\dfrac{51 + 9 + 100}{88 \div 11}$

   h) $\dfrac{11 \times 2 \times 5}{27 - 16}$

3 Add one pair of brackets to each of these calculations to make them correct.

   a) $1 + 6 \times 2 \times 8 = 112$

   b) $18 \div 2 \times 7 + 3^2 = 144$

   c) $160 - 2^3 + 3 \times 12 = 28$

   d) $8 \times 5^2 + 20 - 6 = 354$

   e) $11 + 14 \div \sqrt{25} \times 2 = 10$

   f) $2 \times \sqrt[3]{216} \times 9 - 3 = 72$

4 Write these calculations out as a division with brackets. Then, work out the answer by entering this into your calculator.

   a) $\dfrac{18 + (7 \times 2)}{56 \div (3 + 4)}$

   b) $\dfrac{(12 + 12) \times 2^2}{(8 \times 6) \div 24}$

   c) $\dfrac{36 \div (13 - 4)}{10 - (18 \div 3)}$

   d) $\dfrac{\sqrt[3]{512} \times (11 + 1)}{(6 \times 9) \div 18}$

   e) $\dfrac{(5 + 7) \times 10}{(9 + 1) \times 2}$

   f) $\dfrac{(3^3 + 15) \div 7}{(6 \times 5) \div 15}$

5 Calculate the reciprocals of these calculations.

a) $26 - \sqrt{484}$

b) $(29 + 3^3) - \sqrt{1296}$

c) $(3^4 \div 9) + (6^2 - \sqrt[3]{125})$

d) $(30 + 2) \div (21 - 19)^4$

e) $(24 + \sqrt{121}) + (2^6 + 1)$

f) $(2^6 + 8) \div 3^2$

g) $(12 - 8)^4 - (47 + 3^2)$

h) $16^2 \div (2^2 + 2^3 + 2^2)$

i) $(5 + 6)^2 - (50 - 3^2)$

6 Calculate the reciprocals of the following calculations.

a) $\dfrac{7 + (9 \times 3^3)}{50 \div 10}$

b) $\dfrac{\sqrt{576} \times 3}{6^2}$

c) $\dfrac{6^2 \div 3^2}{22 - (2^5 - 12)}$

d) $\dfrac{\sqrt[3]{64} \times (20 + 15)}{(9^2 + 3) \div 12}$

e) $\dfrac{(5 + 3^3) \times 10^2}{(5^2 + 5^2) \div 5}$

f) $\dfrac{\sqrt[4]{625} + 95}{(4^4 + 119) \div 15}$

Checking Answers using Inverses

One way to check your answers is to do the <u>inverse</u> calculation.
The inverse is just another word for opposite.

Addition and **subtraction** are opposites.

Multiplying and **dividing** are opposites.

Powers and **roots** are opposites.

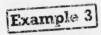 **What inverse calculation could you do to check that $14^3 = 2744$?**

1. First identify what sort of calculation the question is.
   This calculation contains a **power**.

   $14^{\circled{3}} = 2744$

2. **Roots** are the opposite of **powers**.
   Taking the cube root is the opposite of cubing
   something. If you take the cube root of your answer,
   you should get the number you started with.

   $\sqrt[3]{2744} = 14$

Exercise 2

1 Write an inverse calculation to check the following.

a) $56 + 88 = 144$

b) $14 + 77 = 91$

c) $97 - 61 = 36$

d) $66 - 13 = 53$

e) $119 - 54 = 65$

f) $24 + 94 = 118$

2 Write an inverse calculation for each of the following.

a) $3 \times 55 = 165$ b) $180 \div 5 = 36$ c) $19 \times 11 = 209$

d) $12 \times 43 = 516$ e) $252 \div 18 = 14$ f) $612 \div 12 = 51$

3 Write an inverse calculation for each of the following.

a) $12^2 = 144$ b) $15^3 = 3375$ c) $4^4 = 256$

d) $\sqrt[4]{1296} = 6$ e) $\sqrt{289} = 17$ f) $3^5 = 243$

g) $\sqrt[3]{729} = 9$ h) $2^8 = 256$ i) $4^6 = 4096$

4 Use an inverse calculation to check these calculations.
Put a tick by the ones that are correct, and a cross by the ones that are incorrect.

a) $167 + 774 = 930$ b) $528 \div 22 = 24$ c) $32 \times 31 = 992$

d) $22^2 = 484$ e) $982 - 555 = 427$ f) $663 \div 17 = 39$

g) $\sqrt[3]{2744} = 15$ h) $19 \times 46 = 874$ i) $7^4 = 2401$

j) $8^5 = 32\ 796$ k) $\sqrt[7]{16\ 384} = 4$ l) $537 - 493 = 45$

m) $56 \times 31 = 1730$ n) $18^3 = 5832$ o) $\sqrt[3]{9261} = 21$

Investigate — Inverse Functions

Look at this function machine:

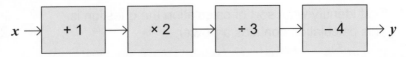

$$x \rightarrow \boxed{+1} \rightarrow \boxed{\times 2} \rightarrow \boxed{\div 3} \rightarrow \boxed{-4} \rightarrow y$$

a) Write these instructions out as a mathematical formula to find y in terms of x. Make sure it follows the rules of BODMAS by putting brackets where necessary.

b) Now draw an inverse function machine that would allow you to go backwards from y to find x.

c) Use your answer to **b)** to write an 'inverse' formula to the one you made in part **a)**. Can you see how to get from one to the other without the function machines?

d) Try this out with some different instructions of your own. Does your method always work?

Section 2 — Approximations

2.1 Rounding

Decimal Places

Numbers are sometimes <u>approximated</u> or <u>rounded</u> to make them easier to work with.

You can round to different numbers of <u>decimal places</u> (d.p.).

For example, a number like 4.728 could be rounded: to one decimal place (= 4.7)

to two decimal places (= 4.73)

Example 1   Round 6.8352 to...

a) ... two decimal places.

1. Look at the digit in the third decimal place.

2. It's 5, so round up.

a) 6.8352
round up to **6.84**

b) ... three decimal places.

1. Look at the digit in the fourth decimal place.

2. It's less than 5, so round down.

b) 6.8352
round down to **6.835**

Exercise 1

1   Round each of these numbers to one decimal place.

    a) 3.42   **b)** 6.83   **c)** 8.91   **d)** 0.62   **e)** 0.08

    f) 0.078   **g)** 12.38   **h)** 2.869   **i)** 14.217   **j)** 0.99

2   Write down all the numbers from the box that round to 2.8 to the nearest tenth.

| 2.87 | 2.83 | 2.91 | 2.78 | 2.75 | 2.765 | 2.699 | 2.827 | 2.748 | 2.772 |

3   Write down four numbers that round to 9.3 to one decimal place.

4   Round the following numbers to 2 decimal places.

    a) 4.628   **b)** 9.292   **c)** 0.247   **d)** 0.006

    e) 1.065   **f)** 2.0345   **g)** 0.9949   **h)** 7.999

5 Write down all the numbers from the box that round to 1.38 to the nearest hundredth.

1.369	1.378	1.384	1.338	1.388
1.395	1.3658	1.3862	1.3821	1.3846

6 Round the following numbers to 3 decimal places.

a) 7.2184 b) 5.0436 c) 8.5045 d) 0.0465

e) 2.7005 f) 7.980621 g) 1.0098 h) 3.999898

7 Round the following numbers to the number of decimal places specified.

a) 2.818 — to 1 d.p. b) 11.92945 — to 3 d.p. c) 0.6023 — to 2 d.p.

d) 27.6254 — to 2 d.p. e) 0.04078 — to 3 d.p. f) 29.994 — to 1 d.p.

8 Tom is 1.682 m tall. Round his height to two decimal places.

9 The mass of a walrus is 1.458 tonnes.
Round this mass to one decimal place.

10 The nearest recycling centre is 2.9998 km from Rob's house.
Round this distance to three decimal places.

11 A number, when rounded to one decimal place, equals 2.4.
What is the smallest possible value of this number?

> ### Investigate — Importance of Zeroes
>
> In an experiment, a scientist makes some very precise
> measurements and needs to round them to 3 decimal places.
> She rounds a measurement of 0.1001999 mm to 0.1 mm.
>
> a) Has she made a mistake? Is 0.1 the same as 0.100?
>
> b) Why might the zeroes be important? (*Hint — think about the
> different ranges of possible values for the two rounded numbers.*)

Significant Figures

You can also round to different numbers of <u>significant figures</u> (s.f.).

For example, 126 409 could be rounded: to one significant figure (= 100 000)

to two significant figures (= 130 000)

to three significant figures (= 126 000)

Zeros at the start of a decimal do not count as significant figures.
The first significant figure is the first non-zero digit — so 0.00152 to 1 s.f. is 0.002.

Example 2   Round 40.621 to...

a) ... **one significant figure.**
  1. Look at the second digit.
  2. It's less than 5, so round down.

a) 40.621
    round down to **40**

b) ... **two significant figures.**
  1. Look at the third digit.
  2. It's greater than 5, so round up.

b) 40.621
    round up to **41**

c) ... **three significant figures.**
  1. Look at the fourth digit.
  2. It's less than 5, so round down.

c) 40.621
    round down to **40.6**

Exercise 2

1 Round the following numbers to one significant figure.

a) 523	**b)** 27	**c)** 345	**d)** 0.684
e) 32	**f)** 1024	**g)** 0.00257	**h)** 9399
i) 11 459	**j)** 2.077	**k)** 156 092	**l)** 330 763

2 Round the following numbers to two significant figures.

a) 568	**b)** 932	**c)** 0.0629	**d)** 6566
e) 3478	**f)** 0.2984	**g)** 25 693	**h)** 12 371
i) 78 452	**j)** 130.89	**k)** 5.672	**l)** 0.002059

3 Round the following numbers to three significant figures.

   a) 9281   **b)** 3736   **c)** 123.59   **d)** 13.892

   e) 0.005078   **f)** 75 614   **g)** 67 839   **h)** 0.03896

   i) 176 378   **j)** 576 514   **k)** 738.094   **l)** 2.0076

4 Round the following numbers to the number of significant figures (s.f.) indicated.

   a) 0.0829 — to 1 s.f.   **b)** 37.62 — to 2 s.f.   **c)** 85.729 — to 3 s.f.

   d) 4782 — to 2 s.f.   **e)** 3929 — to 1 s.f.   **f)** 274.65 — to 3 s.f.

   g) 0.007976 — to 2 s.f.   **h)** 438 967 — to 3 s.f.   **i)** 96 849 — to 1 s.f.

5 A racing snail has a top speed of 28 mm/s.
Round this speed to one significant figure.

6 In one year, 164 578 people visited a theme park.
Round this number to two significant figures.

7 The mass of a rock is 22.784 kg. Round this mass to three significant figures.

8 The area of a pond is 0.0004999 km². Round this area to two significant figures.

9 The number of people at a concert has been rounded to 20 000.
What are the smallest and largest numbers of people if this has been rounded to:

   a) 1 significant figure?

   b) 2 significant figures?

   c) 3 significant figures?

10 Round each of these measurements to an appropriate degree of accuracy.

   a) A population of 56 897   **b)** A race time of 13.24582 seconds

   c) A height of 2.8067 m   **d)** A mass of 0.142832 kg

2.2 Estimating

Estimating Answers by Rounding

You can <u>estimate</u> the answer to a calculation by <u>rounding</u> numbers in the calculation to numbers that are easier to use — usually by rounding to one <u>significant figure</u>.

Even though the answer isn't exactly right, it can still be useful.

> **Example 1** Estimate the value of $\dfrac{9.8 \times 43}{0.987 \times 19.7}$ by rounding each number to one significant figure.
>
> 1. Round each number in the calculation to one significant figure.
>
>   To 1 s.f. 9.8 rounds to 10, 43 rounds to 40, 0.987 rounds to 1 and 19.7 rounds to 20.
>
> 2. Rewrite the calculation using the rounded numbers (≈ means 'approximately equal to').
>
> $\dfrac{9.8 \times 43}{0.987 \times 19.7} \approx \dfrac{10 \times 40}{1 \times 20}$
>
> 3. Work out the answer.
>
> $= \dfrac{400}{20} = \mathbf{20}$

Exercise 1

1 Use rounding to estimate the answer to each of these calculations.

    a) 44 × 2.8   **b)** 19 × 7.2   **c)** 97 × 3.6

    d) 78 ÷ 3.9   **e)** 62 ÷ 3.2   **f)** 89.2 ÷ 8.8

2 Use rounding to estimate the answer to each of these calculations.

    a) 756 ÷ (19.2 + 23.8)   **b)** (1826 ÷ 537) × 18

    c) 52 × (198 ÷ 97)   **d)** (4276 ÷ 38.9) − (3.2 × 13)

3 By rounding each number to one significant figure, estimate the answer to each of these calculations.

    a) $\dfrac{11.2 \times 29}{4.9 \times 6.1}$ **b)** $\dfrac{21.3 \times 3.8}{5.1 \times 1.8}$

    c) $\dfrac{9.9 \times 52}{4.8 \times 5.2}$ **d)** $\dfrac{19.8 \times 5.1}{1.1 \times 21.2}$

4 By rounding each number to one significant figure, estimate the answer to each of these calculations.

a) $\dfrac{39.8 \times 4.9}{0.989 \times 20.8}$

b) $\dfrac{0.995 \times 49.6}{1.95 \times 5.01}$

c) $\dfrac{31.2 \times 0.95}{10.98 \div 1.96}$

d) $\dfrac{97.86 \div 5.06}{51.1 \div 9.89}$

5 Abigail says "I worked out 313.6 ÷ 32 and got the answer 98".

a) By rounding to one significant figure, estimate 313.6 ÷ 32.

b) Use your answer to part **a)** to decide whether Abigail is correct.
Explain your answer.

6 Luna has done the calculation 14.2 × 27.9 on her calculator. She got the answer 3961.8.
Her friend Milo has done the same calculation and got the answer 396.18.

a) By rounding to one significant figure, estimate 14.2 × 27.9.

b) Use your answer to part **a)** to decide who was correct, Luna or Milo.
Explain your answer.

7 Use rounding to choose the correct answer (A, B or C) to the following calculations.

a) 2.72 × 18.68	A: 50.8096	B: 25.7862	C: 108.96
b) 48.5 × 23.1	A: 146.15	B: 530.35	C: 1120.35
c) 577.1 ÷ 29	A: 19.9	B: 12.2	C: 32.1
d) 2272.86 ÷ 36.6	A: 621.12	B: 62.1	C: 6.21
e) (12.7 + 23.6) × 3.1	A: 942.42	B: 350.04	C: 112.53

8 The decimal points have been missed out from the answer to each of these calculations.
Use rounding to find an approximate answer in each case, and then decide where the decimal point should be.

a) 11.8 × 52.3 = 61714

b) 2062.72 ÷ 58.6 = 352

c) 92.7 × 1.8 = 16686

d) 38.08 ÷ 28 = 136

e) (22.6 + 76.3) × 18.2 = 179998

f) (433.84 ÷ 13.6) + 271 = 3029

Rounding Errors

The rounding error is the difference between the rounded number and the actual number.

Rounding error = rounded value – actual value

The maximum rounding error is half the rounding unit. So if you were rounding to the nearest 10, the maximum rounding error would be 5 and if you were rounding to the nearest whole number, the maximum rounding error would be 0.5.

You can use inequalities to show the maximum and minimum values of a rounded number.

For example, if a number x has been rounded to 70 to the nearest 10, the possible values of x would be anything from 65 up to (but not including) 75.

Using inequality notation, this is written as $65 \le x < 75$.

Example 2   A length x has been measured as 2.6 m to 1 d.p.

a) What is the maximum possible rounding error?

1. The measurement has been rounded to 1 d.p. so the rounding unit is 0.1.

    Rounding unit = 0.1

2. Divide this value by 2 to find the maximum possible rounding error.

    $0.1 \div 2 = \textbf{0.05 m}$

b) Show the range of the possible values of x using inequality notation.

1. To find the minimum and maximum values of x, add and subtract half the rounding unit to and from the rounded measurement.

    $2.6 + 0.05 = 2.65$
    $2.6 - 0.05 = 2.55$

2. Write this using inequalities.

    $\textbf{2.55} \le x < \textbf{2.65}$

Exercise 2

1   Find the maximum possible rounding error when a number is rounded to:

   a) the nearest 100   **b)** the nearest 10   **c)** the nearest whole number

   d) the nearest 1000   **e)** one decimal place   **f)** two decimal places

2   Find the rounding error for each of the following numbers after they have been rounded to the nearest 10.

   a) 65   **b)** 12   **c)** 74

   d) 27   **e)** 189   **f)** 199

3 Find the rounding errors when the following numbers are rounded as specified.

a) 44 (rounded to the nearest 10) **b)** 11.8 (rounded to the nearest whole number)

c) 6.46 (rounded to 1 d.p.) **d)** 314 (rounded to the nearest 100)

e) 275.258 (rounded to 2 d.p.) **f)** 12 485 (rounded to the nearest 1000)

4 Show the range of possible values for each of the following.
Give your answer using inequality notation.

a) u = 25 000 when rounded to the nearest 1000

b) v = 130 when rounded to the nearest 10

c) w = 1800 when rounded to the nearest 100

d) x = 224 when rounded to the nearest whole number

e) y = 8.0 when rounded to 1 d.p.

f) z = 14.84 when rounded to 2 d.p.

5 x = 1000. Using inequality notation, show the range of possible values of x when it has been rounded to:

a) the nearest 1000 **b)** the nearest 100

c) the nearest 10 **d)** the nearest whole number

6 When rounded to one significant figure, n = 30 000.
Show the range of possible values of n using inequality notation.

> ### Investigate — Rounding Errors
>
> A decorator is ordering flooring and skirting boards for a rectangular room. He has measured the room and found the length to be 10 m and the width to be 7 m, both rounded to the nearest whole number.
>
> **a)** Do you think this is a sensible way to round the measurements? What would you choose to round to?
>
> **b)** What are the maximum and minimum possible values for the length, width, perimeter and area of the room?
>
> **c)** What else would you need to think about or measure when knowing how much flooring and skirting board to order?

Section 3 — Powers

3.1 Power Laws

Multiplying and Dividing

Use these power laws to multiply and divide <u>powers</u> with the same <u>base</u>.

- To multiply two powers with the same base, add the powers: $a^m \times a^n = a^{m+n}$

- To divide two powers with the same base, subtract the powers: $a^m \div a^n = a^{m-n}$

- To raise one power to another power, multiply the powers: $(a^m)^n = a^{m \times n}$

There are two other important power facts you need to know.

- Anything to the power 1 is itself: $a^1 = a$

- Anything to the power 0 is 1: $a^0 = 1$

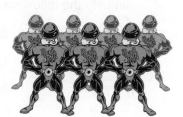

| **Example 1** | **Simplify the following.**
 Leave your answers with powers. |

a) $4^7 \times 4^4$

This is a multiplication, so add the powers. $\qquad 4^7 \times 4^4 = 4^{7+4} = \mathbf{4^{11}}$

b) $\dfrac{6^7}{6^4}$

This is a division ($\dfrac{6^7}{6^4} = 6^7 \div 6^4$),

so subtract the powers. $\qquad 6^7 \div 6^4 = 6^{7-4} = \mathbf{6^3}$

c) $(3^9)^2$

This is one power raised to another power,
so multiply the powers. $\qquad (3^9)^2 = 3^{9 \times 2} = \mathbf{3^{18}}$

Exercise 1

Answer these questions **without using a calculator**.

1 Simplify the following, leaving your answers with powers.

    a) $2^3 \times 2^5$ **b)** $9^8 \times 9^2$ **c)** $5^7 \times 5^6$ **d)** 6×6^8

    e) $8^4 \times 8^{10}$ **f)** $7^3 \times 7^3$ **g)** $4^9 \times 4$ **h)** $3^6 \times 3^7$

    i) $10^3 \times 10^5$ **j)** $2^{10} \times 2^{10}$ **k)** $11^5 \times 11^4$ **l)** $3^{12} \times 3$

2 Simplify the following, leaving your answers with powers.

a) $3^6 \div 3^2$ **b)** $7^8 \div 7^4$ **c)** $5^7 \div 5^2$ **d)** $3^5 \div 3^3$

e) $9^{15} \div 9^{13}$ **f)** $2^{10} \div 2^2$ **g)** $6^6 \div 6^5$ **h)** $4^7 \div 4^5$

i) $8^8 \div 8$ **j)** $11^3 \div 11^2$ **k)** $13^8 \div 13^2$ **l)** $12^3 \div 12$

3 Evaluate the following.

a) 4^1 **b)** 5^0 **c)** 11^0 **d)** 123^1

4 Simplify the following, leaving your answers with powers.

a) $(2^5)^5$ **b)** $(13^4)^3$ **c)** $(60^4)^{12}$ **d)** $(8^7)^4$

e) $(12^{13})^5$ **f)** $(23^2)^3$ **g)** $(2^{32})^2$ **h)** $(15^5)^5$

i) $(7^7)^7$ **j)** $(100^2)^3$ **k)** $(5^{12})^{12}$ **l)** $(3^3)^8$

5 Simplify the following, leaving your answers with powers.

a) $5^7 \times 5^{15}$ **b)** $16^{11} \div 16^5$ **c)** $(7^6)^7$ **d)** $3^{21} \div 3^7$

e) $(13^5)^6$ **f)** $12^{15} \times 12^4$ **g)** 111×111^5 **h)** $66^{17} \div 66^7$

i) $(152^8)^4$ **j)** $202^3 \times 202^4$ **k)** $\dfrac{2^4}{2}$ **l)** $\dfrac{34^{110}}{34^{104}}$

6 For each of the following, find the number that should replace the star (★).

a) $7^7 \times 7^3 = 7^{★}$ **b)** $(9^{10})^7 = 9^{★}$ **c)** $7^{15} \div 7^9 = 7^{★}$ **d)** $\dfrac{19^8}{19^7} = ★$

7 For each of the following, find the number that should replace the star (★).

a) $3^{★} \times 3^{13} = 3^{17}$ **b)** $14^9 \times 14^{★} = 14^{18}$ **c)** $4^{24} \div 4^{★} = 4^{21}$ **d)** $8^{★} \div 8^4 = 8^9$

e) $12^2 \times 12^{★} = 12^9$ **f)** $11^{★} \div 11^5 = 11^5$ **g)** $3^{★} \times 3^{26} = 3^{30}$ **h)** $5^{31} \div 5^{★} = 5^{22}$

8 For each of the following, find the number that should replace the star (★).

a) $(14^2)^{★} = 14^{18}$ **b)** $(4^{★})^7 = 4^{21}$ **c)** $(3^{★})^8 = 3^{32}$ **d)** $(★^4)^4 = 5^{16}$

e) $(22^{25})^4 = 22^{★}$ **f)** $(100^5)^{★} = 100^{35}$ **g)** $(2014^{15})^{★} = 2014^{30}$ **h)** $(★^{10})^7 = 6^{70}$

Example 2 Simplify each expression without using a calculator. Leave your answers with powers.

a) $3^7 \times 3^5 \div 3^4$

The power of the result will be $7 + 5 - 4$.

$3^7 \times 3^5 \div 3^4 = 3^{7+5-4}$
$= 3^8$

b) $\dfrac{3^6 \times 3^2}{3^9 \div 3^3}$

1. Work out the top and bottom lines of the fraction separately.

2. Then do the final division.

$\dfrac{3^6 \times 3^2}{3^9 \div 3^3} = \dfrac{3^{6+2}}{3^{9-3}} = \dfrac{3^8}{3^6}$
$= 3^{8-6}$
$= 3^2$

Exercise 2

Answer these questions without using a calculator.

1 Simplify each expression, leaving your answers with powers.

a) $2^3 \times 2^5 \times 2^9$ **b)** $7^{12} \times 7^4 \times 7$ **c)** $12^3 \times 12 \times 12$

d) $5^5 \times 5^6 \times 5^7$ **e)** $4^9 \times 4^2 \div 4^7$ **f)** $6^7 \times 6^5 \div 6^9$

g) $8^{15} \div 8^3 \times 8^3$ **h)** $2^6 \div 2^3 \div 2^2$ **i)** $5^5 \div 5^2 \div 5$

2 Simplify each expression, leaving your answers with powers.

a) $(3^7)^3 \times 3^4$ **b)** $(2^4)^7 \div 2^8$ **c)** $5^3 \times (5^2)^7$ **d)** $7^{34} \div (7^2)^4$

3 Simplify each expression, leaving your answers with powers.

a) $(8^3 \times 8^2)^6$ **b)** $(16^{12} \div 16^5)^4$ **c)** $(12^2 \times 12^{15})^3$ **d)** $(100^8 \div 100^4)^2$

4 Simplify each expression, leaving your answers with powers.

a) $\dfrac{5^2 \times 5^6}{5^3}$ **b)** $\dfrac{2^8}{2^4 \div 2^3}$ **c)** $\dfrac{3^3 \times 3^7}{3^2 \times 3^3}$

d) $\dfrac{7^6 \times 7^3}{7^2}$ **e)** $\dfrac{6^4 \times 6^3}{6 \times 6^5}$ **f)** $\dfrac{4^{10} \times 4}{4^9 \times 4}$

g) $\dfrac{8^4 \times 8^4}{8^{10} \div 8^7}$ **h)** $\dfrac{12^9 \div 12^5}{12^6 \div 12^5}$ **i)** $\dfrac{10^{17} \div 10^2}{10^3 \times 10^{10}}$

5 Simplify each expression, leaving your answers with powers.

a) $\left(\dfrac{7^4 \times 7^8}{7^7}\right)^5$

b) $\dfrac{3^2 \times 3^9}{(3^3)^3}$

c) $\dfrac{(9^7)^5 \div 9^{12}}{9^4 \times 9^9}$

d) $\dfrac{(2^{12} \div 2^{10})^5}{2^8 \div 2^2}$

e) $\dfrac{5^4 \times (5^3)^5}{(5^4)^2}$

f) $\dfrac{4^4}{(4^4 \div 4^2)^2}$

g) $\left(\dfrac{12^7}{12^2 \times 12^3}\right)^5$

h) $\dfrac{6^8 \div 6}{(6^3)^2}$

6 Simplify each expression, leaving your answers with powers.

a) $\dfrac{(2^2)^3 \times 2}{2^4}$

b) $\dfrac{5^4 \times 5^4}{(5^2)^4}$

c) $\dfrac{(7^3)^3}{(7^2 \times 7^2)^2}$

d) $\dfrac{(11^7 \times 11^2)^3}{11^{26} \div 11^3}$

e) $\dfrac{(3^6 \div 3^3)^3}{3^4}$

f) $\dfrac{(6^7 \times 6^2)^2}{6^{20} \div 6^4}$

7 Which of the expressions in the box are equal to 1?

$$\dfrac{5^5 \div 5^2}{5} \qquad \dfrac{8^{16}}{8^9 \times 8^7} \qquad \dfrac{2^9 - 2^8}{2} \qquad \dfrac{4^{12} \times 4^3}{(4^3)^5} \qquad \dfrac{(6^4)^4 - 6^4}{6^8}$$

8 Simplify the following, giving your answers as powers of 2.

a) $2 \times 4 \times 8$

b) $2^3 \times 4^2$

c) $\dfrac{2^6 \times 4}{8}$

Investigate — Other Powers

1 a) Write out $\dfrac{2 \times 2}{2 \times 2 \times 2}$ as: **i)** a fraction in its simplest form.
ii) a single power of 2 using the power laws.

b) Repeat for $\dfrac{2 \times 2}{2 \times 2 \times 2 \times 2}$ and $\dfrac{2 \times 2}{2 \times 2 \times 2 \times 2 \times 2}$.

c) What do your answers tell you about negative powers?

d) Can you use your answers to write 3^{-1}, 3^{-2} and 3^{-3} as fractions?

2 Look at the expression $\left(2^{\frac{1}{2}}\right)^2$.

a) Use the power law to write this as a number with a single power.

b) Can you use this to work out what it means to have a power of $\dfrac{1}{2}$?

Negative Powers

A number to the power of $-m$ is the same as the reciprocal of the number to the power m.

$$a^{-m} = \frac{1}{a^m}$$

Example 3 Write 10^{-3} as:

a) **a fraction.**

1. Write 10^{-3} as the reciprocal of 10^3.

   $$10^{-3} = \frac{1}{10^3}$$

2. Simplify the number on the bottom.

   $$= \frac{1}{1000}$$

b) **a decimal.**

1. Use your answer from part **a)** to write 10^{-3} as a fraction.

   $$10^{-3} = \frac{1}{1000}$$

2. Write one thousandth as a decimal with a 1 in the thousandths column — the third decimal place.

   $$= 0.001$$

Exercise 3

1 Write the following as fractions in their simplest terms.

a) 2^{-3} b) 5^{-2} c) 2^{-4} d) 3^{-3}

e) 7^{-4} f) 6^{-2} g) 4^{-4} h) 8^{-1}

i) 12^{-2} j) 7^{-2} k) 12^{-1} l) 2^{-11}

2 Write each negative power of 10 as: i) a fraction
                                         ii) a decimal

a) 10^{-7} b) 10^{-5} c) 10^{-2} d) 10^{-4}

3 Write these decimals as negative powers of 10.

a) 0.001 b) 0.000001 c) 0.00000001 d) 0.1

4 Simplify these expressions without a calculator. Leave your answers with powers.

a) $3^9 \times 3^{-5}$ b) $5^8 \div 5^{-1}$ c) $8^{-4} \times 8^7$ d) $2^2 \div 2^{-1}$

3.2 Standard Form

Standard form is used to make it easier to write very large or very small numbers, like 2 670 000 000 000 and 0.0000000000014. In standard form, numbers are written as a multiple of a power of 10, like this:

A can be any number between 1 and 10 (but not 10 itself) $\longrightarrow$ $A \times 10^n$ $\longleftarrow$ n can be any whole number

Large Numbers in Standard Form

Example 1 Write 279 000 in standard form.

1. First, write 279 000 as a number between 1 and 10 multiplied by a multiple of ten.

$$279\ 000 = 2.79 \times 100\ 000$$

2. Rewrite the multiple of 10 as a power.

$$2.79 \times 100\ 000 = \mathbf{2.79 \times 10^5}$$

Exercise 1

1 Which of these numbers are **not** written in standard form?

5.2×10^9 $\qquad$ 3.5×12^2 $\qquad$ 55×10^6

$\qquad$ 3×10^8 $\qquad$ $1.25 \times 10^{1.5}$

6.5×100^2 $\qquad$ 2.5×10^{11} $\qquad$ 0.5×10^7

2 Fill in the gaps to show how these numbers can be written in standard form.

a) $200\ 000 = \text{......} \times 100\ 000 = \text{......} \times 10^5$

b) $3\ 000\ 000 = 3 \times \text{.................} = 3 \times \text{......}$

3 Write these numbers in standard form.

a) 200   b) 2000   c) 40 000   d) 600 000

e) 8000   f) 900   g) 5 000 000   h) 70 000 000

i) 450 000   j) 4100   k) 625 000   l) 54 000

> **Example 2** Write 3.5×10^3 as an ordinary number.
>
> 1. First, rewrite the power of 10 in full as an ordinary number.
>
> $3.5 \times 10^3 = 3.5 \times 1000$
>
> 2. Do the multiplication to find the value of the standard form number.
>
> $3.5 \times 1000 = \mathbf{3500}$

4 Fill in the gaps to show how these can be written as ordinary numbers.

a) $8 \times 10^3 = $ .... $\times 1000 = $ ....

b) $5 \times 10^6 = 5 \times $ .... $= $ ....

5 Write each of these as an ordinary number.

a) 4×10^3 b) 5×10^2 c) 8×10^6 d) 7×10^9

e) 6.2×10^3 f) 1.4×10^5 g) 6.9×10^7 h) 7.2×10^8

i) 6.05×10^4 j) 7.27×10^5 k) 3.65×10^9 l) 5.201×10^4

6 Put each of these groups of numbers in order, from smallest to largest.

a) 4×10^5, 2×10^3, 3×10^2, 6×10^4, 7×10^3, 2×10^2

b) 2.5×10^3, 4.6×10^6, 1.5×10^4, 9.8×10^2, 1.1×10^6, 6.8×10^4

c) $410\,100$, 4.105×10^6, 4.11×10^6, $4\,100\,000$, 4.105×10^5, $4\,101\,000$

7 By writing each of the numbers as an ordinary number first, work out these calculations. Give your answers in standard form.

a) $(2 \times 10^3) + (5 \times 10^2)$ b) $(3 \times 10^4) + (6 \times 10^4)$

c) $(8.5 \times 10^6) + (7.7 \times 10^5)$ d) $(2.05 \times 10^5) + (6.02 \times 10^4)$

e) $(8 \times 10^4) - (2 \times 10^4)$ f) $(5 \times 10^7) - (9 \times 10^6)$

8 The population of country A is 5.3×10^7 and the population of country B is 3.1×10^6. How many more people live in country A than in country B?

Small Numbers in Standard Form

Small numbers can be written in <u>standard form</u> by using negative powers of 10.

Example 3 **Write the following numbers in standard form.**

a) 0.0002

1. Write 0.0002 as a number between 1 and 10 multiplied by a decimal containing only 0s and a 1.

$0.0002 = 2 \times 0.0001$

2. Rewrite the decimal as a negative power of 10.

$2 \times 0.0001 = \mathbf{2 \times 10^{-4}}$

b) 0.00486

1. Write 0.00486 as a number between 1 and 10 multiplied by a decimal containing only 0s and a 1.

$0.00486 = 4.86 \times 0.001$

2. Rewrite the decimal as a negative power of 10.

$4.86 \times 0.001 = \mathbf{4.86 \times 10^{-3}}$

Exercise 2

1 Fill in the gaps to show how these numbers can be written in standard form.

a) $0.04 = \ldots\ldots \times 0.01 = \ldots\ldots \times 10^{-2}$

b) $0.008 = \ldots\ldots \times 0.001 = \ldots\ldots \times 10^{-3}$

c) $0.0006 = 6 \times \ldots\ldots\ldots\ldots\ldots = 6 \times \ldots\ldots$

2 Write these numbers in standard form.

a) 0.003   b) 0.4   c) 0.07   d) 0.0005

e) 0.06   f) 0.2   g) 0.009   h) 0.0008

3 Fill in the gaps to show how these numbers can be written in standard form.

a) $0.32 = \ldots\ldots \times 0.1 = \ldots\ldots \times 10^{-1}$

b) $0.056 = \ldots\ldots \times 0.01 = \ldots\ldots \times 10^{-2}$

c) $0.0017 = 1.7 \times \ldots\ldots\ldots\ldots\ldots = 1.7 \times \ldots\ldots$

4 Write these numbers in standard form.

a) 0.045   b) 0.12   c) 0.0075   d) 0.052

e) 0.67   f) 0.0021   g) 0.099   h) 0.0082

5 Write these numbers in standard form.

    a) 0.0305   **b)** 0.000675   **c)** 0.215   **d)** 0.000889

 Example 4   Write 6.5×10^{-3} as an ordinary number.

    1. Rewrite 10^{-3} as a decimal. $6.5 \times 10^{-3} = 6.5 \times 0.001$

    2. Do the multiplication to find the
       value of the standard form number. $6.5 \times 0.001 = \textbf{0.0065}$

---

6 Fill in the spaces to show how these can be written as ordinary numbers.

    a) 4×10^{-2} = ... × 0.01 = ...

    b) 3.3×10^{-4} = ... × 0.0001 = ...

    c) 5.6×10^{0} = 5.6 × .... = ...

7 Write each of these as an ordinary number.

    a) 6×10^{-1} **b)** 7×10^{-4} **c)** 2×10^{0}

    d) 1.2×10^{-4} **e)** 3.4×10^{-2} **f)** 5.5×10^{-3}

    g) 1.5×10^{0} **h)** 2.3×10^{-3} **i)** 4.1×10^{-6}

8 Put the numbers in each list in order, from smallest to largest.

    a) 2×10^{-2}, 2×10^{-3}, 2×10^{-6}, 2×10^{-5}, 2×10^{-4}, 2×10^{-1}

    b) 9.1×10^{-2}, 6.5×10^{-6}, 3.4×10^{-7}, 1.3×10^{-2}, 8.9×10^{-7}, 1.2×10^{-1}

    c) 3.45×10^{-6}, 2.34×10^{-1}, 9.08×10^{-3}, 9.08×10^{-2}, 7.56×10^{-1}, 1.08×10^{-1}

9 Put the numbers in each list in order, from smallest to largest.

    a) 5×10^{-5}, 5×10^{5}, 5×10^{-2}, 5×10^{0}, 5×10^{-4}, 5×10^{2}

    b) 3.8×10^{-7}, 4.9×10^{10}, 7.1×10^{-7}, 5.1×10^{-2}, 2.1×10^{3}, 1.8×10^{-1}

    c) 7.79×10^{3}, 7.79×10^{0}, 1.29×10^{-3}, 6.03×10^{-2}, 1.80×10^{-2}, 1.08×10^{2}

10 Put each of these numbers into standard form and then put each list in order, from smallest to largest.

   a) 0.000313, 3.13×10^{-5}, 312 000 000, 3.1×10^5, 3.1, 3.13×10^{-6}

   b) 1.75×10^6, 0.0175, 715 000, 7.14×10^3, 0.00714, 7.1×10^{-3}

   c) 21 300, 2.12×10^{-2}, 0.00021, 2.14×10^6, 2.14, 2.13×10^{-5}

11 The weight of one sand particle is 8.7×10^{-7} kg and the weight of another is 2.1×10^{-6} kg. Calculate their combined weight.

12 What is the difference between the width of the two cells shown? Give your answer in standard form.

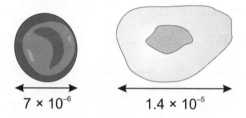

7×10^{-6} 1.4×10^{-5}

Investigate — Standard Form in Science

   a) Look up or estimate the diameter or width of each of the following things:

a hydrogen atom,	a red blood cell,
a flea,	a dinner plate,
a mountain,	the moon,
the Earth,	the Sun,
the Milky Way,	the observed Universe.

   You'll probably find that the very small and very large numbers are given in standard form.

   b) Arrange the objects in size order, then try to estimate the scale factor between each one.

   c) How many times bigger is the Sun than the Earth?

   d) How many times bigger is the Milky Way than a flea? Can you use standard form to help?

3.3 Roots

Roots are the <u>inverse</u> of powers.

So 3^4 ("3 to the power of 4") is 81, and $\sqrt[4]{81}$ ("the fourth root of 81") is 3.

Most roots are <u>irrational</u> — they give infinitely long, non-<u>recurring</u> decimals when you work them out. Leaving them as roots (e.g. $2\sqrt{2}$) or rounded <u>decimals</u> (e.g. 2.83 to 2 d.p.) is sometimes easier.

Every positive number has two <u>square roots</u> — one positive ($\sqrt{x}$) and one negative ($-\sqrt{x}$). Your calculator will only give you the positive one, so you need to remember to give both. The same applies to all even roots (square roots, fourth roots, sixth roots). Negative numbers don't have even roots.

Example 1 | **Calculate all possible answers to the following roots, giving your answers to 2 d.p.**

a) The square roots of 2.

1. The square root of 2 is an even root, so it can be positive or negative. Work out the positive root using your calculator. $\sqrt{2}$ = 1.4142...

2. Round to 2 d.p.   **1.41 (to 2 d.p.)**

3. Now write down the negative version.   **or –1.41 (to 2 d.p.)**

b) The cube root of 7.

1. A cube root is not an even root, so it only has one answer — use your calculator to work it out. $\sqrt[3]{7}$ = 1.9129...

2. Round to 2 d.p.   **1.91 (to 2 d.p.)**

Exercise 1

1 Find both square roots of these numbers. You may use a calculator if you need to.

    a) 256   **b)** 361   **c)** 400   **d)** 10 000

2 Find both square roots of these numbers using a calculator. Round your answers to 2 d.p.

    a) 48   **b)** 963   **c)** 578   **d)** 8000

    e) 478   **f)** 264   **g)** 182   **h)** 365

3 Use your calculator to find the cube root of each of these numbers:

    a) 1331   **b)** 729   **c)** –343   **d)** –1728

4 Use your calculator to find the cube root of each of these numbers.
Round your answers to 2 d.p.

    a) 653   **b)** 1221   **c)** −585   **d)** 979

    e) 9000   **f)** −5874   **g)** 396   **h)** 754

5 Find these square and cube roots using your calculator.

    a) $\sqrt{1.44}$ **b)** $\sqrt[3]{0.008}$ **c)** $\sqrt[3]{-0.027}$ **d)** $\sqrt[3]{0.343}$

6 Find these square and cube roots using your calculator. Round your answers to 2 d.p.

    a) $\sqrt{438}$ **b)** $\sqrt[3]{15.65}$ **c)** $\sqrt{0.55}$ **d)** $\sqrt[3]{-0.346}$

    e) $\sqrt[3]{0.0932}$ **f)** $-\sqrt{0.0412}$ **g)** $\sqrt[3]{-0.02342}$ **h)** $-\sqrt{14.4}$

7 Use your calculator to find these roots.

    a) $\sqrt[7]{2187}$ **b)** $\sqrt[7]{-78\,125}$ **c)** $\sqrt[5]{0.03125}$ **d)** $\sqrt[8]{1\,679\,616}$

8 Use your calculator to work out these calculations. Round your answers to 2 d.p.

    a) $\sqrt{5} + \sqrt{6}$ **b)** $\sqrt{4} + \sqrt[5]{5}$ **c)** $\sqrt[4]{84} + \sqrt[5]{84}$

    d) $\sqrt[3]{21} - \sqrt{345}$ **e)** $\sqrt[4]{65} - \sqrt[3]{15}$ **f)** $-\sqrt{322} - \sqrt[4]{214}$

9 Work out the value of x in each of these calculations. Do **not** use a calculator.

    a) $\sqrt[3]{x} = 10$ **b)** $\sqrt[x]{32} = 2$ **c)** $\sqrt{4} = \sqrt[3]{x}$ **d)** $\sqrt{x} = 3^2$ **e)** $\sqrt[3]{125} = \sqrt[x]{25}$

> ### Investigate — Messy Roots
>
>   **a)** Work out $\sqrt{2}$ on your calculator, then $\sqrt{8}$.
>   You should get long messy decimals
>   – they're both irrational numbers.
>
>   **b)** Now try $\sqrt{2} \times \sqrt{8}$. What do you get?
>   Was that what you expected?
>   Try again but with $\sqrt{18}$ instead of $\sqrt{8}$.
>
>   **c)** Investigate to find which roots will give you whole numbers when you
>   multiply by $\sqrt{2}$. Can you see a pattern? Can you find an explanation?

Section 4 — Multiples, Factors and Primes

4.1 Multiples and Factors

Multiples and LCM

The <u>multiples</u> of a number are just the numbers that are in its times table.

So the multiples of 3 are 3, 6, 9, 12, 15, ... and the multiples of 10 are 10, 20, 30, 40, 50, ...

A <u>common multiple</u> is a number that's in the times table of two or more different numbers.

The <u>lowest common multiple</u> (LCM) of a group of numbers is the smallest common multiple of those numbers. It's the lowest number they all divide into exactly.

Example 1   **Find the lowest common multiple of 4 and 5.**

1. Write down the multiples of 4 and 5:

    multiples of 4:
    4, 8, 12, 16, (20) 24, ...
    multiples of 5:
    5, 10, 15, (20) 25, ...

2. The lowest common multiple is the smallest number that's in both lists.

    The LCM of 4 and 5 is **20**.

Example 2   **Chris weeds his garden every 6 days. His next-door neighbour Kim weeds her garden every 8 days. If they both weeded today, how many days will it be before they weed on the same day again?**

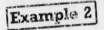

You need to find the lowest common multiple of 6 and 8:

Chris weeds his garden on day
6, 12, 18, (24) 30, ...
Kim weeds her garden on day
8, 16, (24) 32, ...

So they will next weed on the same day after **24 days**.

Exercise 1

1 Find the lowest common multiple (LCM) of each of the following pairs of numbers.

   a) 3 and 5   **b)** 2 and 7   **c)** 3 and 4

   d) 5 and 9   **e)** 3 and 7   **f)** 8 and 9

2 Find the LCM of each of the following pairs of numbers.

   a) 4 and 6   **b)** 8 and 10   **c)** 9 and 12

3 **a)** Write down the first eight multiples of 4, 6 and 8.

b) Find the lowest common multiple of 4, 6 and 8.

4 **a)** Write down the first eight multiples of 3, 6 and 9.

b) Find the lowest common multiple of 3, 6 and 9.

5 Find the LCM of each of the sets of numbers below.

a) 2, 3 and 4   **b)** 3, 5 and 6   **c)** 5, 10 and 15

d) 5, 6 and 10   **e)** 5, 8 and 10   **f)** 4, 9 and 12

6 Find the lowest common multiple of the following pairs of numbers:

a) 12 and 15   **b)** 20 and 24

c) 12 and 16   **d)** 16 and 20

7 Coralie visits the hairdresser every 8 weeks. Victor visits the same hairdresser every 12 weeks. They go for the first time in Week 0, and keep going for a year.

a) In which weeks does Coralie visit the hairdresser?
Write down all possible answers.

b) In which weeks does Victor visit the hairdresser?
Write down all possible answers.

c) In which week will they next visit the hairdresser at the same time?

8 Tabitha empties her bins every 5 days and Peter empties his bins every 7 days. If they both emptied their bins today, how many days will it be before they both empty them on the same day again?

9 Miss Norfolk splits a class of children into 10 equal groups. Mr Wales splits the same class into 15 equal groups. What is the smallest possible number of children in the class?

10 x and y are whole numbers less than 24. The lowest common multiple of x and y is 24. Find all the possible values of x and y.

Factors and HCF

The <u>factors</u> of a number are all the numbers that divide into it ('go into it') exactly.

So the factors of 6 are 1, 2, 3 and 6 — all these numbers go into 6 exactly.

A <u>common factor</u> is a number that divides exactly into two or more different numbers.

The <u>highest common factor</u> (HCF) of a group of numbers is the largest common factor of those numbers. It's the biggest number that divides into all of them exactly.

Example 3	**Find the highest common factor of 18 and 27.**

1. Write down the factors of 18 and 27:

    factors of 18:
    1, 2, 3, 6, (9) 18
    factors of 27:
    1, 3, (9) 27

2. The highest common factor is the biggest number that's in both lists.

    The HCF of 18 and 27 is **9**.

Exercise 2

1 Find the highest common factor (HCF) of each of the following pairs of numbers.

    a) 4 and 16   **b)** 8 and 32   **c)** 7 and 28

    d) 5 and 35   **e)** 6 and 24   **f)** 10 and 40

2 Find the HCF of each of the following pairs of numbers.

    a) 3 and 8   **b)** 4 and 15   **c)** 8 and 21

    d) 10 and 27   **e)** 13 and 28   **f)** 9 and 32

3 Find the HCF of each of the following pairs of numbers.

    a) 8 and 12   **b)** 6 and 8   **c)** 20 and 30

    d) 14 and 35   **e)** 9 and 24   **f)** 16 and 40

4 **a)** Write down all the factors of 6, 18 and 36.

    b) Find the highest common factor of 6, 18 and 36.

5 Find the HCF of each of the following sets of numbers.

    a) 6, 12 and 24   **b)** 4, 16 and 20

    c) 9, 27 and 36   **d)** 15, 30 and 60

    e) 3, 5 and 14   **f)** 4, 7 and 13

    g) 9, 16 and 23   **h)** 12, 19 and 25

    i) 12, 20 and 28   **j)** 15, 21 and 33

    k) 14, 35 and 49   **l)** 18, 36 and 48

6 Find the highest common factor of the following pairs of numbers:

    a) 48 and 64   **b)** 60 and 80   **c)** 72 and 90

7 Peter and Elaine keep the same number of pet birds.
Peter shares 63 seeds equally between his birds (with no seeds left over).
Elaine shares 81 seeds equally between her birds (with no seeds left over).

What is the largest number of birds they could each have?

8 Some students take part in an outdoor activity day. They are arranged into teams so that each team is the same size, is as large as possible, and has no mixing of boys and girls. There are 36 boys and 42 girls.

    a) How many students are on each team?

    b) How many more girls teams are there than boys teams?

Investigate — Perfect Numbers

    *A number is called perfect if the sum of all its factors is
exactly double the number itself.*

    a) Can you find any perfect numbers between 1 and 10?

    b) Can you find a perfect number that is also prime?

    c) If numbers are not perfect they are called either *abundant* or *deficient*.
Given that *deficient* means 'not having enough' and *abundant* means 'having
a lot', what do you think these terms mean in relation to sums of factors?

    d) Try to find the perfect number that lies between 10 and 50, and see if you
can spot any patterns in which numbers are perfect, abundant or deficient.

4.2 Prime Numbers

Prime Numbers

A prime number is a number that has no factors except itself and 1.

In other words, the only numbers that divide exactly into a prime number are itself and 1.

But remember... 1 is not a prime number.

Here are the first few prime numbers: 2, 3, 5, 7, 11, 13, 17, 19, 23, 29, ...

Example 1   **Which of the numbers in the box are primes?**

| 37 | 38 | 39 | 40 | 41 |

1. Look for factors of each of the numbers.

2. If you can find factors, then the number isn't prime.

3. If there are no factors other than itself and 1, the number is prime.

$38 = 2 \times 19$, so 38 isn't prime
$39 = 3 \times 13$, so 39 isn't prime
$40 = 4 \times 10$, so 40 isn't prime

37 has no factors other than 1 and 37.
41 has no factors other than 1 and 41.

So the prime numbers are **37** and **41**.

Exercise 1

1 Write down all the prime numbers in this box:

| 7 | 15 | 23 | 28 | 35 | 49 | 53 | 59 |

2 **a)** Write down the four prime numbers between 10 and 20.

   b) Find the two prime numbers between 30 and 40.

3 **a)** Find the largest prime number that is less than 70.

   b) Find all the prime numbers between 40 and 50.

4 Explain why 42 is not a prime number.

5 Explain why 41 is a prime number.

6 Is 51 a prime number? Explain your answer.

7 Look at the numbers in the box:

| 71 | 72 | 73 | 74 | 75 | 76 | 77 | 78 | 79 |

Write down all the prime numbers in the box.

8 Without doing any calculations, explain how you can tell that none of the numbers in the box are prime.

| 102 | 104 | 106 | 108 | 110 | 55 | 60 | 65 | 70 | 75 |

9 **a)** Find two prime numbers that add to make 16.

b) Find two prime numbers that add to make 36.

c) Find an example to show that this statement is **false**:

"The sum of two prime numbers is always even".

10 The product of two consecutive primes is 437. What is their sum?

11 Alana multiplies two primes together and gets a very large even number.
She tells her friend Bel the large even number, and asks her to guess the prime numbers she multiplied together. Bel works out very quickly what the two primes are.
Explain how Bel is able to do this.

> ## Investigate — Very Large Primes
>
> *Very large prime numbers, often with over 100 digits, are used in the field of cryptography — making codes to protect information.*
>
> **a)** What is the largest prime number you can think of?
> Think about how you'd go about finding bigger ones.
> How could you check they were prime?
>
> **b)** Research the uses of primes in cryptography.
> How do other people go about finding large primes?

Prime Factors

Integers which are not prime can be broken down into prime factors.
The product of these factors is the original number. (Remember, 'product' means the result of multiplying things).

You can write the prime factors using powers — so $12 = 2 \times 2 \times 3 = 2^2 \times 3$.

Every integer can only be made of one unique set of primes multiplied together (and vice versa). This is called the unique factorisation property.

Example 2   **Write 18 as a product of prime factors.**

Make a factor tree.

1. First find any two factors whose product is 18 (here, $3 \times 6 = 18$). Circle any of these factors that are prime.

2. Repeat step 1 for any factors you didn't circle (here, $6 = 2 \times 3$).

3. Stop when all the branches end in a circle. The product of all the circled primes is the number you started with.

4. You can rewrite the prime factors using powers to simplify.

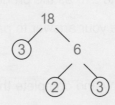

$18 = 2 \times 3 \times 3$

$18 = 2 \times 3^2$

Exercise 2

In the following questions, write any repeated factors as powers.

1 Write the following numbers as the product of prime factors.

a) 4   b) 10   c) 26

d) 34   e) 55   f) 65

2 Use factor trees to write the following numbers as the product of prime factors.

a) 27   b) 30   c) 63

d) 75   e) 99   f) 110

g) 40   h) 56   i) 64

j) 81   k) 108   l) 120

3 Write the following as the product of prime factors.

    a) 20   **b)** 32   **c)** 44

    d) 124   **e)** 144   **f)** 225

    g) 315   **h)** 990   **i)** 1050

4 **a)** Write 96 as the product of prime factors.

    b) Use your answer to part **a)** to write 1440 (= 96 × 15) as the product of prime factors.

5 **a)** Write 210 as the product of prime factors.

    b) Use your answer to part **a)** to write 70 (= 210 ÷ 3) as the product of prime factors.

6 **a)** Copy and complete this factor tree.

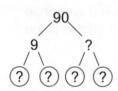

    b) Use your factor tree to write 90 as the product of prime factors.

    c) Use your answer to part **b)** to write 90^2 as the product of prime factors.

7 Work out the missing number in the prime factorisation of 84:

$$84 = 2^2 \times 3 \times \ldots$$

8 **a)** Find the prime factorisation of 24.

    b) The prime factorisation of 648 is $2^3 \times 3^4$.
        Use this, and your answer to **a)**, to work out the missing number in this calculation:

$$648 = 24 \times \ldots$$

Using Prime Factors

Prime factors can be used to find the lowest common multiple (LCM) and highest common factor (HCF) of a pair of numbers.

For example:

$28 = 2 \times 2 \times 7$ and $42 = 2 \times 3 \times 7$

The HCF is the product of the prime factors common to both numbers. They're the ones in the overlap of a Venn diagram containing the prime factors of the numbers.

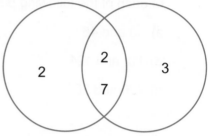

Prime factors   Prime factors
of 28   of 42

The LCM is the product of all the individual prime factors in the diagram — only counting shared factors once.

So the HCF of 28 and 42 is $2 \times 7 = $ **14**. The LCM of 28 and 42 is $2 \times 2 \times 3 \times 7 = $ **84**.

Exercise 3

1 $140 = 2 \times 2 \times 5 \times 7$ and $200 = 2 \times 2 \times 2 \times 5 \times 5$.

   a) Copy and complete this Venn diagram using the prime factors of 140 and 200.

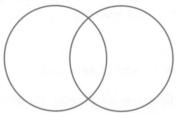

Prime factors of 140   Prime factors of 200

   b) Use the Venn diagram to find the HCF of 140 and 200.

   c) Use the Venn diagram to find the LCM of 140 and 200.

2 **a)** Find the prime factors of 75 and 105.

   b) Show the prime factors of 75 and 105 on a Venn diagram.

   c) Use your answer to **b)** to find the HCF of 75 and 105.

   d) Use your answer to **b)** to find the LCM of 75 and 105.

3 **a)** Write 78 and 96 as products of their prime factors.

   b) Find the HCF of 78 and 96.

   c) Find the LCM of 78 and 96.

4 Use prime factors to find:

   i) the HCF   **ii)** the LCM

of each of the following pairs of numbers:

  a) 38 and 46   **b)** 70 and 65   **c)** 45 and 99

  d) 112 and 124   **e)** 300 and 340   **f)** 162 and 186

  g) 220 and 208   **h)** 170 and 190   **i)** 315 and 405

5 Use prime factors to find the highest number that will divide into both 150 and 160.

6 Use prime factors to find the lowest number that divides exactly by both 320 and 400.

7 The pupils in Year 9 at a school are arranged into 16 equally sized classes for maths and 20 equally sized classes for art. Use prime factors to work out the smallest number of pupils there could be in Year 9. Show your working.

8 A pair of numbers have HCF = 15 and LCM = 150.

  a) Use the HCF and LCM to fill in the Venn diagram with prime factors of the numbers.

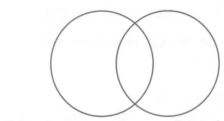

Prime factors of first number   Prime factors of second number

  b) Use your answer to **a)** to find a pair of numbers which have HCF = 15 and LCM = 150.

9 Find a pair of numbers that have HCF = 25 and LCM = 300, using prime factors.

Section 5 — Fractions and Percentages

5.1 Adding and Subtracting Fractions

Adding and Subtracting Fractions

Fractions with different <u>denominators</u> can be added and subtracted. You need to rewrite them with a <u>common denominator</u> first, before adding or subtracting the <u>numerators</u>.

Example 1 Work out $\dfrac{5}{6} - \dfrac{2}{9}$.

1. Use the lowest common multiple of 6 and 9 as a common denominator.

   LCM of 6 and 9 = 18

2. Rewrite the fractions with a common denominator of 18.

$$\overset{\times 3}{\dfrac{5}{6} = \dfrac{15}{18}}\underset{\times 3}{} \qquad \overset{\times 2}{\dfrac{2}{9} = \dfrac{4}{18}}\underset{\times 2}{}$$

3. Now you can subtract the numerators.

$$\dfrac{15}{18} - \dfrac{4}{18} = \dfrac{15-4}{18} = \dfrac{11}{18}$$

Exercise 1

Don't use a calculator for this exercise.

1 Add or subtract these fractions by first rewriting them so they have a common denominator. Give your answers in their simplest terms.

a) $\dfrac{1}{6} + \dfrac{4}{12}$

b) $\dfrac{3}{5} + \dfrac{2}{10}$

c) $\dfrac{3}{4} - \dfrac{5}{12}$

d) $\dfrac{8}{16} - \dfrac{1}{4}$

e) $\dfrac{1}{6} + \dfrac{3}{24}$

f) $\dfrac{17}{20} - \dfrac{3}{4}$

g) $\dfrac{3}{5} + \dfrac{9}{25}$

h) $\dfrac{10}{22} + \dfrac{3}{11}$

i) $\dfrac{2}{6} + \dfrac{4}{18}$

j) $\dfrac{8}{10} - \dfrac{6}{30}$

k) $\dfrac{24}{28} - \dfrac{3}{7}$

l) $\dfrac{4}{5} - \dfrac{7}{15}$

2 Add or subtract these fractions by first rewriting them so they have a common denominator. Give your answers in their simplest terms.

a) $\dfrac{3}{4} + \dfrac{1}{6}$

b) $\dfrac{7}{8} - \dfrac{1}{6}$

c) $\dfrac{1}{2} + \dfrac{1}{5}$

d) $\dfrac{3}{5} - \dfrac{2}{6}$

e) $\dfrac{1}{7} + \dfrac{4}{6}$

f) $\dfrac{4}{5} - \dfrac{2}{8}$

g) $\dfrac{6}{7} - \dfrac{2}{5}$

h) $\dfrac{3}{4} - \dfrac{3}{7}$

3 In a shop, $\frac{4}{15}$ of the kites are red and $\frac{2}{5}$ are blue.

What is the total fraction, in its simplest form, of kites that are either red or blue?

4 Josie has a ribbon that is $\frac{4}{5}$ m long. She cuts off $\frac{2}{7}$ m of the ribbon.

How long is the ribbon now? Give your answer as a fraction.

5 Add or subtract these fractions by first rewriting them so they have a common denominator. Give your answers in their simplest terms.

a) $\frac{1}{8} + \frac{5}{32} + \frac{3}{16}$ **b)** $\frac{2}{5} + \frac{2}{15} + \frac{1}{3}$ **c)** $\frac{3}{5} - \frac{1}{4} + \frac{3}{20}$ **d)** $\frac{5}{6} - \frac{1}{3} - \frac{3}{12}$

6 Add or subtract these fractions by first rewriting them so they have a common denominator. Give your answers in their simplest terms.

a) $\frac{3}{10} + \frac{2}{5} + \frac{1}{6}$ **b)** $\frac{7}{12} + \frac{3}{4} - \frac{8}{9}$ **c)** $\frac{6}{7} - \frac{1}{2} - \frac{1}{4}$ **d)** $\frac{4}{5} - \frac{3}{10} - \frac{1}{6}$

7 Amy buys 3 bags of beads. They weigh $\frac{3}{16}$ kg, $\frac{1}{8}$ kg and $\frac{1}{4}$ kg.

What mass of beads does she have in total?
Give your answer as a fraction in its simplest form.

8 Look at the following fractions:

$$\frac{3}{8} \qquad \frac{1}{3} \qquad \frac{3}{4} \qquad \frac{1}{6} \qquad \frac{7}{12} \qquad \frac{11}{24}$$

a) Which two of these fractions add up to $\frac{5}{8}$?

b) Which two of these fractions have a difference of $\frac{1}{4}$?

9 All the pupils at a school come from one of three villages: Oakwood, Beechfield or Three Pines. $\frac{1}{4}$ of the pupils come from Oakwood. $\frac{3}{5}$ of the pupils come from Beechfield. 102 pupils come from Three Pines.

How many pupils are there in total in the school?

Dealing With Mixed Numbers

To add or subtract <u>mixed numbers</u>, first change them into <u>improper fractions</u> with a <u>common denominator</u>.

Example 2 Work out $1\frac{3}{4} + 2\frac{3}{8}$.

1. Write the mixed numbers as improper fractions.

$1 = \frac{4}{4}$, so $1\frac{3}{4} = \frac{4}{4} + \frac{3}{4} = \frac{7}{4}$

$2 = \frac{16}{8}$, so $2\frac{3}{8} = \frac{16}{8} + \frac{3}{8} = \frac{19}{8}$

2. Rewrite the improper fractions with a common denominator.

$$\overset{\times 2}{\underset{\times 2}{\frac{7}{4} = \frac{14}{8}}}$$

3. Add the numerators. Give your answer as a mixed number in its simplest form.

So $1\frac{3}{4} + 2\frac{3}{8} = \frac{14}{8} + \frac{19}{8} = \frac{33}{8}$

$= \frac{32}{8} + \frac{1}{8} = 4\frac{1}{8}$

Exercise 2

Don't use a calculator for this exercise.

1 Write the following mixed numbers as improper fractions.

a) $1\frac{3}{7}$ b) $1\frac{3}{5}$ c) $3\frac{7}{8}$ d) $3\frac{9}{10}$ e) $4\frac{4}{5}$ f) $8\frac{5}{9}$

g) $12\frac{4}{5}$ h) $13\frac{3}{4}$ i) $12\frac{1}{3}$ j) $4\frac{4}{5}$ k) $9\frac{7}{12}$ l) $5\frac{7}{11}$

2 Write the following improper fractions as mixed numbers in their simplest terms.

a) $\frac{14}{8}$ b) $\frac{10}{6}$ c) $\frac{40}{12}$ d) $\frac{36}{8}$ e) $\frac{21}{9}$

f) $\frac{70}{20}$ g) $\frac{28}{6}$ h) $\frac{57}{11}$ i) $\frac{52}{8}$ j) $\frac{50}{15}$

3 a) Write the mixed number $2\frac{3}{5}$ as an improper fraction.

b) Use your answer to **a)** to work out $2\frac{3}{5} + \frac{4}{5}$ as an improper fraction.

c) Write your answer to **b)** as a mixed number.

4 Work out the following. Give your answers as mixed numbers in their simplest form.

a) $2\frac{3}{4} + \frac{3}{4}$

b) $3\frac{5}{7} - \frac{4}{7}$

c) $1\frac{4}{5} + \frac{3}{5}$

d) $6\frac{5}{7} - \frac{6}{7}$

e) $3\frac{7}{8} + 3\frac{7}{8}$

f) $4\frac{4}{9} - 2\frac{8}{9}$

5 a) Write the following as improper fractions:

  i) $3\frac{1}{4}$

  ii) $1\frac{5}{6}$

b) Use your answers to a) to work out $3\frac{1}{4} + 1\frac{5}{6}$ as a mixed number in its simplest form.

c) Use your answers to a) to work out $3\frac{1}{4} - 1\frac{5}{6}$ as a mixed number in its simplest form.

6 Work out the following. Give your answers as mixed numbers in their simplest form.

a) $2\frac{2}{7} + 1\frac{3}{14}$

b) $3\frac{5}{8} - 1\frac{1}{4}$

c) $4\frac{1}{9} + 3\frac{1}{3}$

d) $4\frac{3}{12} - 2\frac{1}{6}$

7 Work out the following. Give your answers as mixed numbers in their simplest form.

a) $2\frac{2}{3} + 1\frac{2}{5}$

b) $2\frac{6}{7} - \frac{1}{3}$

c) $2\frac{5}{6} + 2\frac{2}{7}$

d) $3\frac{3}{5} + 4\frac{3}{7}$

e) $4\frac{5}{6} + 3\frac{3}{5}$

f) $2\frac{5}{8} + 2\frac{2}{9}$

g) $2\frac{4}{9} - 1\frac{1}{6}$

h) $5\frac{5}{6} + 2\frac{3}{8}$

i) $2\frac{9}{10} + 3\frac{5}{6}$

j) $4\frac{5}{7} - 1\frac{3}{4}$

k) $3\frac{8}{9} - 2\frac{2}{5}$

l) $3\frac{1}{3} + 6\frac{7}{8}$

8 Heather and Ashleigh are making bracelets. Heather has made $5\frac{3}{4}$ bracelets.

Ashleigh has made $7\frac{3}{5}$ bracelets.

How many bracelets have they made altogether?
Give your answer as a mixed number in its simplest form.

9 Ralph has eaten $1\frac{5}{6}$ pizzas. Josh has eaten $\frac{7}{8}$ of a pizza.

How much more pizza has Ralph eaten than Josh?

10 Sabeen is making nine cards for the school fair. She has finished $6\frac{8}{9}$ so far.

How many does she have left to make?
Give your answer as a mixed number in its simplest form.

11 The table shows the number of cakes eaten by three contestants in a cake eating contest.
Calculate the total number of cakes eaten.

Contestant	1	2	3
No. of Cakes Eaten	$2\frac{7}{12}$	$3\frac{3}{4}$	$2\frac{5}{6}$

12 Work out the following. Give your answers as mixed numbers in their simplest form.

a) $1\frac{1}{3} + 2\frac{4}{15} + 1\frac{3}{5}$

b) $5\frac{9}{10} + 2\frac{2}{5} + 1\frac{1}{2}$

c) $1\frac{5}{6} + 2\frac{1}{3} + 2\frac{2}{9}$

d) $4\frac{2}{3} - 1\frac{1}{5} - 1\frac{2}{5}$

e) $2\frac{1}{6} + 2\frac{3}{4} + 1\frac{3}{8}$

f) $6\frac{1}{2} - 3\frac{5}{6} - 1\frac{1}{4}$

13 Find the missing number in these calculations.
Give your answers as mixed numbers in their simplest form.

a) $2\frac{5}{6} + \text{..........} = 4\frac{1}{2}$

b) $\text{..........} - 1\frac{1}{3} = 3\frac{5}{12}$

c) $\text{..........} + 1\frac{3}{4} = 5\frac{7}{12}$

d) $3\frac{1}{10} - \text{..........} = -\frac{1}{5}$

> ### Investigate — Mixed Letters
> The letters a, b, c, and d stand for single digit positive numbers.
>
> **a)** How would you add the two mixed numbers $a\frac{b}{c} + d\frac{b}{c}$?
>
> (Hint: try picking some numbers for a, b, c, and d and doing it with numbers first.)
>
> **b)** Once you've mastered that, try $a\frac{b}{c} + b\frac{c}{d}$.
>
> **c)** How about with more letters: $a\frac{b}{c} + d\frac{e}{f}$.

5.2 Multiplying and Dividing Fractions

Multiplying Fractions

To multiply one fraction by another fraction, first check if any <u>factors</u>
of the numerators and denominators can be cancelled.
Then multiply the <u>numerators</u> together and the <u>denominators</u> together separately.

To multiply <u>mixed numbers</u>, change them to improper fractions first.

Example 1   Work out $\frac{3}{8} \times \frac{2}{3}$.

1. Cancel out the common factors
   by dividing by 3 and then by 2.

$$\frac{{}^1\cancel{3}}{\cancel{8}_4} \times \frac{\cancel{2}^1}{\cancel{3}_1} = \frac{1}{4} \times \frac{1}{1}$$

2. Multiply the numerators.

3. Multiply the denominators.

$$\frac{1}{4} \times \frac{1}{1} = \frac{1 \times 1}{4 \times 1} = \frac{1}{4}$$

Example 2   Work out $2\frac{2}{3} \times 3\frac{1}{4}$.

1. Write the mixed numbers as
   improper fractions.

$$2\frac{2}{3} = \frac{6}{3} + \frac{2}{3} = \frac{8}{3}$$

$$3\frac{1}{4} = \frac{12}{4} + \frac{1}{4} = \frac{13}{4}$$

2. Cancel out common factors
   by dividing by 4.

$$\frac{{}^2\cancel{8}}{3} \times \frac{13}{\cancel{4}_1} = \frac{2}{3} \times \frac{13}{1}$$

3. Multiply the two fractions.

$$\frac{2}{3} \times \frac{13}{1} = \frac{2 \times 13}{3 \times 1} = \frac{26}{3}$$

4. Write your answer as a
   mixed number.

$$\frac{26}{3} = \frac{24}{3} + \frac{2}{3} = 8\frac{2}{3}$$

Exercise 1

Don't use a calculator for this exercise.

1   Work out these multiplications. Give your answers in their simplest terms.

a) $\frac{2}{5} \times \frac{3}{4}$ b) $\frac{1}{4} \times \frac{4}{6}$ c) $\frac{2}{4} \times \frac{3}{12}$ d) $\frac{1}{2} \times \frac{8}{9}$ e) $\frac{3}{3} \times \frac{2}{6}$

f) $\frac{1}{4} \times \frac{4}{7}$ g) $\frac{5}{8} \times \frac{1}{5}$ h) $\frac{2}{3} \times \frac{2}{10}$ i) $\frac{5}{9} \times \frac{3}{5}$ j) $\frac{4}{5} \times \frac{5}{10}$

2 a) Write the following as improper fractions: **i)** $2\frac{1}{3}$ **ii)** $1\frac{1}{4}$

b) Use your answers to **a)** to work out $2\frac{1}{3} \times 1\frac{1}{4}$. Give the answer as a mixed number.

3 Work out these multiplications.
Give your answers as mixed numbers in their simplest terms.

a) $2\frac{1}{3} \times 2\frac{3}{4}$ **b)** $2\frac{2}{5} \times 1\frac{4}{5}$ **c)** $1\frac{4}{5} \times 2\frac{1}{3}$ **d)** $1\frac{3}{5} \times 2\frac{1}{4}$

e) $1\frac{1}{6} \times 2\frac{1}{2}$ **f)** $3\frac{1}{3} \times 1\frac{2}{5}$ **g)** $2\frac{1}{5} \times 3\frac{1}{2}$ **h)** $1\frac{1}{4} \times 3\frac{2}{3}$

i) $2\frac{2}{5} \times 2\frac{1}{5}$ **j)** $3\frac{1}{3} \times 3\frac{1}{6}$ **k)** $1\frac{2}{3} \times 4\frac{2}{5}$ **l)** $2\frac{5}{6} \times 1\frac{1}{8}$

4 Jack spent $3\frac{2}{3}$ hours at the gym one week.

Isaac spent $1\frac{1}{3}$ times longer at the gym than Jack that week.

How long did Isaac spend at the gym?
Give your answer as a mixed number in its simplest form.

5 Jen made $12\frac{3}{4}$ metres of bunting on Saturday.

On Sunday, she made $2\frac{2}{5}$ times more.

Work out the length of bunting that Jen made on Sunday.

6 On Monday Liam cycles $2\frac{3}{5}$ miles. He cycles $1\frac{1}{2}$ times further on Tuesday.

Work out the total distance he travels on Monday and Tuesday.

7 Work out these multiplications.
Give your answers as mixed numbers in their simplest terms.

a) $1\frac{1}{2} \times -1\frac{2}{3}$ **b)** $-2\frac{1}{5} \times -2\frac{2}{3}$ **c)** $-1\frac{4}{5} \times -2\frac{1}{6}$

d) $1\frac{1}{3} \times 1\frac{2}{5} \times 1\frac{1}{4}$ **e)** $1\frac{1}{2} \times 1\frac{1}{5} \times -2\frac{1}{3}$ **f)** $2\frac{1}{6} \times 1\frac{1}{3} \times -1\frac{1}{2}$

Dividing Fractions

To divide by a fraction, you multiply by its <u>reciprocal</u>.
You get the reciprocal by swapping around the <u>numerator</u> and the <u>denominator</u>.

Example 3   **Work out:**

a) $\frac{1}{3} \div \frac{2}{5}$ Multiply $\frac{1}{3}$ by the reciprocal of $\frac{2}{5}$. $\frac{1}{3} \times \frac{5}{2} = \frac{1 \times 5}{3 \times 2} = \frac{5}{6}$

b) $\frac{2}{7} \div 3$ Multiply $\frac{2}{7}$ by the reciprocal of 3.

3 is the same as $\frac{3}{1}$, so its reciprocal is $\frac{1}{3}$. $\frac{2}{7} \times \frac{1}{3} = \frac{2 \times 1}{7 \times 3} = \frac{2}{21}$

c) $8\frac{3}{4} \div 2\frac{1}{3}$ Convert both improper fractions to mixed numbers. $8\frac{3}{4} = \frac{35}{4}, \ 2\frac{1}{3} = \frac{7}{3}$

Multiply $\frac{35}{4}$ by the reciprocal of $\frac{7}{3}$. $\frac{\overset{5}{\cancel{35}}}{4} \times \frac{3}{\cancel{7}_1} = \frac{5 \times 3}{4 \times 1}$

$= \frac{15}{4} = 3\frac{3}{4}$

Exercise 2

Don't use a calculator for this exercise.

1 Work out these calculations. Give your answers in their simplest terms.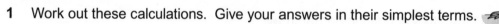

a) $\frac{1}{3} \div \frac{3}{8}$ **b)** $\frac{2}{5} \div \frac{1}{2}$ **c)** $\frac{1}{4} \div \frac{4}{5}$ **d)** $\frac{3}{11} \div \frac{11}{12}$ **e)** $\frac{4}{15} \div \frac{2}{3}$ **f)** $\frac{3}{30} \div \frac{3}{20}$

2 Work out these calculations.

a) $11 \div \frac{3}{9}$ **b)** $7 \div \frac{2}{6}$ **c)** $5 \div \frac{5}{6}$ **d)** $3 \div \frac{4}{12}$ **e)** $12 \div \frac{3}{5}$

3 Work out these calculations. Give your answers in their simplest terms.

a) $\frac{5}{6} \div 5$ **b)** $\frac{6}{9} \div 4$ **c)** $\frac{10}{12} \div 5$ **d)** $\frac{5}{8} \div 5$ **e)** $\frac{3}{11} \div 3$

4 Change the mixed numbers to improper fractions to work out these calculations.
Give your answers in their simplest terms.

a) $2\frac{3}{4} \div 3$ **b)** $1\frac{5}{6} \div 4$ **c)** $4\frac{2}{7} \div 5$ **d)** $3\frac{5}{8} \div 5$ **e)** $2\frac{8}{9} \div 5$

5 Work out these calculations. Give your answers as mixed numbers in their simplest terms.

a) $2\frac{1}{5} \div \frac{1}{3}$ b) $4\frac{2}{7} \div \frac{1}{2}$ c) $2\frac{3}{4} \div \frac{2}{3}$ d) $1\frac{2}{5} \div \frac{3}{5}$ e) $2\frac{2}{3} \div \frac{2}{5}$

6 Work out these calculations. Give your answers as mixed numbers in their simplest terms.

a) $2\frac{4}{5} \div 1\frac{3}{4}$ b) $2\frac{5}{6} \div 2\frac{2}{3}$ c) $2\frac{7}{8} \div 1\frac{3}{4}$ d) $3\frac{2}{3} \div 2\frac{3}{4}$ e) $5\frac{5}{8} \div 2\frac{1}{2}$

7 James shares out $2\frac{6}{8}$ bars of chocolate equally between his 3 brothers.
Work out what fraction of a bar each of his brothers gets.

8 A hard drive has enough storage space left for $7\frac{1}{2}$ hours of TV programs.

How many programs each lasting $\frac{5}{6}$ of an hour can be recorded on the hard drive?

9 Work out: a) $-\frac{2}{7} \div 5$ b) $-\frac{7}{9} \div \frac{5}{6}$ c) $\frac{5}{8} \div -\frac{2}{5}$

10 Find the missing fraction in these calculations:

a) .... $\div \frac{2}{3} = \frac{7}{9}$ b) .... $\div \frac{1}{8} = -\frac{2}{7}$ c) $-\frac{1}{16} \div$ .... $= -\frac{3}{8}$

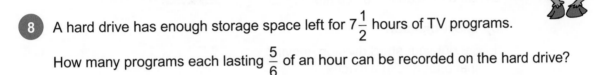

Investigate — Dividing by Tiny Numbers

Unit fractions are those that always have a numerator of 1.
The bigger the denominator of a unit fraction, the smaller the number.

a) What happens when you divide the number 1 by smaller and smaller unit fractions? Try filling in this table to start with.

Unit fractions	$\frac{1}{5}$	$\frac{1}{10}$	$\frac{1}{15}$	$\frac{1}{20}$	$\frac{1}{25}$
1 ÷ unit fraction					

b) Extend the table up to $\frac{1}{100}$. What is happening to the size of the answers?

c) Try plotting the table as a graph (but be careful with the scale for the x-axis).
Can you use the graph to predict what would happen if you divided 1 by 0?

5.3 Changing Fractions to Decimals and Percentages

Fractions and Decimals

All numbers that can be written as fractions are known as rational numbers.

All fractions can be written as a decimal by dividing the numerator by the denominator.

They can either be terminating decimals (with a finite number of decimal places) or recurring decimals. Recurring decimals have a repeating pattern of digits that goes on infinitely.

Example 1 Write $\frac{3}{8}$ as a decimal using:

a) a calculator

Divide 3 by 8 on the calculator.

$\boxed{3} \div \boxed{8} = 0.375$

b) short division

1. Set out your short division, leaving space for decimal places.

$8\overline{)3.000}$

2. Carry out the short division.

0.375
$8\overline{)3.^30^60^40}$

Example 2 Use a calculator to convert the following fractions to decimals.

a) $\frac{2}{3}$

1. Divide 2 by 3 on the calculator.

$\boxed{2} \div \boxed{3}$

2. You get a 'recurring decimal' — one that repeats forever. Show the repeating digit with a dot.

$= 0.66666... = 0.\dot{6}$

b) $\frac{84}{222}$

1. Divide 84 by 222 on the calculator.

$\boxed{8}\boxed{4} \div \boxed{2}\boxed{2}\boxed{2}$

2. You get an answer with a repeating pattern. Show the repeating pattern by putting dots over the first and last digits of the repeated group.

$= 0.378378378... = 0.\dot{3}7\dot{8}$

Exercise 1

1 Use your calculator to write these fractions as decimals.

a) $\frac{5}{8}$ b) $\frac{11}{25}$ c) $\frac{9}{40}$ d) $\frac{1}{16}$ e) $\frac{7}{16}$ f) $\frac{9}{50}$

g) $\frac{9}{375}$ h) $\frac{11}{250}$ i) $\frac{93}{625}$ j) $\frac{33}{24}$ k) $\frac{127}{80}$ l) $\frac{171}{125}$

2 Write these fractions as decimals using short division.

a) $\dfrac{1}{8}$ b) $\dfrac{7}{8}$ c) $\dfrac{17}{8}$ d) $\dfrac{7}{20}$ e) $\dfrac{11}{40}$

3 a) Convert each of these fractions to a decimal:

$\dfrac{5}{8}$ $\dfrac{3}{5}$ $\dfrac{23}{40}$

b) Use your answers to part **a)** to write the three fractions in ascending order.

4 Use your calculator to write these fractions as decimals.

a) $\dfrac{7}{9}$ b) $\dfrac{6}{33}$ c) $\dfrac{5}{18}$ d) $\dfrac{70}{333}$ e) $\dfrac{6}{99}$ f) $\dfrac{12}{88}$

5 Write these mixed numbers as decimals.

a) $2\dfrac{3}{5}$ b) $3\dfrac{7}{8}$ c) $3\dfrac{5}{6}$ d) $2\dfrac{3}{15}$ e) $1\dfrac{6}{125}$ f) $2\dfrac{8}{200}$

6 The fraction $\dfrac{a}{45}$ is equivalent to a decimal between 0.7 and 0.75.

Use a calculator to find the possible integer values of a.

> ## Investigate — Recurring Decimals as Fractions
>
> There's a handy method you can use to change recurring decimals to fractions.
> Let $x = 0.\dot{3}$.
> Here, the repeating bit is 3, so if you multiply by 10
> you'll get one repeating bit on the left of the decimal point: $10x = 3.\dot{3}$
>
> Subtract one from the other: $10x - x = 3.\dot{3} - 0.\dot{3}$
>
> Solve to find x as a fraction: $9x = 3$
>
> $$x = \dfrac{3}{9} = \dfrac{1}{3} \qquad \text{So } 0.\dot{3} \text{ is the same as } \dfrac{1}{3}.$$
>
> Try this with some more recurring decimals.
> If the repeating bit is 2 digits ($0.\dot{1}\dot{8}$) or 3 digits long ($0.\dot{2}3\dot{4}$), multiply by 100 or 1000 to get one repeating chunk to the left of the decimal point.
>
> Are there any patterns in the denominators of the fractions you get from recurring decimals? How is this linked to the method you've been using?

It's easier to write fractions as decimals when the <u>denominator</u> is 10, 100 or 1000.

Remember: $\dfrac{1}{10} = 0.1$ $\dfrac{1}{100} = 0.01$ $\dfrac{1}{1000} = 0.001$

Just put the <u>numerator</u> digits in the right decimal places.

$$\dfrac{135}{1000} = 0.135$$

tenths   hundredths   thousandths

If the fraction has a denominator which is a <u>factor</u> or <u>multiple</u> of 10, 100 or 1000, find the equivalent fraction with a denominator of 10, 100 or 1000 first. Then it's easy to change it into a decimal.

Example 3   **Write $\dfrac{20}{50}$ as a decimal.**

1. First, find a fraction equivalent to $\dfrac{20}{50}$ which has 10, 100 or 1000 as the denominator.

2. Multiply the numerator and denominator by 2 to rewrite the fraction with denominator 100.

$$\dfrac{20}{50} \overset{\times 2}{\underset{\times 2}{=}} \dfrac{40}{100}$$

3. Change the fraction to a decimal. You don't need the extra zero on the end.

$\dfrac{40}{100} = 40$ hundredths

$= 0.40 = \mathbf{0.4}$

Exercise 2

Answer these questions **without using a calculator**.

1 Write these fractions as decimals.

a) $\dfrac{8}{25}$ b) $\dfrac{7}{25}$ c) $\dfrac{3}{5}$ d) $\dfrac{21}{50}$ e) $\dfrac{12}{25}$ f) $\dfrac{11}{25}$ g) $\dfrac{19}{20}$ h) $\dfrac{17}{20}$

2 Write these fractions as decimals.

a) $\dfrac{11}{50}$ b) $\dfrac{13}{25}$ c) $\dfrac{91}{500}$ d) $\dfrac{101}{200}$ e) $\dfrac{201}{500}$ f) $\dfrac{103}{250}$

g) $\dfrac{126}{200}$ h) $\dfrac{99}{200}$ i) $\dfrac{245}{500}$ j) $\dfrac{3}{200}$ k) $\dfrac{9}{250}$ l) $\dfrac{7}{500}$

3 Write the digits 2, 4 and 6 in the gaps to make a correct conversion: $\dfrac{\dotsb}{25} = 0.\dots\ \dots$

4 Damian won some money in a lottery.

He spends $\frac{70}{200}$ of the money and wants to give the rest to charity.

What proportion of the money will he give to charity? Give your answer as a decimal.

You can change a decimal to a fraction by writing it as a fraction with a denominator of 10, 100 or 1000, then simplifying.

Example 4	**Write these decimals as fractions.** **Give your answers in their simplest terms.**

a) 0.4

1. The final digit is in the tenths column, so write a fraction using 10 as the denominator.

2. Simplify the fraction.

$$0.4 = \frac{4}{10} = \frac{2}{5}$$
$\div 2$ (top), $\div 2$ (bottom)

b) 0.142

1. The final digit is in the thousandths column, so write a fraction using 1000 as the denominator.

2. Simplify the fraction.

$$0.142 = \frac{142}{1000} = \frac{71}{500}$$
$\div 2$ (top), $\div 2$ (bottom)

Exercise 3

1 Write these decimals as fractions without using a calculator.
Give your answers in their simplest terms.

a) 0.5   b) 0.8   c) 0.2   d) 0.12   e) 0.44   f) 0.38

g) 0.64   h) 0.04   i) 0.05   j) 0.225   k) 0.045   l) 0.008

2 Write down a fraction that lies between 0.42 and 0.43.

3 Write these decimals as **i)** improper fractions, and **ii)** mixed numbers.

a) 1.03   b) 2.7   c) 1.11   d) 4.39   e) 2.349   f) 1.099

4 Write down 5 fractions between 0.1 and 0.2.

Fractions, Decimals and Percentages

A <u>percentage</u> is a fraction out of 100, so 45% is the same as $\frac{45}{100}$, which simplifies to $\frac{9}{20}$.

To change from a <u>percentage</u> to a <u>decimal</u>, you can divide by 100.
To change from a decimal to a percentage, multiply by 100.

Fraction $\xrightarrow{\text{Divide}}$ Decimal $\xrightarrow{\times\ 100\%}$ Percentage

Fraction $\xleftarrow[\substack{\text{Place Value} \\ \text{(tenths, hundredths etc.)}}]{\text{Use}}$ Decimal $\xleftarrow{\div\ 100\%}$ Percentage

---

Example 5 **Write $\frac{21}{35}$ first as a decimal and then as a percentage.**

1. Divide the top number by the bottom number to get a decimal.

    $21 \div 35 = \mathbf{0.6}$

2. Then multiply by 100 to give the percentage.

    $0.6 \times 100 = \mathbf{60\%}$

Example 6 **Write 45% as both a decimal and as a fraction in its simplest form.**

1. Divide the percentage by 100 to get a decimal.

    $45 \div 100 = \mathbf{0.45}$

2. The final digit of 0.45 is in the hundredths column, so write 0.45 as 45 hundredths.

    $0.45 = \frac{45}{100}$

3. Divide the top and bottom by 5 to simplify the fraction.

    $$\overset{\div\ 5}{\frac{45}{100}} = \frac{9}{20}$$
    $$\underset{\div\ 5}{}$$

Exercise 4

Answer questions 1 to 3 **without using a calculator**.

1 Write these decimals as **i)** percentages, and **ii)** fractions in their simplest form:

    a) 0.67   **b)** 0.77   **c)** 0.01   **d)** 0.84   **e)** 0.45

    f) 0.05   **g)** 0.415   **h)** 0.224   **i)** 0.025   **j)** 0.036

2 Write these fractions as **i)** decimals, and **ii)** percentages:

a) $\dfrac{49}{100}$ b) $\dfrac{3}{10}$ c) $\dfrac{17}{20}$ d) $\dfrac{1}{4}$ e) $\dfrac{11}{25}$ f) $\dfrac{15}{25}$ g) $\dfrac{87}{200}$

3 Write these percentages as **i)** decimals, and **ii)** fractions in their simplest form:

a) 39%   b) 48%   c) 13%   d) 9%   e) 5%   f) 22.5%   g) 4.8%

You **can** use a calculator for questions 4 to 12.

4 Write these fractions as: **i)** decimals, and **ii)** percentages.

a) $\dfrac{13}{20}$ b) $\dfrac{43}{50}$ c) $\dfrac{19}{40}$ d) $\dfrac{33}{40}$ e) $\dfrac{41}{80}$ f) $\dfrac{48}{125}$

5 Jill scored $\dfrac{18}{25}$ in a test. What is her mark as a percentage?

6 James sits an exam and gets a mark of $\dfrac{54}{75}$. What percentage did he get wrong?

7 325 students attend a school. 195 of the students are girls.
Give the proportion of boys at the school as a decimal.

8 $\dfrac{18}{20}$ children in a class prefer dogs to cats. What percentage of the class prefer cats?

9 85% of customers in a cafe ordered soup for lunch.
Write this percentage as a fraction in its simplest form.

10 53% of the people who visited a museum one day were male.
What proportion of the visitors that day were female? Give your answer as a decimal.

11 To pass an exam a student needed to get 0.65 of the questions correct.
How many of the questions out of 200 would she be able to get wrong and still pass?

12 The area of a country is 130 000 km². The area that has been built on is 3000 km².

a) What fraction of the country is built on? Give your answer in its simplest form.

b) Write this fraction as a percentage. Give your answer to 1 decimal place.

Comparing Proportions

If you need to compare some proportions (fractions, decimals or percentages), convert them to the same type of proportion first.

Example 7 Put 16%, $\frac{1}{6}$, and 1.6 in order, from smallest to largest.

Write the amounts in the same form.
(Here, I've chosen to write them all as decimals.)

1. Calculate 16 ÷ 100 to write 16% as a decimal. $\qquad$ 16 ÷ 100 = 0.16

2. Calculate 1 ÷ 6 to write $\frac{1}{6}$ as a decimal. $\qquad$ $\frac{1}{6} = 0.166... = 0.1\dot{6}$

3. Put the decimals in order, from smallest to largest. $\qquad$ 0.16, 0.1$\dot{6}$, 1.6

4. Rewrite in their original forms. $\qquad$ 16%, $\frac{1}{6}$, 1.6

Exercise 5

Answer question 1 **without using a calculator**.

1 For each of the following pairs, write down which is larger.

a) 0.44, 40%   b) 0.3, 3%   c) 0.65, 60%   d) 0.08, 80%

e) 0.3, $\frac{29}{100}$ f) 0.1, $\frac{1}{100}$ g) 0.8, $\frac{3}{4}$ h) 0.01, $\frac{2}{20}$

You **can** use a calculator to answer questions 2 to 9 if you need to.

2 Which is bigger:

a) 43% or $\frac{24}{60}$?   b) $\frac{18}{30}$ or 0.51?   c) 0.85 or $\frac{36}{45}$?

d) 0.41 or $\frac{22}{55}$?   e) $\frac{5}{25}$ or 0.25?   f) 0.9 or $\frac{19}{20}$?

3 Write each set of numbers in order, starting with the smallest:

a) $\frac{11}{44}$, 0.11, 24%   b) 2%, 0.8, $\frac{8}{40}$ c) 0.7, $\frac{21}{28}$, 76%

4 For each of the following lists, write down which amount is **not** equal to the others.

a) 0.25, 40%, $\frac{4}{10}$ **b)** 0.6, 60%, $\frac{6}{100}$ **c)** 0.12, 12%, $\frac{1}{12}$ **d)** 0.3, 3%, $\frac{3}{10}$

e) 0.6, 6%, $\frac{3}{5}$ **f)** 0.4, 44%, $\frac{22}{50}$ **g)** 0.33, 33%, $\frac{33}{50}$ **h)** 0.12, 25%, $\frac{3}{25}$

5 Put the numbers in each of the following lists in order, from largest to smallest.

a) 0.91, 95%, $\frac{18}{20}$ **b)** 0.5, 51%, $\frac{1}{5}$ **c)** 0.6, 23%, $\frac{6}{25}$ **d)** 0.03, 31%, $\frac{3}{10}$

6 Put the numbers in each of the following lists in order, from smallest to largest.

a) 1.02, 92%, $1\frac{2}{10}$ **b)** 13.2, 132%, $1\frac{2}{3}$ **c)** 6.0, 60%, $\frac{6}{100}$

d) 0.9, 91%, $9\frac{2}{10}$ **e)** 2.2, 124%, $2\frac{23}{100}$ **f)** 0.155, 150%, $\frac{15}{100}$

7 Cat buys three identical pies.
On Monday, she eats $\frac{1}{5}$ of the first pie. On Tuesday, she eats 25% of the second pie.
On Wednesday, she eats 0.3 of the third pie.
One which day does she eat the most pie?

8 Arthur is keeping a record of the wildlife in his garden. Of the wildlife he has seen
this month, 22% were birds, 0.12 were hedgehogs and $\frac{23}{50}$ were squirrels.
Which type of wildlife did Arthur see the most of?

9 In a test, Sophie scores 78%. Calum scores $\frac{66}{75}$.
Nadia got 0.89 of the total number of questions correct.
Who got the highest mark?

10 Tom wins at chess 180 times in every 250. Daisy wins three quarters of the time.
Jacob wins 328 times in every 400.

Without using a calculator, work out who has the best percentage score.

5.4 Percentages of Amounts

Finding Percentages Without a Calculator

Finding a <u>percentage</u> of an amount just means finding a <u>proportion</u> of the total number.

Example 1   Without using a calculator, find 40% of £55.

1. 40% is the same as $\frac{2}{5}$. $40\% = \frac{40}{100} = \frac{2}{5}$

2. So find 40% of £55 by dividing by 5 $55 \div 5 \times 2 = \mathbf{£22}$
   and multiplying by 2.

Example 2   Find 17% of £40 without a calculator.

1. First find 10% of £40.

   10% is the same as $\frac{1}{10}$, so divide 40 by 10. $40 \div 10 = 4$

2. Next, find 5%, 1% and 2% of 40:
   5% is 10% ÷ 2. $4 \div 2 = 2$
   1% is 10% ÷ 10. $4 \div 10 = 0.4$
   2% is 1% × 2. $0.4 \times 2 = 0.8$

3. Add together 10%, 5% and 2%   17% of 40 is 4 + 2 + 0.8
   to find 17%. $= \mathbf{£6.80}$

Exercise 1

Do not use a calculator for this exercise.

1   Find each of these percentages:

     a) 10% of 15   **b)** 30% of £120   **c)** 70% of 70 m   **d)** 15% of 90

     e) 35% of 60 cm   **f)** 5% of £500   **g)** 45% of £220   **h)** 80% of 200

2   Dan buys a bike costing £450. He has to leave a 20% deposit at the shop.
    How much is the deposit?

3   240 people filled in a survey about pets.
    10% owned a cat and 35% owned a dog.

     a) How many people owned a cat?

     b) How many people owned a dog?

4 Find each of these percentages:

   a) 20% of 10   **b)** 15% of 20   **c)** 50% of 86 kg   **d)** 2% of 400

   e) 5% of £5.40   **f)** 15% of £180   **g)** 25% of 56   **h)** 3% of 1000

   i) 70% of 220 miles **j)** 4% of 200 m   **k)** 25% of 900   **l)** 13% of 300 g

5 Find each of these percentages:

   a) 1% of £200   **b)** 1% of 6000 km   **c)** 3% of 900   **d)** 1% of 800

   e) 2% of 500   **f)** 6% of 600   **g)** 1% of 400   **h)** 1% of 1000 kg

   i) 4% of 450   **j)** 3% of 150 miles   **k)** 27% of 150   **l)** 16% of £70

6 Find each of these percentages:

   a) 110% of 50   **b)** 125% of 200   **c)** 130% of 300   **d)** 180% of 250

7 Ashley made £60 by selling cupcakes. She donated 31% of this to charity.
   How much did she donate to charity?

8 Mark gets 98% on a science test. How many questions did he get right out of 600?

9 Find each of these percentages:

   a) 2.5% of 80   **b)** 12.5% of £120   **c)** 17.5% of 400 km   **d)** 22.5% of 160 g

---

Investigate — Per-sept-ages

Imagine a number system based on the number 7 instead of a decimal system (based on the number 10). In this number system, proportions are given as 'per-sept-ages', which is the relative number out of 7, rather than out of 100.

For example, 1 percept of 35 would be $\frac{1}{7}$ of 35, or $\frac{35}{7}$ = 5.

a) What would 10 persept of 35 be?

b) What about 10 persept of 100?

c) Can you see any problems with getting answers with decimal places? Can you think of any way to overcome this?

Finding Percentages Using a Calculator

You can also work out percentages of amounts by multiplying the amount by the percentage as a <u>decimal</u>. This decimal is sometimes called a <u>multiplier</u>.

> **Example 3** **Find 87% of 2.8 using your calculator.**
>
> 1. Change 87% to a decimal equivalent $87 \div 100 = 0.87$
>   by dividing by 100.
> 2. Multiply the amount by this decimal. $2.8 \times 0.87 = \mathbf{2.436}$

Exercise 2

Use a calculator to answer these questions.

1   Find each of the following.

   a) 79% of 265   **b)** 52% of 480   **c)** 46% of 250   **d)** 82% of 600

   e) 57% of 216   **f)** 138% of 684   **g)** 9% of 542   **h)** 199% of 214

2   Answer each of the following.

   a) What is 12% of 68 kg?   **b)** What is 65% of 46 cm?   **c)** What is 93% of 178 miles?

   d) What is 7% of 360 km?   **e)** What is 171% of £69?   **f)** What is 128% of £28?

3   Work out:

   a) 16% of 28.4   **b)** 17% of 16.8   **c)** 66% of 26.6   **d)** 18% of 88.8

   e) 169% of 120.6 cm   **f)** 173% of 36.5 kg   **g)** 24.5% of 860 g   **h)** 106.5% of £120

   i) 24.6% of 250 m   **j)** 3.4% of £1200   **k)** 58.2% of 60 kg   **l)** 33.3% of 90 cm

4   Paul is 88% of the way through a 250 mile journey. How far does he have left to travel?

5   The cost of an adult's ticket for a theme park is £36. A child's ticket is 62.5% of the price of an adult's ticket. How much does it cost for one adult ticket and two children's tickets?

6   Kate has 800 g of flour. She uses 17.5% of the flour to make a cake, and 65% of the flour to make some bread. How much flour is left?

5.5 Percentage Change

If something increases by 10%, you've now got 110% of it.

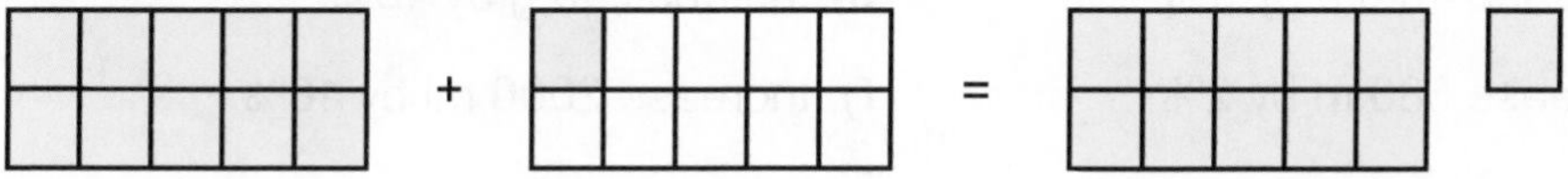

original amount $\frac{1}{10}$ (10% of the original amount) $\frac{11}{10}$ (110% of the original amount)

If something decreases by 10%, you've now got 90% of it left.

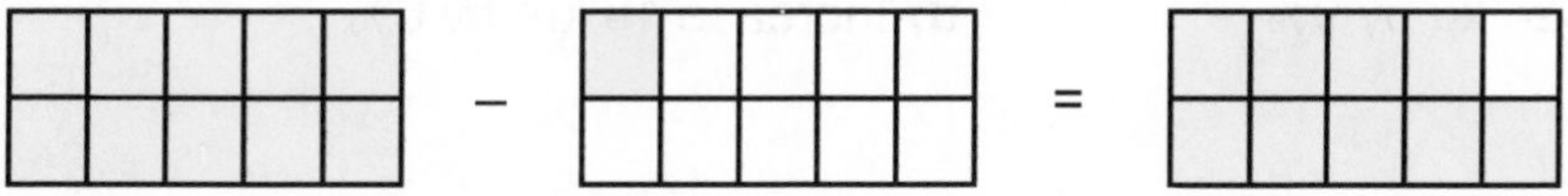

original amount $\frac{1}{10}$ (10% of the original amount) $\frac{9}{10}$ (90% of the original amount)

Example 1 **Increase 250 by 20%:**

a) by using multipliers

1. Work out the total percentage you need to find. $100\% + 20\% = 120\%$

2. You can write this as a fraction... $120\% = \frac{120}{100}$

3. ...and a decimal. $120\% \div 100 = 1.2$

4. Multiply the amount by the decimal to find the answer. $250 \times 1.2 = \mathbf{300}$

b) without using a calculator

1. First find 10% of 250... $10\%: \ 250 \div 10 = 25$

2. ...and use this to find 20%. $20\%: \ 25 \times 2 = 50$

3. Add this to 100% (which is just the full amount that you started with). $120\% = 250 + 50 = \mathbf{300}$

Exercise 1

1 Without using a calculator, increase:

a) 140 by 10%   b) 40 by 30%   c) 600 by 20%   d) 180 by 15%

2 Work out the new amounts when you:

   a) Increase 150 kg by 70%   **b)** Increase 225 km by 98%

   c) Increase 40 cm by 8%   **d)** Increase 15 g by 15%

   e) Increase 580 m by 2%   **f)** Increase 2000 ml by 16%

3 Work out the new amounts when you:

   a) Increase £16 by 20%   **b)** Increase 45 cm by 14%

   c) Increase 124 kg by 9%   **d)** Increase 18 km by 6%

4 For each of these percentage decreases:

   i) convert the percentage to a decimal,
   ii) work out the multiplier by subtracting your decimal in part **i)** from 1,
   iii) multiply the original amount by the multiplier.

   a) Decrease 140 by 24%   **b)** Decrease 80 by 59%

   c) Decrease 700 by 43%   **d)** Decrease 54 by 62%

5 Work out the new amounts when you:

   a) Decrease 800 by 26%   **b)** Decrease 224 by 20%

   c) Decrease 720 by 25%   **d)** Decrease 200 by 13%

   e) Decrease 84 by 45%   **f)** Decrease 90 by 37%

6 **Without** using a calculator, decrease:

   a) 160 by 20%   **b)** 90 by 40%   **c)** 800 by 30%   **d)** 160 by 25%

7 Richard's phone bill is £35 each month. The price goes up by 6%.
How much will he pay each month now?

8 What was the original price of a jacket costing £31.45 that has been reduced by 15% in a sale?

Section 6 — Ratio, Proportion and Rates of Change

6.1 Comparing Quantities Using Fractions and Ratios

Comparing Quantities Using Fractions

You can write one number as a <u>fraction</u> of another by putting the first number over the second and <u>cancelling down</u>. If the first number is bigger than the second, you'll end up with a fraction greater than 1.

If you multiply the fraction by the second number, you end up with the first number again.

Example 1

a) **Write 27 as a fraction of 36.**
   Put 27 over 36 and cancel down.

   $$\div 9$$
   $$\frac{27}{36} = \frac{3}{4}$$
   $$\div 9$$

b) **What fraction must you multiply 36 by to get 27?**
   This is the fraction you've just found.

   Check your answer by doing the
   multiplication: $36 \times \dfrac{3}{4} = 27$.

   $\dfrac{3}{4}$

Exercise 1

For this exercise, give any **fractions** as improper fractions in their **simplest terms**.

1 a) Write 44 as a fraction of 50.   b) Write 125 as a fraction of 150.

    c) Write 19 as a fraction of 95.   d) Write 47 as a fraction of 141.

2 a) Write 85 as a fraction of 15.   b) Write 99 as a fraction of 22.

    c) Write 153 as a fraction of 45.   d) Write 200 as a fraction of 16.

3 a) i) Write 51 as a fraction of 136.   ii) Write 136 as a fraction of 51.

    b) What fraction must you multiply 136 by to get 51?

4 a) i) Write 102 as a fraction of 104.   ii) Write 104 as a fraction of 102.

    b) What fraction must you multiply 102 by to get 104?

5 a) Write 88 as a fraction of 160.

b) Use your answer to part **a)** to write 88 as a percentage of 160.

6 a) Write 96 as a fraction of 40.

b) Use your answer to part **a)** to write 96 as a percentage of 40.

7 a) Write 48 as a percentage of 160.　　**b)** Write 55 as a percentage of 125.

c) Write 18 as a percentage of 360.　　**d)** Write 130 as a percentage of 500.

8 a) Write 19 as a percentage of 10.　　**b)** Write 65 as a percentage of 50.

c) Write 99 as a percentage of 44.　　**d)** Write 300 as a percentage of 240.

9 The contents of a packet of jelly sweets are as follows:

a) Write the number of orange jelly sweets as a fraction of the total number of jelly sweets in the packet.

b) Write the number of red jelly sweets as a fraction of the number of pink jelly sweets.

c) Complete this sentence:

Colour	Number of jelly sweets
Red	16
Yellow	12
Pink	6
Green	8
Orange	7

The number of ☐ sweets as a fraction of the number of ☐ sweets is $\frac{4}{3}$.

10 There are 36 Year 7 students, 27 Year 8 students and 42 Year 9 students on a trip.

a) Write the number of Year 8 students as a percentage of the number of Year 7 students.

b) Write the number of Year 9 students as a fraction of the number of Year 8 students.

11 What fraction must you multiply 75 by to get 135?

12 Fill in the gap in the following multiplication: 98 × ☐ = 154

Comparing Quantities Using Ratios

You can use ratios to compare amounts of things.

You can turn a ratio into a fraction by putting one bit of the ratio on top of the other.

Example 2 A recipe calls for two and a half times as much flour as sugar.

a) Write the amount of flour to the amount of sugar as a ratio.

'Two and a half times' as much flour means that for every 1 part of sugar there must be 2.5 parts of flour. Write this as a ratio. You can multiply both parts of the ratio by 2 to get rid of the decimal.

flour : sugar
= 2.5 : 1
= 5 : 2

b) Write the amount of sugar compared to the amount of flour as a fraction.

Put the numbers from your ratio into a fraction, using the ratio that doesn't have decimals in it. You want to show the amount of sugar, so put that part of the ratio on the top of the fraction.

The recipe needs $\frac{2}{5}$ as much sugar as flour.

Exercise 2

1   Write the following statements as ratios of CDs to DVDs:

   a) Lucy has three and a half times as many CDs as DVDs.

   b) Ricky has one-third as many DVDs as CDs.

   c) Amir has three-fifths as many CDs as DVDs.

   d) Nancy has four and a half times as many DVDs as CDs.

2   Neil has six and a half times as many sheep as cows, and half as many goats as cows on his farm. Write this information as a ratio. Give your answer in the form sheep : cows : goats.

3   A choir has two-thirds as many female members as male members.

   a) Write the number of female to male members as a ratio.

   b) Complete the statement: There are ☐ times as many males as females.

4   A bakery sells only white and wholemeal loaves of bread.
The ratio of white loaves to wholemeal loaves sold is 7 : 3.

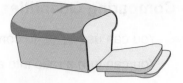

   a) Write the number of wholemeal loaves sold as a fraction
of the number of white loaves sold.

   b) Write the number of white loaves sold as a fraction
of the number of wholemeal loaves sold.

   c) Write the number of white loaves sold as a fraction
of the total number of loaves sold.

5   Harry is given a box of toy lorries and cars. $\dfrac{4}{15}$ of the vehicles in the box are lorries.

   a) What fraction of the vehicles are cars?

   b) Write down the ratio of lorries to cars.

   c) Write the number of cars as a fraction of the number of lorries.

6   The ratio of Irish Setters to Labradors to Great Danes in a class at a dog show is 5 : 3 : 2.
All the dogs in the class are either Irish Setters, Labradors or Great Danes.

   a) Write the number of Irish Setters as a fraction of the number of Labradors.

   b) Write the number of Irish Setters as a percentage of the number of Great Danes.

   c) Write the number of Labradors as a fraction of the total number of dogs in the class.

   <u>**Investigate — Ratio Functions**</u>

   The height and width of a digital photo are to be kept in the
same ratio, no matter how much the photo is enlarged.
The original image is 1200 (height) × 1800 (width) pixels.

   a) Write the ratio of height : width in its simplest form.
(*This is known as the aspect ratio.*)

   b) Write a formula to calculate the height
for any given width.

   c) Draw a graph that would allow you to look up the height
for any given width (and vice versa).

   d) Use the internet to look up different standard aspect ratios
for photos, and repeat steps **a)-c)** for these ratios.

6.2 Ratio Problems

Simplifying Ratios

You can simplify ratios in different ways:

- To simplify integer ratios, divide all the numbers by their highest common factor.

- To write ratios involving decimals as integer ratios, multiply all the numbers by whatever will make them all integers, then cancel down as necessary.

- To write ratios in the form $1:n$ or $n:1$, divide both numbers either by the number on the left (for $1:n$) or by the number on the right (for $n:1$).

Example 1   **Write the ratio 3.5 cm : 21 mm in its simplest form.**

1. Rewrite the ratio so that the units are the same on both sides. Then remove the units altogether.

    1 cm = 10 mm, so 3.5 cm = 35 mm.
    3.5 cm : 21 mm = 35 mm : 21 mm,
    so the ratio is 35 : 21

2. 7 divides into both 35 and 21, so use this to simplify the ratio.

    $35 ÷ 7 = 5$ and $21 ÷ 7 = 3$

    So the ratio can be written as **5 : 3**, which is the simplest form.

Exercise 1

1 Write each of the following ratios in its simplest form.

    a) 20 cm : 1 m   **b)** 20 seconds : 1 minute   **c)** 30p : £1.20

    d) 45 minutes : 1 hour   **e)** 600 g : 1 kg   **f)** 4 cm : 25 mm

    g) 3 km : 900 m   **h)** 30 minutes : 2 hours   **i)** 60p : £2

    j) 2 kg : 300 g   **k)** 6 mm : 18 cm   **l)** 1.8 m : 160 cm

2 For this rectangle, find the ratio of the longer side to the shorter side in its simplest form.

    1.4 m

    70 cm

3 A 3 m ribbon is cut into two pieces. The shorter length measures 0.75 m. Write the ratio of the shorter length to the longer length in the simplest form $a : b$, where a and b are both integers.

4 Write each of the following ratios in its simplest form.

    a) 6 : 3 : 3   **b)** 30 : 18 : 6   **c)** 80 mm : 12 cm : 16 cm

Example 2	Jenny dilutes 500 ml of squash with 2.5 litres of water. Write the ratio of squash to water in the form $1:n$.

1. Write the ratio of squash to water.   500 ml : 2.5 litres

2. Rewrite the ratio so that the units are the same on both sides. Then remove the units altogether.   1 litre = 1000 ml, so 2.5 litres = 2500 ml. The ratio is 500 : 2500

3. Simplify the ratio — it needs to be in the form $1:n$, so divide both sides by 500. $500 \div 500 = 1$ and $2500 \div 500 = 5$ So the ratio is **1:5** — for every ml of squash, Jenny uses 5 ml of water.

Exercise 2

1 Write each of the following ratios in the form $1:n$.

a) 2 : 10   b) 3 : 18   c) 6 : 9   d) 8 : 20

e) 20 : 15   f) 12 : 6   g) 40 : 24   h) 100 : 45

2 Write each of the following ratios in the form $n:1$.

a) 18 : 9   b) 25 : 5   c) 12 : 10   d) 8 : 5

e) 6 : 20   f) 4 : 25   g) 40 : 200   h) 45 : 180

3 a) Write each of the following ratios in the form $1:n$.

i) 40 cm : 1 m   ii) 30 seconds : 2 mins   iii) £3.60 : 90p   iv) 3 litres : 300 ml

b) Write each of the following ratios in the form $n:1$.

i) 4.5 km : 900 m   ii) £4.80 : 60p   iii) 30 minutes : 4 hours   iv) 750 g : 1.5 kg

4 Jim has 14 pencils and 35 pens. Write the ratio of pencils to pens in the form $1:n$.

5 Lisa makes some green paint by mixing 400 ml of blue paint with 3.2 litres of yellow paint. How much blue paint does she use for every litre of yellow paint?

6 Sarah and Anna share $600 between them. Sarah gets $278. Write the ratio of Sarah's money to Anna's in the form $1:n$, rounding your ratio to 2 decimal places.

Using Ratios

You can use ratios to solve problems.

You can scale up a ratio by multiplying each side of the ratio by the same number.

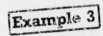 **Example 3** The ratio of caster sugar to demerara sugar in a recipe is 5:4. If 250 g of demerara sugar is used, how much caster sugar is used?

1. Work out what you need to multiply by to go from 4 to 250 on the right-hand side.

2. Multiply the left-hand side by the same number to find the amount of caster sugar used.

$250 \div 4 = 62.5$

caster sugar : demerara sugar

$\times 62.5 \left(\begin{array}{c} 5:4 \\ 312.5:250 \end{array} \right) \times 62.5$

So **312.5 g of caster sugar** is used

Exercise 3

1   Purple paint is made by mixing blue paint and red paint in the ratio 5:12.
    If 12.5 litres of blue paint are used, how many litres of red paint are needed?

2   In a recipe, flour and butter are used in the ratio 8:3.
    If 100 g of flour are used, how much butter is needed?

3   Shaun and Ben share some money in the ratio 11:7.
    If Ben gets £45.50, how much does Shaun get?

4   The ratio of Tom's height to Lisa's height is 8:5. If Tom is 1.68 m tall, how tall is Lisa?

5   Milly and Lotte are knitting scarves. For every 6 cm that Milly knits, Lotte knits 11 cm.
    If Milly knits a scarf that is 1.2 m long, how long will Lotte's scarf be in metres?

6   Jacqueline invests some money in bank accounts A and B in the ratio 12:13.
    If she invests £3750 in account A, how much does she invest in account B?

7   The ratio of Leo's age to Caroline's age is 2:3. Caroline is 15 years old.
    In how many years will the ratio of their ages be 3:4?

You can use ratios to <u>divide</u> an amount into two or more shares. Use the total number of parts to find the size of one part, then use this to find the size of each share.

| Example 4 | Divide £51 in the ratio 2:3. |

1. Add up the numbers in the ratio to find the total number of parts.

    2 + 3 = 5 parts altogether

2. Work out the amount for one part.

    5 parts = £51,
    so 1 part = £51 ÷ 5 = **£10.20**

3. Then multiply the amount for one part by the number of parts in each share.

    £10.20 × 2 = £20.40
    £10.20 × 3 = £30.60

4. To check, add up the shares — you should get the original amount.

    So the shares are **£20.40** and **£30.60**
    (and £20.40 + £30.60 = £51).

Exercise 4

1 **a)** Divide 24 in the ratio 1:3. **b)** Divide 31.5 in the ratio 3:4.

  c) Divide 95 in the ratio 3:7. **d)** Divide 136.5 in the ratio 6:7.

2 Share 40 kg in the following ratios:

  a) 1:3 **b)** 1:7 **c)** 5:11 **d)** 15:17

3 Find the larger amount when each of these amounts is divided into the given ratio.

  a) 170 ml in the ratio 7:13 **b)** 127.5 cm in the ratio 11:14

  c) £300 in the ratio 11:13 **d)** 550 g in the ratio 9:11

4 Justin and Lee share £6350 in the ratio 17:23. How much does each person get?

5 In a school of 1600 pupils, the ratio of pupils who wear glasses to pupils who don't wear glasses is 31:69. How many pupils don't wear glasses?

6 Hannah bakes 200 cakes. She puts $\frac{2}{5}$ of the cakes in the freezer.

  She ices the remaining cakes with white or blue icing in the ratio 1:2. How many cakes have blue icing?

> **Example 5** Green paint is made by mixing blue paint and yellow paint in the ratio 4:9. It takes 26 litres of paint to paint a room. How much yellow paint is needed?
>
> 1. Add up the numbers in the ratio to find the total number of parts.
>   4 + 9 = 13 parts altogether
>
> 2. Work out the amount for one part.
>   13 parts = 26 litres,
>   so 1 part = 26 litres ÷ 13 = 2 litres
>
> 3. Then multiply the amount for one part by the number of parts for yellow paint.
>   2 litres × 9 = **18 litres** of yellow paint

Exercise 5

1 Sonya and Alfonse each have a job that pays them £5 per hour. The ratio of the hours they work is 2:3, and they work for 125 hours in total between them. How much does Alfonse earn?

2 Alyssa and Paul have a combined height of 240 cm. Their heights are in the ratio 5:7. To ride a rollercoaster at a theme park, you must be over 1.1 m tall. Is Alyssa tall enough to ride the rollercoaster?

3 Leanne and Kyle have a combined age of 72. Their ages are in the ratio 2:7. How much older than Leanne is Kyle?

4 Katie is making bags of cake mixture. Each bag weighs 750 g, and the ratio of flour to sugar in each bag is 16:9. How many grams of sugar will she need to make 6 bags?

5 A ship is carrying gold bars and silver bars in the ratio 13:17. The ship's load weighs 600 kg in total. If each bar weighs 5 kg, how many gold bars is the ship carrying?

> ## Investigate — Birthday Money
>
> A girl is exactly one year older than her little brother. Every year on their joint birthday, they receive £100, split in the ratio of their ages.
>
> **a)** What happens to the difference in the amounts they receive as they grow up? Will the boy receive the same amount on his tenth birthday as his sister did on her tenth birthday?
>
> **b)** Is this a fair way to split up the money? Does it get more or less fair as time goes on, or does it stay the same?

6.3 Percentage Change Problems

Percentage Increase and Decrease Problems

To increase or decrease something by a percentage, first find the <u>percentage change</u> as a decimal (called the <u>multiplier</u>), then multiply the original amount by the multiplier to find the new amount.

> For a percentage increase, the multiplier is greater than 1
> (so for an increase of 20%, multiply by 1 + 0.2 = 1.2).
> For a percentage decrease, the multiplier is less than 1
> (so for a decrease of 20%, multiply by 1 − 0.2 = 0.8).

Example 1 | **A dress costing £52 is reduced by 12% in a sale. What is the new price of the dress?**

1. Work out the multiplier as a decimal.   1 − 0.12 = 0.88

2. Multiply the original amount by the   £52 × 0.88 = £45.76
   multiplier to find the new amount.   So the dress costs **£45.76** in the sale.

Exercise 1

1 After a baby boom, the number of penguins in a zoo increases by 25%.
   There were 56 penguins originally. How many are there after the baby boom?

2 A TV costing £450 is reduced by 11% in a sale.
   What is the new price of the TV?

3 Standard concert tickets cost £48. A front-row ticket costs 72% more.
   How much does a front-row ticket cost?

4 In a coffee shop, it costs 5% more to sit inside the shop.
   If a takeaway coffee costs £2.20, how much would it cost
   to have the same coffee inside?

5 A cardigan usually costs £18.50, but is being sold with a 16% discount
   because it has a button missing. What is the new price of the cardigan?

6   Morgan earns £638 a month. He gets a pay rise of 2.5%.
How much does he now earn each month?

7   At the start of the year, 120 girls and 125 boys were having swimming lessons.
During the year, the number of girls having swimming lessons increased by 15%
and the number of boys having swimming lessons decreased by 20%.
How many children in total were having swimming lessons at the end of the year?

8   Bus fares increase by 8%. How much would a £2.25 ticket cost after the increase?

9   A meal at a restaurant cost £145. The restaurant adds on a 12%
service charge to the bill. The Snow family decide to leave an
extra tip of 5% of the new total. How much did they pay in total?

10 A hotel bill came to £364. Sam has a voucher for 10% off. The hotel then decided to
knock 15% off his final bill because of building work. How much did Sam pay in total?

11 In January, the cost of a TV is £400. In February, the shop increases the cost by 15%.
In March, the shop has a 15% off sale. What is the cost of the TV in March?

12 A market trader increases his prices by 5%. Six months later, he increases them again,
this time by 8%. A watch cost £50 before the increases. Find its new price.

Finding the Percentage Change

To find a percentage change (either an increase or decrease):
*   calculate the difference between the new amount and the original amount
*   find this as a percentage of the original amount using the formula:

$$\textbf{percentage change} = \frac{\textbf{change}}{\textbf{original}} \times \textbf{100}$$

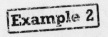 **Example 2**   **In a sale, the cost of a pair of shoes is reduced from
£60 to £51. Find the percentage decrease.**

1. Find the difference between the   £60 – £51 = £9
    new cost and the original cost.
                                          percentage change = $\frac{9}{60} \times 100$
2. Put the numbers into the formula
    to find the percentage decrease.   = **15%**

Exercise 2

1 **a)** Find the percentage increase when:

      i) a price of £32 is increased to £36.48.   **ii)** a price of £55 is increased to £70.95.

   b) Find the percentage decrease when:

      i) a price of £14 is decreased to £12.32.   **ii)** a price of £46 is decreased to £34.96.

2 At 8 am, there are 36 cars parked on a car park. At 9 am, there are 45 cars parked on the same car park. Find the percentage increase in the number of cars parked.

3 At the start of a race, the mass of fuel in a car is 145 kg. Halfway through the race, the mass has dropped to 92.8 kg. Find the percentage decrease in fuel.

4 Moyo's monthly rent increases from £425 to £463.25. Find the percentage increase.

5 Eddie's swimming pool has sprung a leak. At the start of the day, the depth of water in the pool was 1.96 m, and by the end of the day the depth was 1.47 m. Find the percentage decrease in the depth of the water.

6 A house increases in price from £245 000 to £279 300. What is the percentage increase?

7 Ty buys a boat for £134. It loses £5.36 in value each month. Find the percentage loss after 6 months.

8 A motorbike is bought for £8300. Two years later, it is sold for £5976. After another five years, it is sold for £2689.20.

   a) Find the percentage decrease in the motorbike's price over the first two years.

   b) Find the percentage decrease in the motorbike's price over the next five years.

   c) Find the percentage decrease in the motorbike's price over the whole seven years.

9 It costs £42 to make 15 gingerbread houses. They are all sold at a Christmas fair for £4.06 each. Work out the percentage profit.

Finding the Original Value

If you know the <u>percentage change</u> and the new value, you can use this information to find the original value. There are two ways of doing this:

Divide to find 1% then multiply to find 100%:
- Write the amount in the question as a percentage of the original value.
- Divide to find 1% of the original value.
- Multiply by 100 to give the original value (= 100%).

The multiplier method:
- First find the <u>multiplier</u> (remember that for a 10% increase, the multiplier is 1.1, and for a 10% decrease the multiplier is 0.9).
- Divide the new value by the multiplier — this will give you the original value.

Example 3   **Lisa's monthly salary increases by 10% to £770.**
What was her monthly salary before the increase?

1. An increase of 10% means £770 represents 110% of the original value.   £770 = 110%

2. Divide by 110 to find 1% of the original value.   £770 ÷ 110 = £7 (= 1%)

3. Multiply by 100 to find the original value.   £7 × 100 = **£700** (= 100%)

Example 4   **In a sale, a t-shirt is reduced by 20% to £12.80.**
Find what it cost before the sale.

1. Find the multiplier.   1 − 0.2 = 0.8

2. Divide the new amount by the multiplier to find the original amount.   £12.80 ÷ 0.8 = £16
So the t-shirt cost **£16** before the sale.

Exercise 3

1   A shop increases its prices by 20% The new price of a toaster is £24.

a) What percentage of the original amount does £24 represent?

b) Find 1% of the original value.

c) Use your answer to part **b)** to find the original value.

d) What multiplier would you use to answer the same question?

2 A shop is having a 10% off sale. The sale prices of a number of items are given below. Find the original price of each item.

a) a scarf costing £9 in the sale.

b) a skirt costing £13.50 in the sale.

c) a belt costing £5.40 in the sale.

3 A restaurant automatically adds on a 20% service charge to every bill. Find the price before the service charge for a bill of:

a) £36

b) £60

c) £78

4 An armchair costs £175 after a 30% discount. Find the original price of the armchair.

5 Brandon receives an electricity bill of £32.55, which is 5% higher than the bill for the previous month. How much was his bill last month?

6 A statue has increased in value by 40% and is now worth £840. Find the original value of the statue.

7 Linda is selling her car for £6600, which is 45% less than the price she paid for it. How much did she pay for the car?

8 A house increases in value by 12% to £252 000. How much was it originally worth?

9 A red dress costs £55.20 after an 8% discount. A blue dress costs £56.96 after an 11% discount. Which dress cost more before the discounts?

10 Jamie sells his house for £320 000, which is 25% more than he bought it for. When he bought it, he had a budget of £260 000. How much under his budget was the house when he bought it?

Interest

Simple interest is where a certain percentage of an initial investment or loan is added on to it at regular intervals (e.g. once a month or once a year). This means that the amount of interest is the **same** every time it's added on.

Compound interest is where each amount of interest is calculated using the new total, rather than the original amount, so the amount of interest **changes** each time it's added. Banks often pay compound interest instead of simple interest.

| Example 5 | Grace invests £500 in an account that pays 3% interest each year. Work out how much will be in the account after two years if the interest is: |

a) Simple

1. Each year, she earns 3% of £500, so multiply 500 by 0.03.

   $£500 \times 0.03 = £15$
   She earns £15 interest in 1 year

2. Multiply this amount by 2 to find the interest earned in two years, and add this on to the original amount.

   $£15 \times 2 = £30$
   $£500 + £30 = £530$

b) Compound

1. Multiply 500 by 1.03 to find the amount in the account after 1 year.

   $£500 \times 1.03 = £515$

2. Then multiply this new amount by 1.03 to find the amount in the account after 2 years.

   $£515 \times 1.03 = £530.45$

Exercise 4

1 Theo invests £800 in an account that pays 2% simple interest each year.

a) Work out how much interest is earned in a year.

b) Work out how much there will be in the account after 5 years.

c) Work out how much there will be in the account after 10 years.

2 Kamui invests £2000 in an account that pays 1% simple interest each month. Work out how much will be in the account:

a) after 3 months

b) after 8 months

c) after 1 year

3 When Jessica was born, her parents invested £2500 in an account that pays 2.5% simple interest each year. Work out how much will be in the account on Jessica's 21st birthday.

4 Emilia invests £5000 in an account that pays 2% simple interest and leaves it for 5 years. Lucy invests £4500 in an account that pays 5% simple interest and leaves it for 3 years.

a) Who will have the most money at the end of the investment period?

b) How much more money will she have?

5 Philip invests £1500 in an account that pays 3% compound interest each year. Work out how much will be in the account, to the nearest penny:

a) after 1 year   **b)** after 2 years   **c)** after 4 years

6 A bank pays 4% compound interest each year. Work out how much money will be in each account at the end of the investment. Give your answers to the nearest penny.

a) £400 invested for 2 years   **b)** £600 invested for 3 years

c) £500 invested for 4 years   **d)** £800 invested for 5 years

7 William has a debt of £1500 which increases by 2% compound interest each year. Work out how much money, to the nearest penny, he will owe:

a) after 3 years   **b)** after 5 years

8 Lloyd invests £2000 in an account that pays 1.5% interest each year. Work out how much will be in the account after 4 years, to the nearest penny, if the interest is:

a) simple   **b)** compound

9 Stefan wants to invest £5000 for 6 years. Account A pays 2.5% simple interest each year. Account B pays 2% compound interest each year. Which account should he choose?

> ## Investigate — Compound Decay
>
> A radioactive substance decays at a compound rate of 2% per day. A scientist has 250 g of the substance.
>
> **a)** How much will there be after 1 day? How much will there be after 2 days? How much will be left after 4 days?
>
> **b)** How many days will it take before there is less than 200 g left?
>
> **c)** Can you come up with a quick way to work out the amount of the substance left after a larger number of days?

6.4 Direct and Inverse Proportion

Direct Proportion

If two things are in <u>direct proportion</u>, then the <u>ratio</u> between them is always the same. If you increase one thing, the other increases at the same rate.

The graph of two things in direct proportion is a straight line that goes through the <u>origin</u>. The <u>equation</u> of a straight line through the origin is $y = Ax$ for some number A, so all direct proportions can be written as an equation in this form.

Example 1 200 ml of honey weighs 280 g.

a) Given that mass and volume are directly proportional, work out how much 300 ml of honey will weigh.

1. Divide 280 by 200 to find how much 1 ml of honey weighs.

   1 ml:
   $280 \div 200 = 1.4$ g

2. Multiply by 300 to find how much 300 ml of honey weighs.

   300 ml:
   $1.4 \times 300 = \textbf{420 g}$

b) Let m be the mass of honey in grams and v be the volume in millilitres. Write an equation in the form $m = Av$ to represent this direct proportion.

1. Find the value of A by putting $m = 280$ and $v = 200$ into the equation.

   $280 = 200A$
   $1.4 = A$

2. Put the value of A back into the equation. $m = \textbf{1.4}v$

c) Sketch a graph to represent this direct proportion.

Draw a straight line from the origin and label a point with the values you know (volume = 200 ml, mass = 280 g).

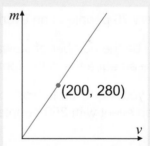

Exercise 1

1 Which of these three graphs shows a direct proportion?

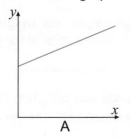

A

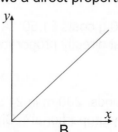

B

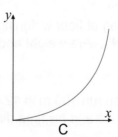

C

2 In an hour, 4 children can pick 34 kg of apples from an orchard.
How many kg of apples could 9 children pick in an hour?

3 A team of 6 cleaners can clean 165 hotel rooms per day.
How many rooms per day could a team of 10 cleaners clean?

4 At a coffee morning, 3 people serve 165 cups of coffee in an hour.

a) How many cups of coffee could 8 people serve in an hour?

b) Let C be the number of cups of coffee served and p be the number of people serving coffee. Write an equation in the form $C = Ap$ to represent this direct proportion.

c) Sketch a graph to represent this direct proportion.

5 A piece of metal with a volume of 200 cm³ has a mass of 500 g.

a) How much would a piece of the same metal with a volume of 900 cm³ weigh?

b) Let m be the mass in grams and v be the volume in cm³.
Write an equation in the form $m = Av$ to represent this direct proportion.

c) Sketch a graph to represent this direct proportion.

6 For every 75 people at an event, there must be 6 stewards.

a) Let s be the number of stewards and p be the number of people.
Write an equation in the form $s = Ap$ to represent this direct proportion.

b) Use your equation to work out how many stewards there must be
for an event with 250 people attending.

7 A direct proportion is represented by the equation $b = 0.2c$.
Work out the value of c when $b = 35$.

8 A small bag of flour weighing 600 g costs £1.50. A large bag of flour weighing 1.5 kg costs £2.40. Are weight and cost directly proportional? Give a reason for your answer.

9 Jordan can run 100 m in 12 seconds, 200 m in 24 seconds and 500 m in 100 seconds.
Are distance and his time directly proportional? Give a reason for your answer.

Inverse Proportion

If two things are in <u>inverse proportion</u>,
one increases as the other decreases.

The general <u>equation</u> for inverse proportion is

$y = \dfrac{A}{x}$ for some number A.

The graph of an inverse proportion looks like this:

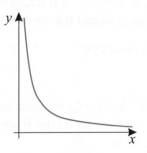

Example 2	A team of 12 window cleaners take 20 minutes to clean the windows of an office. If there are 15 window cleaners in the team, it takes them 16 minutes.

a) How long would it take a team of 8 window cleaners?

1. First, work out how long it would take 1 window cleaner by multiplying 20 minutes by 12. (You can check this value by dividing by 15 to see if it gives you the time for 15 window cleaners.)

   $12 \times 20 = 240$ minutes for 1 window cleaner ($240 \div 15 = 16$ minutes for 15 window cleaners, as expected)

2. Divide by 8 to find the time for 8 window cleaners.

   $240 \div 8 = \textbf{30 minutes}$ for 8 window cleaners

b) Let t be the time taken and w be the number of window cleaners.

Write an equation in the form $t = \dfrac{A}{w}$ to represent this inverse proportion.

1. Find the value of A by putting $w = 12$ and $t = 20$ into the equation.

   $20 = \dfrac{A}{12}$, so A = 240

2. Put the value of A back into the equation.

   $t = \dfrac{240}{w}$

Exercise 2

1   Some children are doing a litter pick. It takes 10 children 4 hours to pick up all the litter on a beach. How long would it take 16 children to pick up the litter from the same beach?

2   It takes 4 chefs 15 minutes to cut all the vegetables for the soup of the day. How long would it take 3 chefs to chop the same amount of vegetables?

3   It takes 3 children 6 hours to build a snow fort. How long would it take 12 children to build the same snow fort?

4   It takes 5 teachers 6 hours to mark a set of exam papers.
How long would it take to mark the same set of exams if there were:

   a) 15 teachers   **b)** 6 teachers   **c)** 12 teachers?

5   It takes 6 parents an hour and a half to make paper chains for a party.
How long would it take 9 parents to make the same paper chains?

6   It takes 7 people 30 minutes to move a pile of logs onto a trailer.
How long would it take 6 people to move the same pile of logs?

7   It takes 3 prisoners 8 months to dig a tunnel.

   a) How long would it take 4 prisoners to dig the same tunnel?

   b) Let t be the time taken to dig the tunnel and p be the number of prisoners.
   Write an equation in the form $t = \dfrac{A}{p}$ to represent this inverse proportion.

8   It takes 12 gardeners 15 minutes to plant some roses.

   a) How long would it take 5 gardeners to plant the same number of roses?

   b) Let t be the time taken to plant the roses and n be the number of gardeners.
   Write an equation in the form $t = \dfrac{A}{n}$ to represent this inverse proportion.

   ### Investigate — Other Types of Proportion

   There are other types of direct proportion.
   For example, the area of an enlarged shape is
   proportional to the scale factor squared.
   The graph of this proportion would look like this:

   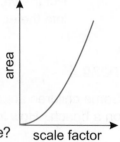

   a) A square with an area of 25 cm² is enlarged by a
   scale factor of 2. What is the area of the enlarged square?

   b) Find the area if the same square is enlarged by a scale factor of 3, 4 or 5.

   c) Use your results from part **b)** to write proportionality statements.
   For example, for part **a)**, 'when you enlarge by a scale factor of 2,
   the area is 4 times bigger'. Do this for a scale factor of 3, 4 and 5.

   d) Can you think of any other situations where
   one thing is proportional to another thing squared?

Section 7 — Units and Scales

7.1 Changing Units

Metric and Imperial Conversions

You can convert between different <u>metric units</u> using these conversions:

Length:	Mass:	Volume:
1 cm = 10 mm	1 kg = 1000 g	1 litre (l) = 1000 ml
1 m = 100 cm	1 tonne = 1000 kg	1 ml = 1 cm^3
1 km = 1000 m		

You can use these conversions to convert <u>areas</u> too — but you have to use the <u>conversion factor</u> twice. So to convert mm^2 to cm^2, divide by 10, then divide by 10 again.

Example 1   **Convert 0.182 m^2 into cm^2.**

1. There are 100 cm in 1 metre, so the conversion factor is 100 (remember, for areas use the conversion factor twice).

         1 m = 100 cm

    0.182 m^2 = (0.182 × 100 × 100) cm^2

2. cm^2 are smaller than m^2, so multiply by the conversion factor twice.

         = **1820 cm^2**

Exercise 1

For questions **1-3**, convert each measurement into the units given.

1
   a) 6 cm into mm
   b) 4 litres into ml
   c) 6 kg into g

   d) 3 km into m
   e) 7 kg into tonnes
   f) 48 cm^3 into ml

   g) 3.15 tonnes into kg
   h) 2.25 cm into m
   i) 5.26 kg into g

   j) 1.05 tonnes into kg
   k) 2273 cm^3 into litres
   l) 0.271 km into mm

2
   a) 30 mm into cm
   b) 5000 g into kg
   c) 8000 ml into litres

   d) 12 g into kg
   e) 63 mm in m
   f) 280 kg into tonnes

   g) 9430 ml into litres
   h) 35 m into mm
   i) 2000 cm into km

   j) 81 cm^3 into litres
   k) 2.31 tonnes into g
   l) 292.2 m into km

3 a) 12.8 m into mm   **b)** 2150 cm³ into litres   **c)** 4400 cm into km

    d) 0.74 tonnes into g   **e)** 495 mm into m   **f)** 874 100 g into tonnes

    g) 4.15 litres into cm³   **h)** 6.892 m into mm   **i)** 7.65 km into cm

4 Convert the following area measurements into the units given.

    a) 4 cm² into mm²   **b)** 5 km² into m²   **c)** 1600 cm² into m²

    d) 50 000 mm² into m²   **e)** 12 km² into m²   **f)** 6 130 000 cm² into km²

5 Write each set of measurements in order of size, starting with the smallest.

    a) 76 cm, 745 mm, 0.704 m   **b)** 51 mm, 0.5 cm, 0.5 m

    c) 2 km, 2100 m, 2.01 km   **d)** 0.4 km, 491 cm, 4.2 m

    e) 254 cm, 2544 mm, 0.25 m   **f)** 1002 m, 1.02 km, 1 km

    g) 0.61 km, 6100 cm, 611 m   **h)** 0.02 km, 22 m, 202 cm

    i) 0.2 km, 2010 cm, 20 m   **j)** 5 cm, 0.005 km, 0.5 m

6 Write each set of areas in order of size, starting with the smallest.

    a) 1 km², 1 m², 1 cm²   **b)** 44 m², 400 cm², 0.4 km²

    c) 18 100 cm², 1.08 m², 0.0018 km²   **d)** 22 m², 222 000 cm², 0.0000002 km²

    e) 62 m², 0.00062 km² , 62 100 000 cm²,   **f)** 0.14 m², 0.0014 km², 140 000 cm²

7 A bottle contains 1.2 litres of lemonade. Amy drinks 0.4 litres of the lemonade and Jack drinks 650 ml of the lemonade. How much of the lemonade is left?

8 Sugar is sold in bags with a mass of 2 kg.
Chloe runs a cake-baking business.
She bakes 20 cakes a day. She uses 340 g of sugar in each cake.
How many bags of sugar does Chloe use in 5 days?

9 A pot of paint will cover an area of 8000 cm².
How many pots will be needed to paint a wall with area 3.2 m²?

Imperial units are things like inches, feet and miles for lengths, pounds and ounces for mass and pints and gallons for volume.

You can convert between different imperial units using these conversions:

Length:

1 foot = 12 inches

1 yard = 3 feet

Mass:

1 pound = 16 ounces

1 stone = 14 pounds

Volume:

1 gallon = 8 pints

You can convert between metric and imperial units using these conversions:

Length:

1 inch ≈ 2.5 cm

1 foot ≈ 30 cm

1 yard ≈ 90 cm

1 mile ≈ 1.6 km

Mass:

1 ounce ≈ 28 g

1 pound ≈ 450 g

1 stone ≈ 6400 g

1 kg ≈ 2.2 pounds

Volume:

1 pint ≈ 0.57 litres

1 gallon ≈ 4.5 litres

'≈' means 'approximately equal to'.

Example 2 **Convert these units:**

a) 3.5 gallons into pints.

1. There are 8 pints in 1 gallon, so the conversion factor is 8.

2. Pints are smaller than gallons, so multiply by the conversion factor.

$\qquad$ 1 gallon = 8 pints

$\qquad$ 3.5 gallons = (3.5 × 8) pints

$\qquad$ = **28 pints**

b) 1800 g into pounds.

1. There are approximately 450 g in 1 pound, so the conversion factor is 450.

2. Pounds are bigger than grams, so divide by the conversion factor.

$\qquad$ 450 g ≈ 1 pound

$\qquad$ 1800 g ≈ (1800 ÷ 450) pounds

$\qquad$ = **4 pounds**

Exercise 2

For questions **1-4**, convert each measurement into the units given.

1 **a)** 27 feet into yards

b) 3.5 pounds into ounces

c) 120 pints into gallons

d) 160 ounces into pounds

2 **a)** 18 inches into feet and inches

b) 104 pounds into stones and pounds

3   **a)** 10 inches into cm   **b)** 6 pounds into g   **c)** 2 stone into g

   d) 15 yards into cm   **e)** 3 ounces into g   **f)** 4 gallons into litres

   g) 15 feet into cm   **h)** 8 miles into km   **i)** 7 pints into litres

4   **a)** 360 cm into yards   **b)** 64 000 g into stones   **c)** 72 litres into gallons

   d) 114 litres into pints   **e)** 210 cm into feet   **f)** 1350 g into pounds

   g) 75 cm into inches   **h)** 11 pounds into kg   **i)** 182 g into ounces

5   **a)** Convert 5 feet into cm.

   b) Use your answer to part **a)** to convert 5 feet into m.

6   **a)** Convert 9 pints into litres.

   b) Use your answer to part **a)** to convert 9 pints into cm³.

7   **a)** Convert 58 yards into metres and centimetres.

   b) Convert 1.95 m into feet and inches.

   c) Convert 50 pounds into kilograms and grams.

   d) Convert 5 feet and 8 inches into metres and centimetres.

8   An electric car can travel 245 miles on one charge. Paula has a meeting 400 km away.
   Can she drive there without stopping to charge the car?

9   A wind-up robot can travel 20 m on a single wind. How many times
   will it need winding to cover a distance of half a mile?

10   The height of a house is 7 yards. A tree next to the house is 6 feet high, and grows at an
   average rate of 3 inches per month. If the tree is not cut down, estimate how long it will be
   before the tree is taller than the house.

7.2 Compound Measures — Speed and Density

Calculating Speed, Distance and Time

Speed, distance and time are connected by the formula:

$$\text{Speed} = \frac{\text{Distance}}{\text{Time}}$$

Speed units (e.g. km/h) are a combination of the distance units (e.g. km) and time units (e.g. hours).

You can rearrange the speed formula to find distance or time:

$$\text{Distance} = \text{Speed} \times \text{Time} \qquad \text{Time} = \frac{\text{Distance}}{\text{Speed}}$$

The units of the answer will be in terms of the units in the question — so if you had a speed in mph and a time in hours, the distance would be in miles.

Example 1

Sunita walks 4 km to her friend's house at an average speed of 6 km/h. She sets off at 10:30 am. What time will she arrive at her friend's house?

1. Use the formula for time and put in the numbers for speed and distance.

$$\text{Time} = \frac{\text{Distance}}{\text{Speed}} = \frac{4}{6} = \frac{2}{3} \text{ of an hour}$$

2. Convert your answer into minutes.

$$\left(\frac{2}{3} \times 60\right) \text{ mins} = 40 \text{ mins}$$

3. Add on the number of minutes to the time she set off to find her arrival time.

Arrival time = 10:30 am + 40 mins
= **11:10 am**

Exercise 1

1 Work out each speed from the time (t) and distance (d) given.

    a) t = 3 seconds, d = 6 m   **b)** d = 18 m, t = 4 seconds   **c)** t = 12 seconds, d = 72 m

    d) d = 6 km, t = 24 mins   **e)** t = 82 mins, d = 262.4 km   **f)** d = 224 km, t = 3.2 h

2 Mo can run a mile in 6 minutes. Use conversions to work out his average speed in km/h.

3 Jess cycles for 15 minutes at an average speed of 24 km/h.
Charlie cycles for 30 minutes at an average speed of 10 mph. Who cycled the furthest?

4 Joe starts work at 9 am. He sets off for work at 8.45 am.
He works 18 miles away from home, and drives at an average speed of 45 mph.
How many minutes late for work will he be?

5 A train travels between Ashford and Bromley. The distance between Ashford and Bromley is 45 miles. A train leaves Ashford at 18:35 and arrives at Bromley at 20:05.

a) Calculate the average speed of the train in miles per hour.

The following day the train leaves Ashford on time but arrives in Bromley 10 minutes late.

b) Calculate the difference between the average speed of the train on the two days.

6 Amy leaves London by helicopter at 12 noon. She must be at a helipad in Manchester by 1.15 pm. The distance from London to Manchester is 260 kilometres and her helicopter has a maximum speed of 60 m/s. Is it is possible for Amy to get to Manchester in time?

Calculating Density

Density is a compound measure — it is a measure of mass per unit volume.

Density, mass and volume are connected by this formula:
$$\text{Density} = \frac{\text{Mass}}{\text{Volume}}$$

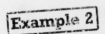
Example 2 Calculate the density of butter if a 250 g block has a volume of 274 cm³. Give your answer to 2 decimal places.

1. Substitute the values for the mass and volume into the formula for density.

$$\text{Density} = \frac{\text{Mass}}{\text{Volume}}$$

$$\text{Density} = \frac{250}{274} = 0.9124...$$

2. The units of density are always mass/volume.
$$= 0.91 \text{ g/cm}^3$$

Exercise 2

For this exercise, round your answers to **2 decimal places** where necessary.

1 For each of the following, use the mass and volume to calculate the density.

a) mass = 480 kg, volume = 320 m³
b) mass = 123 g, volume = 14.25 cm³

c) volume = 1.88 m³, mass = 17 kg
d) volume = 1218 cm³, mass = 3428 g

e) mass = 6422 g, volume = 6.04 m³
f) volume = 0.0095 km³, mass = 7392 kg

g) mass = 322 kg, volume = 43.4 m³
h) volume = 0.43 km³, mass = 44392 kg

2 What is the density of a chocolate bar with a volume of 134.61 cm³ and a mass of 175.5 g?

3 What is the density of a pebble with a volume of 0.04 m³ and a mass of 0.286 kg?

Calculating Volume and Mass

You can rearrange the formula for density to find mass and volume. $\boxed{\text{Mass} = \text{Density} \times \text{Volume}}$ $\boxed{\text{Volume} = \dfrac{\text{Mass}}{\text{Density}}}$

Example 3 **The density of a block of wood is 0.67 g/cm³.**
Find the mass if the block has a volume of 9.5 cm³.

1. Rearrange the formula for density so that the mass is expressed in terms of the density and volume.   Mass = Density × Volume

2. Substitute the values for the density and volume into the formula.   = 0.67 × 9.5

3. The units of density here are g/cm³, so the mass is in g.   = **6.365 g**

Exercise 3

1 For each of the following, use the density and the volume to calculate the mass.

a) volume = 321 m³, density = 1.28 kg/m³   **b)** density = 0.92 g/cm³, volume = 0.25 cm³

c) density = 16.2 kg/m³, volume = 21 m³   **d)** volume = 2123 cm³, density = 9.38 g/cm³

2 For each of the following, use the density and the mass to calculate the volume.

a) mass = 63.19 kg, density = 1.78 kg/m³   **b)** density = 0.92 g/cm³, mass = 7.59 g

3 A marble statue has a volume of 1.9 m³. Marble has a density of 2560 kg/m³.

a) Write down the formula to calculate a mass from a volume and a density.

b) Calculate the mass of the statue.

4 The density of a gold necklace is 19.3 g/cm³. What is the volume of a necklace with a mass of 56.22 g? Give your answer in cm³ to 2 d.p.

5 Find the width (to 3 s.f.) of a perfect cube of ice weighing 10 g with a density of 0.92 g/cm³.

> **Investigate — Density**
>
> The density of air at room temperature is approximately 1.2 kg/m³.
> Estimate the mass of air in your classroom.

7.3 Scale Drawings

Maps and Map Scales

Maps use a scale to accurately show large distances on a smaller drawing. A scale of 1 cm : 100 m means that 1 cm on the map represents an actual distance of 100 m.

A scale without units (e.g. 1 : 100) means you can use any units — but you must put the same units on both sides. For example, 1 cm : 100 cm or 1 mm : 100 mm.

Example 1   The scale on a map is 1 : 200.

a) What is the actual distance (in metres) between two points which are 25 cm apart on the map.

1. Write the scale down using cm
   (to match the units given in the question).   1 cm : 200 cm

2. Multiply both sides of the scale
   by the same number (here it's 25).   1 cm represents 200 cm
   so 25 cm represents 5000 cm

3. Give your answer using the correct units.   5000 cm = (5000 ÷ 100) m
   = **50 m**

b) Rewrite the scale in the form 1 cm : x m.

1. The scale is currently in the form 1 cm : 200 cm.   1 cm : 200 cm

2. 1 m = 100 cm. So to convert 200 cm into metres,
   you need to divide by 100.   200 ÷ 100 = 2
   1 cm : 2 m

Exercise 1

1 A map scale is given as 1 : 500. Convert these lengths on the map to actual distances. Give your answers in m.

    a) 3 cm   **b)** 5 cm   **c)** 8 cm

    d) 6.5 cm   **e)** 2.25 cm   **f)** 9.75 cm

2 A 20 km road is to be drawn on a map with a scale of 1 : 500 000. How long will the road be on the map? Give your answer in cm.

3 A map uses the scale 1 : 50 000. Find the actual distances in km represented by:

    a) 2.5 cm   **b)** 5.6 cm   **c)** 9.7 cm

4 Karen is drawing a plan of the grounds of a stately home on a piece of A4 paper. The grounds cover an area measuring roughly 7 km by 5 km. The drive is 2.5 km long. Suggest a suitable scale for her plan, and work out how long the drive would be on the plan using this scale.

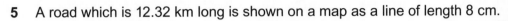

5 A road which is 12.32 km long is shown on a map as a line of length 8 cm.

a) Express the scale in the form 1 cm : n km.

b) Express the scale in the form 1 : k.

6 On the plans for a house, 4 cm represents the length of a garden with actual length 12 m.

a) Find the map scale in the form 1 : n.

b) On the plan, the width of the garden is 2.3 cm. What is its actual width in metres?

c) The kitchen has a length of 5.16 m. What is the corresponding length on the plan?

7 A map is drawn with a scale of 1 cm : 0.5 km. The distance between two towns on this map is 11.6 cm. A second map is drawn with a scale of 1 : 200 000. Work out the distance between the two towns on the second map.

Scale Drawings

Scale diagrams and plans also use <u>scales</u> to show actual distances on a drawing.

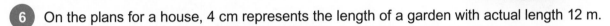

| Example 2 | The diagram shows a rough sketch of a park. Use the scale 1 cm : 5 m to draw an accurate plan of the park. |

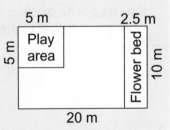

1. Use the scale to work out the lengths for the plan.
   1 cm = 5 m, so divide the lengths in m by 5 to find the lengths in cm on the plan.
   5 m: 5 ÷ 5 = 1 cm
   2.5 m: 2.5 ÷ 5 = 0.5 cm
   20 m: 20 ÷ 5 = 4 cm
   10 m: 10 ÷ 5 = 2 cm

2. Use these lengths to draw an accurate plan.

Exercise 2

1   An architect has been asked to draw the plans for a building using a scale of 1 cm : 1.5 m.
    Find the lengths he should draw on the plan to represent these actual distances.

    a) 6 m   **b)** 21 m   **c)** 9 m   **d)** 4.8 m

2   A plan of an office is drawn using a scale of 2 cm : 1 m.
    Find the actual dimensions if they are given on the plan as:

    a) 6 cm   **b)** 10 cm   **c)** 7 cm   **d)** 1.5 cm

3   These scale drawings have been drawn using the scale 1 cm : 1 m. By measuring
    the scale drawings, give the actual lengths of sides a, b and c in each shape.

    a)   **b)**

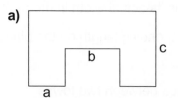   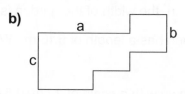

4   A sketch of part of a zoo has been drawn.

    a) Use the scale 1 cm : 5 m to draw an
    accurate plan of the zoo.

    b) Use your plan to find the real-life distance between
    the two points labelled A and B on the sketch.
    Give your answer to the nearest metre.

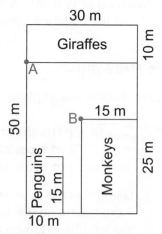

5   A model plane uses a scale of 1 : 250. Use the actual measurements
    given here to find the measurements of the model in cm.

    a) Height of tail: 5 m   **b)** Length of body: 10 m

    c) Width of cockpit: 3 m   **d)** Length of wing: 7.5 m

6   A model of a building uses a scale of 1 : 1000.
    The height of the tower on the model is 5 cm.
    Work out its actual height, giving your answer in m.

7 Jack, Will, Elizabeth and Davy are standing on an island.
Jack is standing 5 metres south of Will.
Elizabeth is standing 8 metres west of Will.
Davy is standing 2 metres north of Elizabeth.

a) Draw a scale drawing of the positions of Jack, Will, Elizabeth and Davy, using the scale 1 cm : 2 m.

b) Use your drawing to work out how far away Jack is standing from Davy.

8 Isabel has made a sketch of her shed. Draw an accurate plan of the shed, using a scale of 1 : 50.

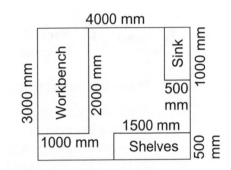

9 A garden is 15 metres long and 9 metres wide.

a) Use the sketch to draw an accurate plan of this garden, using the scale 4 cm : 3 metres.

b) Use your sketch to accurately measure angles $a - d$.

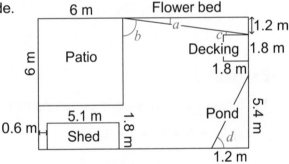

Investigate — Scale Drawings

a) Create a scale drawing of your classroom.
Think about what a sensible scale would be.
Include a few details, like tables, desks and shelves.

b) Use your scale drawing to find the distance between different things in the classroom. Compare the measurements you get from your drawing to the actual measurements to see how accurate your drawing is.

c) Use your scale drawing to measure various angles around your classroom. Compare your readings with a friend.

Section 8 — Algebraic Expressions

8.1 Simplifying Expressions

Simplifying Expressions

Expressions can sometimes be simplified by collecting like terms. 'Like terms' contain exactly the same letters raised to the same powers, but may have different coefficients. Numbers on their own in an expression are treated as like terms.

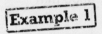 **Simplify the expression $6a + 2a^2 + ab + 8 + 8ab - 2 - a$ by collecting like terms.**

1. There are four sets of like terms:

   i) terms involving just a $+6a$ and $-a$
   ii) terms involving a^2 $+2a^2$
   iii) terms involving ab $+ab$ and $+8ab$
   iv) terms involving just numbers $+8$ and -2

2. Collect the different sets together separately.

    $(6a - a) + 2a^2 + (ab + 8ab) + (8 - 2)$
    $= 5a + 2a^2 + 9ab + 6$

Exercise 1

1 Simplify the following expressions by collecting like terms.

  a) $2y + 7y + 10 + 7 + 5x + 2x$ **b)** $8a - 2c + 6 - 12 + 9a + 7c$

  c) $12 - 5r + 7s - 3 + 8s - 6r$ **d)** $9t + 11t - 11 + 10s + 4 - 6s$

  e) $8a - 5b + 12a + 9 - 4 + 3b$ **f)** $7m + 8 + 7m - 4p + 3 - 9p$

  g) $7y + 11 - 6 - 8y - 5z + 8z$ **h)** $2 - 6c + 9b + 2c - 11b + 8$

  i) $11 + 7p - 9q + 4p - 2q + 8$ **j)** $5g + 11g - 12 + 9h - 7 - 11h$

2 Simplify the following expressions by collecting like terms.

  a) $x^2 + x^2 + 6 + 8$ **b)** $2a^2 - a^2 + 9 - 3$ **c)** $4c^2 + c^2 - 5 + 7$

  d) $6 + 12 + 6f^3 - 3f^3$ **e)** $4n^2 - 6n^2 - 3 - 4$ **f)** $5k^3 + 11 + 7k^3 - 2$

  g) $11z^2 + 10 - 3 + 2z^2$ **h)** $10 - 11 + 4b^3 + 10b^3$ **i)** $9c^2 + 9 - 8c^2 + 12$

  j) $7g^2 + 3 + 12 - 5g^2$ **k)** $11w^2 - w^2 + 7 + 6$ **l)** $10u^3 - 8 + 5u^3 - 8$

3 Simplify the following expressions by collecting like terms.

a) $2y^2 + 4y^2 + y + 5y + 4 + 2$

b) $8g^2 - 2g^2 + 4 - 6g + 7g + 8$

c) $6v - 1 + v^2 - 2v + 9v^2 + 6$

d) $11d^2 - 7 + 4d + 6d^2 + 2d + 3$

e) $7p^3 - 4p^3 + 5 + 9p^2 + 8p^2 - 6$

f) $6a^2 + a^3 + 2 + 9 + a^2 + 9a^3$

g) $2y^2 + 8y - 3 - 11 - y^2 - 12y$

h) $12h^3 - 3h + 9 + 6h - 12 + 4h^3$

4 Simplify these expressions by collecting like terms.

a) $3wv + 7wv - 9w + 3w$

b) $2g^4 + 8g^4 - 3gh - 8gh$

c) $5xy + y - 3xy + 12x$

d) $10ab + 8b^3 + a - 7ab$

e) $2p + 8pq - 3pq + 9q$

f) $5fg + fg + 8fg + 3f^2$

g) $5s + 4st - 2st + 6t$

h) $4ij + 6ij + 12j^2 + 10i^2$

5 Simplify the following expressions by collecting like terms.

a) $9xy + yx + 2x - 3x$

b) $8ab - 7a + 8ba + 3a$

c) $5pq - qp + p^2 + 4p^2$

d) $11rt + 4tr - t^2 + r^2$

e) $7yz - 2yz + 7zy + z^2$

f) $2mn + nm + 7m + 6m$

g) $4g + 7h - gh + 7hg$

h) $2jk - 3j^2 + 4k^2 + 9kj$

i) $3u + 7uv - 9uv^2 + 8v^2u$

j) $12qr^2 + 2p - 9rq^2 + 8qr^2$

6 Simplify the following expressions by collecting like terms.

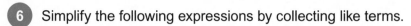

a) $\frac{2}{3}xy + \frac{1}{3}yx + 2x - 3x$

b) $8ab - \frac{1}{2}a + 4ba + \frac{1}{2}a$

c) $\frac{3}{5}st - s^2 + 2t^2 + \frac{2}{5}st$

d) $mg + \frac{1}{2}m^2 - 5mg + \frac{1}{2}m^2$

7 Simplify the following expressions by collecting like terms.

a) $7\frac{y}{z} - 2\frac{y}{z} + 7\frac{z}{y} + z^2$

b) $2\frac{m}{n} + \frac{m}{n} + \frac{5}{7}m + \frac{2}{7}m$

c) $\frac{x}{w} + \frac{w}{x} + 7\frac{w}{x} - 2xw$

d) $\frac{u}{s} - 2\frac{u}{s} + \frac{2}{9}s + 4us$

e) $4\frac{a}{e} + 2\frac{e}{a} + 4a + 5\frac{a}{e} - 4\frac{e}{a}$

f) $\frac{i}{k} - i^2 + j^2 - \frac{k}{i} + 4\frac{i}{k} - 6\frac{k}{i} + j^2$

8.2 Expanding Brackets

One Set of Brackets

You can <u>expand</u> brackets by multiplying everything inside the brackets by the term or number in front of the brackets. This removes the brackets from the expression.

> **Example 1** Simplify the expression $7(x - 6) + 2x(3 - y)$.
>
> 1. Expand both sets of brackets.
> $(7 \times x) + (7 \times -6) + (2x \times 3) + (2x \times -y)$
> $= 7x - 42 + 6x - 2xy$
>
> 2. Then collect like terms.
> $= 13x - 2xy - 42$

Exercise 1

1 Expand the brackets in the following expressions.

a) $3(a + 4)$ 　　　 b) $2(b + 1)$ 　　　 c) $4(p + 6)$ 　　　 d) $5(5 + y)$

e) $6(h - 3)$ 　　　 f) $8(q - 2)$ 　　　 g) $-3(t - 12)$ 　　　 h) $-7(2 + x)$

i) $-11(a - 6)$ 　　 j) $-9(8 + p)$ 　　 k) $-8(8 + s)$ 　　 l) $-7(11 - y)$

2 Expand the brackets in the following expressions.

a) $v(v + 7)$ 　　　 b) $y(y - 5)$ 　　　 c) $r(11 - r)$ 　　　 d) $p(p + 8)$

e) $-q(q - 10)$ 　　 f) $-j(j + 6)$ 　　 g) $-k(8 + k)$ 　　 h) $-l(-5 - l)$

3 Expand the brackets in the following expressions.

a) $3a(a + 3)$ 　　 b) $2v(v + 5)$ 　　 c) $4r(5 - r)$ 　　 d) $11x(x + 11)$

e) $5h(h - 3)$ 　　 f) $-8q(q - 7)$ 　　 g) $6t(t - 12)$ 　　 h) $-9y(y - 8)$

i) $-11b(7 + b)$ 　 j) $-4w(12 - w)$ 　 k) $-12z(8 + z)$ 　 l) $7q(9 - q)$

4 Expand the brackets and simplify the following expressions.

a) $2(b + 4) + 4(b + 6)$ 　　　 b) $3(x + 5) + 3(x + 3)$ 　　　 c) $10(5 - g) - 2(g + 4)$

d) $8h(h + 11) - 6(h + 1)$ 　　 e) $5(d - 4) - d(e + 2)$ 　　 f) $6(e - 7) + 3e(p + 3)$

g) $4m(m - 12) + 2m(m + 2)$ 　 h) $8n(q - 5) - 2n(n + 1)$ 　 i) $9v(7 + v) + 3v(x + 2)$

Two Sets of Brackets

To expand two sets of brackets, you need to multiply each term in the right bracket by each term in the left bracket.

$$(a + b)(c + d) = ac + ad + bc + bd$$

Example 2 Expand $(x + 2)(x + 3)$.

1. Multiply each term in the right bracket by each term in the left bracket.

$$(x + 2)(x + 3) = x^2 + 3x + 2x + 6$$

2. Simplify by collecting like terms.

$$x^2 + 5x + 6$$

Exercise 2

1 Expand the brackets in the following expressions.

a) $(b + 2)(b + 1)$

b) $(a + 3)(a + 3)$

c) $(x + 4)(x + 1)$

d) $(p + 12)(p + 4)$

e) $(q + 9)(q + 9)$

f) $(t + 11)(t + 6)$

g) $(z + 7)(9 + z)$

h) $(g + 4)(12 + g)$

i) $(8 + y)(10 + y)$

2 Expand the brackets in the following expressions.

a) $(a - 5)(a + 6)$

b) $(u + 3)(u - 7)$

c) $(m - 7)(m + 6)$

d) $(g + 4)(g - 11)$

e) $(z - 6)(z + 2)$

f) $(n + 11)(n - 3)$

g) $(q - 4)(q + 11)$

h) $(g - 10)(g + 6)$

i) $(q + 8)(q - 12)$

3 Expand the brackets in the following expressions.

a) $(r - 5)(r - 9)$

b) $(x - 3)(x - 8)$

c) $(h - 7)(h - 4)$

d) $(z - 3)(z - 5)$

e) $(w - 7)(w - 1)$

f) $(c - 10)(c - 3)$

g) $(y - 4)(y - 12)$

h) $(b - 7)(b - 8)$

i) $(x - 6)(x - 10)$

4 Expand the brackets in the following expressions.

a) $(7 + x)(x - 6)$

b) $(p - 2)(6 + p)$

c) $(g + 5)(5 + g)$

d) $(4 + x)(x - 9)$

e) $(10 - s)(s - 4)$

f) $(d - 8)(3 + d)$

g) $(v + 2)(1 + v)$

h) $(3 - a)(a + 10)$

i) $(h + 5)(4 - h)$

5 Expand the brackets in the following expressions.

a) $2(h + 2)(a + 4)$

b) $4(x + 2)(h + 6)$

c) $4(p - 1)(t + 3)$

d) $6(s + 4)(t + 2)$

e) $6(a - 4)(d - 2)$

f) $8(w - 7)(x - 3)$

g) $12(a + 2)(4 - v)$

h) $4(s - 5)(h - 2)$

i) $12(n - 4)(u - 1)$

j) $2(a + 6)(a + 5)$

k) $3(h + 4)(h - 2)$

l) $2(d - 12)(d + 3)$

m) $8(d - 2)(d + 1)$

n) $4(a - 3)(a - 2)$

o) $7(s + 4)(s - 3)$

6 Expand the brackets in the following expressions and simplify your answer.

a) $(x + 2)(x + 3) + (x + 4)(x + 5)$

b) $(x + 1)(x + 6) - (x + 8)(x + 7)$

c) $(x + 4)(x - 2) + (x - 10)(x + 3)$

d) $(x + 5)(x - 7) - (x - 2)(x - 12)$

7 Expand the brackets in the following expressions.

a) $(2a + 4)(3a + 1)$

b) $(h + 1)(5h - 6)$

c) $(2d - 5)(4d + 2)$

d) $(4s + 8)(2s + 4)$

e) $(3v + 9)(7 - v)$

f) $(2x - 3)(3 - 2x)$

8 Expand the brackets in the following expressions.

a) $(6h + 6)(8 - h)$

b) $(4d - 12)(4d + 2)$

c) $(3a - 10)(6a - 2)$

d) $(s + 6)(2s - 5)$

e) $(3p - 4)(5p + 6)$

f) $(4g - 5)(3g - 8)$

9 A rectangle has a width of $(x - 6)$, and a length that is 8 units bigger than its width.

a) Write an expression, in brackets, for the area of the rectangle.

b) Expand the brackets in the expression.

| **Example 4** | Expand $(x + 1)(x + 3)(x - 4)$. |

1. Expand $(x + 3)(x - 4)$ by multiplying each term in the left bracket by each term in the right bracket.

$(x + 1) \times (x^2 - 4x + 3x - 12)$

2. Collect like terms.

$= (x + 1) \times (x^2 - x - 12)$

3. Now multiply the second bracket by $(x + 1)$. Multiply each term in the left bracket by each term in the right bracket.

$= x^3 - x^2 - 12x + x^2 - x - 12$

4. Collect like terms again.

$= x^3 - 13x - 12$

Exercise 4

1 Expand the brackets in the following expressions.

a) $(b + 3)(b + 2)(b + 1)$ **b)** $(m + 4)(m - 2)(m + 5)$ **c)** $(p - 6)(p + 1)(p - 8)$

d) $(v - 5)(v - 3)(v - 2)$ **e)** $(x - 2)(x - 8)(x + 9)$ **f)** $(n + 1)(n + 5)(n - 3)$

2 Expand the brackets in the following expressions.

a) $(y + 3)(y + 2)^2$ **b)** $(s + 2)(s - 4)^2$ **c)** $(b - 12)(b + 4)^2$

d) $(c + 6)(c - 5)^2$ **e)** $(v - 3)(v - 9)^2$ **f)** $(i - 10)(i - 6)^2$

Investigate — Special Pairs of Brackets

Expand and simplify the following sets of brackets:

$$(x + 1)(x - 1), (x + 2)(x - 2), (x + 3)(x - 3)... \text{ etc}$$

a) Look at your final answers. Are they connected to the numbers in the brackets? If so, how?

b) Can you find a general rule for expanding $(x + y)(x - y)$?

c) Can you use your rule to write down a simplified expansion of $(a + 10)(a - 10)$ straight away?

d) Could you put the expression $b^2 - 64$ into two brackets?

e) Use your results to work out $101^2 - 99^2$ and check your results on a calculator. Make up some similar calculations and work them out.

8.3 Factorising

One Set of Brackets

<u>Factorising</u> is the opposite of expanding brackets. It's putting brackets into an expression.

Look for the <u>highest common factor</u> (HCF) of all the terms in an expression, and 'take it outside' a pair of brackets.

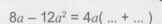

> **Example 1** Fully factorise $8a - 12a^2$.
>
> 1. $4a$ is the highest common factor of $8a$ and $12a^2$, so write a pair of brackets with $4a$ outside. $\qquad$ $8a - 12a^2 = 4a(\ldots + \ldots)$
>
> 2. Divide each term in the expression by $4a$ and write the results in the brackets. $\qquad$ $8a \div 4a = 2$
> $\qquad -12a^2 \div 4a = -3a$
>
> $\qquad\qquad\qquad\qquad\qquad\qquad\qquad 8a - 12a^2 = \mathbf{4a(2 - 3a)}$

Exercise 1

1 Fully factorise these expressions.

a) $8c - 36$ b) $16p - 12$ c) $49 - 14x$

d) $14a + 3a^2$ e) $6a + 5a^2$ f) $11u^2 + 4u$

g) $5h + 12h^3$ h) $6j + 5j^2$ i) $13k^3 - 3k^2$

2 Fully factorise these expressions.

a) $14a + 2a^2$ b) $15v^2 + 5v$ c) $8c + 12c^2$

d) $16f - 4f^2$ e) $2d^3 + 8d$ f) $7q + 14q^2$

g) $6y^2 + 9y$ h) $15r - 10r^3$ i) $30z^2 - 3z$

3 Fully factorise these expressions.

a) $8ab - 3a$ b) $15su^2 + 25u^2$ c) $3v^2 + 30vy$

d) $8xy^2 + 16xy + 4y$ e) $6pq^2 + 15p^2q$ f) $9x^2y - 3xy^2$

g) $21cd^2 + 35c^2d$ h) $12gh^2 - 6hg^2$ i) $56n^2t + 24nt^2$

j) $18r^2 - 27rs - 45r$ k) $15uvw + 10uv + 20vw$ l) $16a^2b^2c^2 + 24a^2bc + 8abc$

Two Sets of Brackets

A quadratic expression is one of the form $ax^2 + bx + c$ where a, b and c are constants (and a is not 0). You can factorise some quadratics using two brackets.

Example 2   **Factorise $x^2 + 4x - 21$.**

1. Write down the initial brackets with x on the left. $(x \quad)(x \quad)$

2. List all the pairs of factors of 21.   1 and 21, 3 and 7

3. Find the right pair of factors that multiply to give 21 and add or subtract to give 4 (ignore the +/– signs for now). $3 \times 7 = 21$ Add/subtract to give 10 or 4

4. Put the pair of numbers into the brackets. $(x \quad 3)(x \quad 7)$

5. Now fill in the +/– signs so that 3 and 7 add to give +4 and multiply to give –21. $(x - 3)(x + 7)$

Exercise 2

1   Write down the values for a, b and c for each of these quadratic expressions.

a) $x^2 + 6x + 8$ b) $x^2 + 5x + 12$ c) $x^2 + 24x + 89$ d) $2x^2 + 5x + 7$

e) $3x^2 + 8x + 10$ f) $5x^2 + 7x + 15$ g) $x^2 - 4x + 9$ h) $6x^2 + 2x - 12$

i) $2x^2 + x - 24$ j) $3x^2 - 6x$ k) $-x^2 - 100$ l) $4x^2$

2   For the quadratic expression $x^2 + 7x + 10$:

a) Find the values of a, b and c.

b) Write down all the pairs of factors of c.

c) Find the pair of factors that add/subtract to give b.

d) Use your answer from c) to fully factorise the expression.

3   For each of these quadratic expressions: i)   find the values of a, b and c
                                                ii)   write down the pair of numbers that multiply
                                                    together to give c and add together to give b
                                               iii) fully factorise the expression

a) $x^2 + 6x + 5$ b) $x^2 + 7x + 6$ c) $x^2 + 5x + 6$ d) $x^2 + 3x + 2$

4 For the quadratic expression $x^2 - 18x + 32$:

a) Find the values of a, b and c.

b) Write down all the factors of c.

c) Find the pair of factors that add/subtract to give b.

d) Use your answer from **c)** to fully factorise the expression.

5 For each of these quadratic expressions: **i)** find the values of a, b and c
                                               ii) write down the pair of numbers that multiply
                                                  together to give c and add together to give b
                                             iii) fully factorise the expression

a) $x^2 + x - 56$ **b)** $x^2 - 14x + 49$ **c)** $x^2 + 2x - 24$ **d)** $x^2 + 3x - 28$

6 Factorise these quadratic expressions.

a) $x^2 + 2x + 1$ **b)** $x^2 + 5x + 4$ **c)** $x^2 + 11x + 18$ **d)** $x^2 + 8x + 15$

e) $x^2 + 3x + 2$ **f)** $x^2 + 10x + 25$ **g)** $x^2 + 6x + 9$ **h)** $x^2 + 6x + 8$

i) $x^2 + x - 12$ **j)** $x^2 - x - 2$ **k)** $x^2 + 2x - 24$ **l)** $x^2 - 3x - 28$

m) $x^2 - 3x - 54$ **n)** $x^2 - 10x + 16$ **o)** $x^2 - 10x - 24$ **p)** $x^2 - 7x - 18$

Investigate — Square Areas

A square has a width of $a + b$.
The area of the square is given as $a^2 - 10a + 25$.

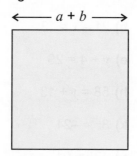

a) Can you use these facts to work out the value of b?

b) Make notes about how you're solving the problem as you work on it.

c) Does your answer tell you anything about the size of a? If so, what?

Section 9 — Equations and Inequalities

9.1 Solving Equations

Solving Simple Equations

Equations are made up of two expressions, one on each side of an equals sign. Equations contain an unknown variable, usually shown by a letter.

To solve an equation, do the same operation to both sides until you have the letter on its own on one side of the equation.

Example 1	Solve the equation $5 + \dfrac{2x}{3} = 8$.

1. Get the x terms on one side and the numbers on the other by subtracting 5 from both sides.

   $$5 + \frac{2x}{3} - 5 = 8 - 5$$
   $$\frac{2x}{3} = 3$$

2. To get x on its own from $\dfrac{2x}{3}$,

   multiply both sides by 3 then divide by 2.

   $$\frac{2x}{3} \times 3 = 3 \times 3$$
   $$2x = 9$$
   $$2x \div 2 = 9 \div 2$$
   $$x = 4.5$$

Exercise 1

1   Find the value of the unknown in each of these equations.

a) $x + 5 = 17$

b) $21 - x = 13$

c) $15 + x = 4$

d) $x - 11 = 25$

e) $y + 4 = 29$

f) $15 = y - 12$

g) $y - 17 = 29$

h) $58 = y + 13$

i) $7z = 56$

j) $15z = 135$

k) $3z = -24$

l) $36z = 45$

m) $14a = 84$

n) $13b = 91$

o) $\dfrac{m}{8} = 9$

p) $\dfrac{s}{20} = -4$

q) $15 = \dfrac{n}{4}$

r) $-8 = \dfrac{u}{5}$

$\boxed{\text{Example 3}}$ **Expand $5(y + 2)^2$.**

1. Write out $(y + 2)^2$ as $(y + 2)(y + 2)$.

$5 \times (y + 2)(y + 2)$

2. Multiply each term in the left bracket by each term in the right bracket.

$= 5 \times (y^2 + 2y + 2y + 4)$

3. Collect like terms inside the brackets.

$= 5 \times (y^2 + 4y + 4)$

4. Multiply everything by 5.

$= 5y^2 + 20y + 20$

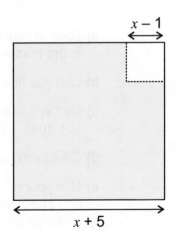

Exercise 3

1 Expand the brackets in the following expressions.

a) $(x + 2)^2$ **b)** $(v - 5)^2$ **c)** $(c - 4)^2$

d) $(m + 3)^2$ **e)** $(n - 9)^2$ **f)** $(p - 3)^2$

g) $2(x + 4)^2$ **h)** $3(u + 2)^2$ **i)** $10(s - 6)^2$

j) $6(t + 7)^2$ **k)** $4(x - 2)^2$ **l)** $5(y - 5)^2$

2 Expand the brackets in the following expressions.

a) $(2b + 3)^2$ **b)** $(10c - 5)^2$ **c)** $(8d - 3)^2$

d) $(5n + 2)^2$ **e)** $(2x - 1)^2$ **f)** $(2q - 3)^2$

g) $(3r + 2)^2$ **h)** $(1 + 2s)^2$ **i)** $(2z - 10)^2$

j) $(2 + 2p)^2$ **k)** $(7 - 2y)^2$ **l)** $(2u - 6)^2$

3 A shape is made by cutting a small square from a larger square. The smaller square has a width of $(x - 1)$ cm and the larger square has a width of $(x + 5)$ cm.

a) Write an expression, in brackets, for the area of:
 i) the smaller square
 ii) the larger square.

b) Write an expression for the area of the shaded shape.

c) Expand the brackets in this expression and simplify.

d) Find the widths of the larger and smaller square if the area of the shaded shape is 60 cm².

2 Find the value of x for each of the following.

a) $8x + 6 = 62$ b) $5x + 15 = 125$ c) $6x + 9 = 69$ d) $12x + 16 = 88$

e) $80 - 7x = 17$ f) $47 - 12x = 11$ g) $70 - 6x = 16$ h) $17 - 13x = 82$

i) $2.2x - 4.2 = 20$ j) $1.5x - 8 = 11.5$ k) $1.8x - 7 = -25$ l) $3.2x - 9 = 39$

3 Solve these equations.

a) $3(x + 2) = 15$ b) $2(2 + x) = 14$ c) $44 = 4(x - 1)$ d) $5(x + 1) = 45$

e) $11(y + 2) = 55$ f) $7(y + 3) = 105$ g) $4(y + 8) = 36$ h) $8(y + 5) = 72$

i) $13(z - 8) = -91$ j) $1.5(z + 2) = 90$ k) $3.6(z + 2.6) = 54$ l) $125 = 5(12 - z)$

4 Find the value of x in each of these equations.

a) $\dfrac{2x}{3} = 7$ b) $\dfrac{5x}{6} = 25$ c) $\dfrac{4x}{5} = 14$ d) $\dfrac{4x}{9} = 3$

e) $\dfrac{x}{0.5} = 3$ f) $\dfrac{x}{0.25} = 7$ g) $\dfrac{x}{0.4} = 1.5$ h) $\dfrac{x}{0.7} = 2.2$

5 Solve the following. Give your answers as simplified fractions where appropriate.

a) $\dfrac{x}{7} + 3 = 7$ b) $\dfrac{2x}{5} - 8 = 3$ c) $\dfrac{2x}{3} + 26 = 74$

d) $\dfrac{4x}{5} - \dfrac{3}{7} = \dfrac{4}{7}$ e) $\dfrac{4x}{9} + \dfrac{1}{3} = \dfrac{2}{3}$ f) $\dfrac{2x}{3} - \dfrac{3}{8} = -\dfrac{5}{8}$

6 Find the value of x for each of these, giving your answers as simplified fractions.

a) $\dfrac{1}{x} = 5$ b) $\dfrac{3}{x} = 21$ c) $\dfrac{5}{4x} = 2$ d) $\dfrac{1}{x + 4} = -2$

7 Solve to find the value of x. Give your answers as decimals where appropriate.

a) $-\dfrac{4x}{5} - 5 = 5$ b) $18 - \dfrac{7x}{4} = -3$ c) $22 - \dfrac{5x}{2} = 5$ d) $-\dfrac{2x}{7} - 8 = 3$

Harder Equations

Some equations have an 'unknown' on both sides. To solve them, get all the terms with letters on one side and the numbers on the other, then solve as normal.

> **Example 2** Solve the equation $3x + 4 = 5x - 12$.
>
> 1. Subtract $3x$ from both sides. This leaves an x term on only one side of the equation.
>
> $3x + 4 - 3x = 5x - 12 - 3x$
> $4 = 2x - 12$
>
> 2. Now solve the equation as before. Add 12 to both sides and then divide by 2.
>
> $4 + 12 = 2x - 12 + 12$
> $16 = 2x$
> $16 \div 2 = 2x \div 2$
> $8 = x$ or $x = 8$

Exercise 2

1 Solve these equations. Start by subtracting an x term from both sides.

    a) $9x - 8 = 5x + 20$ **b)** $14x - 2 = 7x + 19$ **c)** $17x - 3 = 9x + 45$

    d) $17x - 2 = 7x + 8$ **e)** $9x - 26 = 5x - 14$ **f)** $2x + 8 = 13x + 63$

2 Solve these equations. Start by adding an x term to both sides.

    a) $9x - 41 = 39 - 7x$ **b)** $3x - 13 = 50 - 6x$ **c)** $5x - 17 = 83 - 5x$

    d) $13x - 16 = 24 - 7x$ **e)** $12x - 13 = 53 - 10x$ **f)** $17x - 21 = 51 - 19x$

3 Solve these equations. Start by multiplying out the brackets.

    a) $2(x + 5) = x + 14$ **b)** $7(x + 4) = 5x + 57$ **c)** $11(x - 1) = 3x + 21$

    d) $7(x - 6) = 2x + 3$ **e)** $8(x + 2) = 5x + 76$ **f)** $9(x + 1) = 6x + 78$

4 Find the value of x for each of the following:

    a) $23x - 23 = 14x + 4$ **b)** $2x - 16 = 62 - 11x$ **c)** $36(x + 2) = 12(x - 1)$

    d) $87 - 11x = 15 - 9x$ **e)** $17x - 5 = 11x + 49$ **f)** $-4x - 17 = 145 - 22x$

    g) $22x - 7 = 6x + 41$ **h)** $3(x + 4) = 6(x - 3)$ **i)** $10(x - 8) = 2(x - 2)$

Example 3	Solve the equation $\frac{x}{5} = 9 - 3x$.
	Give the value of x to 1 decimal place.

1. Multiply both sides by 5.

$$\frac{x}{5} \times 5 = (9 - 3x) \times 5$$
$$x = 5(9 - 3x)$$

2. Multiply out the brackets.

$$x = 45 - 15x$$

3. Then solve as normal.

$$x + 15x = 45 - 15x + 15x$$
$$16x = 45$$
$$16x \div 16 = 45 \div 16$$
$$x = 2.81... = \mathbf{2.8\ (1\ d.p)}$$

Exercise 3

1 Solve the following equations. Give your answers as decimals.

a) $\frac{x}{3} = 1 - x$

b) $\frac{x}{4} = 8 - x$

c) $\frac{x}{7} = 12 - 2x$

d) $\frac{x}{3} = 5 - x$

e) $\frac{x}{8} = 1 - 3x$

f) $\frac{x}{2} = x + 4$

g) $\frac{x}{5} = 15 - x$

h) $\frac{x}{5} = x + 4$

i) $-\frac{x}{4} = -15 - x$

j) $-\frac{x}{2} = 12 - x$

k) $-\frac{x}{3} = x - 11$

l) $\frac{4x}{7} = -5 - 3x$

2 Find the value of x in each of the following, giving your answers to 2 d.p.

a) $\frac{x}{5} = 3(x - 8)$

b) $\frac{x}{3} = 5(x - 11)$

c) $\frac{x}{7} = 4(x + 13)$

d) $\frac{x}{4} = 5(x + 9)$

e) $\frac{x}{6} = -6(x + 28)$

f) $\frac{x}{4} = 6(x - 33)$

g) $\frac{x}{2} = 2(x + 0.5)$

h) $\frac{x}{5} = 7(3 + x)$

i) $\frac{x}{8} = 6(5 - x)$

3 Find the value of x in each of the following.

a) $\frac{x}{7} + \frac{x}{7} = 4$

b) $\frac{2x}{3} - \frac{x}{3} = 4$

c) $\frac{4x}{5} - \frac{2x}{5} = 7$

d) $\frac{x}{6} + \frac{x}{4} = 3$

e) $-\frac{x}{5} + \frac{x}{4} = 2$

f) $\frac{x}{3} - \frac{x}{6} = 5$

Example 4 Solve the equation $\dfrac{x+5}{4} = \dfrac{x-3}{3}$.

1. Multiply the top of each fraction by the bottom of the other. (This is the same as multiplying both sides by 3 and then by 4.)

2. Then solve in the normal way.

$$\dfrac{x+5}{4} \diagup\!\!\!\!\diagdown \dfrac{x-3}{3}$$

$$3(x+5) = 4(x-3)$$

$$3x + 15 = 4x - 12$$

$$15 = x - 12$$

$$x = 27$$

Exercise 4

1 Solve the following equations.

a) $\dfrac{x-5}{5} = \dfrac{x+2}{10}$

b) $\dfrac{x+8}{3} = \dfrac{x+12}{4}$

c) $\dfrac{x+6}{8} = \dfrac{x-1}{4}$

d) $\dfrac{x+7}{6} = \dfrac{x+4}{5}$

e) $\dfrac{x-3}{3} = \dfrac{x-2}{6}$

f) $\dfrac{x+8}{6} = \dfrac{x+20}{9}$

2 Solve the following equations.

a) $\dfrac{x-3}{3} = \dfrac{10-x}{4}$

b) $\dfrac{x+2}{2} = \dfrac{1-2x}{6}$

c) $\dfrac{x+8}{2} = \dfrac{2x+22}{7}$

d) $\dfrac{x-6}{2} = \dfrac{2x-5}{3}$

e) $\dfrac{x+8}{6} = \dfrac{3x-1}{12}$

f) $\dfrac{x-2}{15} = \dfrac{15+2x}{11}$

Investigate — Solving Equations

Not all equations have one solution. Some equations have more than one solution, some don't have any.

a) These equations have two solutions. Can you find them?

$x^2 = 9$ $\qquad$ $x^2 = 81$ $\qquad$ $x^2 = 125$ $\qquad$ $(x+3)^2 = 16$

b) The equation $x^2 = -64$ has no solutions.
Why is this? What happens when you try to solve it?

c) Some equations are true for all values of x. They are called identities and are often written with an $\equiv$ sign. Here are some:

$$3x + 5x \equiv 8x \qquad 3(x+2) \equiv 3x + 6 \qquad \dfrac{3x}{4} \equiv \dfrac{x}{4} + \dfrac{2x}{4}$$

Can you see how they're different to normal equations?
Have a go at coming up with some identities of your own.

9.2 Inequalities

Write inequalities using these symbols:

> greater than   ≥ greater than or equal to

< less than   ≤ less than or equal to

Sometimes you can get "two inequalities in one".

For example, $4 < x ≤ 10$ means that both of the following are true: $4 < x$ and $x ≤ 10$.
So $4 < x ≤ 10$ means: x is between 4 and 10 (including 10, but not including 4).

You might sometimes see the symbol ≠, which means 'not equal to'.

Example 1   **Show the following inequalities on a number line.**

a) $x > -3$

Use an empty circle to show −3
is not included... $x = -3$ does **not**
satisfy the inequality.

b) $x ≤ 3$

Use a solid circle to show 3 is
included... $x = 3$ **does** satisfy
the inequality.

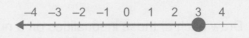

c) $-2 ≤ x < 3$

1. Write down the two separate
inequalities.

     $-2 ≤ x < 3$ means $-2 ≤ x$ and $x < 3$.

2. Find the number x is greater than...
...and the number x is less than.

     $-2 ≤ x$ is the same as $x ≥ -2$
     So $x ≥ -2$ and $x < 3$.

3. Draw the number line.
−2 is included, but not 3.

Exercise 1

1   Convert these sentences into inequalities.

a) x is less than 6

b) x is less than or equal to 7

c) x is greater than or equal to 5

d) x is greater than −2

2   Convert each of these inequalities into a sentence.

   a) $x \geq 8$ **b)** $x < 9$ **c)** $x > -1$ **d)** $x \leq 4$

   e) $x < 3$ **f)** $x \leq -12$ **g)** $x \geq 5$ **h)** $x > -8$

3   Form an inequality by inserting the correct symbol (> or <) into each box.

   a) 8 ☐ 4   **b)** -4 ☐ 2   **c)** 3 ☐ -7 **d)** -13 ☐ -4

4   Rewrite each of the following so that x is on the left-hand side.

   a) $3 \geq x$ **b)** $-2 < x$ **c)** $24 > x$ **d)** $-8 \leq x$

5   Draw each of these inequalities on a number line.

   a) $x \geq 9$ **b)** $x < 13$ **c)** $x < 4$ **d)** $x \geq 31$

   e) $x > -9$ **f)** $x \leq 4$ **g)** $x < 16$ **h)** $x > -7$

   i) $x \leq -3$ **j)** $x < 65$ **k)** $x \geq -24$ **l)** $x \leq -10$

6   Draw each of these inequalities on a number line.

   a) $0 < x \leq 6$ **b)** $9 \leq x \leq 14$ **c)** $1 \leq x < 5$

   d) $-2 < x \leq 3$ **e)** $-7 < x < -3$ **f)** $-3 \leq x < 3$

7   Integers are whole numbers, positive and negative (including zero).
   List all the integer values of x that satisfy both inequalities.

   a) $x > 9$, $x < 15$ **b)** $x \geq -2$, $x \leq 5$ **c)** $x \geq 12$, $x < 17$

   d) $x > -1$, $x \leq 7$ **e)** $8 \geq x$, $-3 < x$ **f)** $x \leq 4$, $-3 \leq x$

8   Convert each of these sentences into an inequality.

   a) x is less than 8 and greater than 3.   **b)** x is less than 4 and greater than -2.

   c) x is greater than 12 and less than or equal to 17.

9   Convert each of these inequalities into a sentence.

   a) $2 < x < 6$ **b)** $6 \leq x < 13$ **c)** $38 < x < 56$

   d) $-3 < x \leq -1$ **e)** $-11 \leq x < 11$ **f)** $-5 \leq x \leq -2$

10 Given that x is an integer, list all the possible values of x.

a) $0 < x < 5$ b) $-10 < x \leq -4$ c) $27 \leq x \leq 32$

d) $4 \leq x < 11$ e) $16 \leq x < 21$ f) $45 < x < 52$

g) $-9 \leq x \leq -5$ h) $-4 < x \leq 2$ i) $-2 \leq x \leq 4$

j) $-1 \leq x < 5$ k) $13.2 < x < 20.8$ l) $-3.5 \leq x \leq 1.5$

Solving inequalities is very similar to solving equations — you always do the same thing to both sides of the inequality. Be careful though — multiplying or dividing both sides by a negative number changes the direction of the inequality sign (so > becomes <).

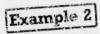 **2**   **Solve the following inequalities and show the solutions on a number line:**

a) $x + 9 \leq 11$

1. Subtract 9 from both sides.

2. Use a solid circle on the number line to show that 2 is included.

$$x + 9 - 9 \leq 11 - 9$$
$$x \leq 2$$

-4 -3 -2 -1 0 1 2 3 4

b) $6 < \dfrac{x}{5}$

1. Multiply both sides by 5.

2. Write the inequality with x on the left. The big end of the inequality sign should still be next to the x.

$$6 \times 5 < \dfrac{x}{5} \times 5$$
$$30 < x$$
$$x > 30$$

3. Use an empty circle on the number line to show that 30 is not included.

29 30 31 32 33 34 35 36 37

Exercise 2

1   Solve these inequalities. Show each of your solutions on a number line.

a) $x - 7 \geq 25$ b) $x - 8 < 5$ c) $x + 11 > 23$ d) $x + 12 \leq 6$

2   Solve each of the following inequalities. Give your answers with x on the left-hand side.

a) $21 < x + 18$ b) $16 \leq x - 7$ c) $12 > x - 7$ d) $29 < x + 53$

e) $15 \geq x + 19$ f) $35 > x - 8$ g) $-6 \leq x - 18$ h) $-15 < x - 2$

3 Solve these inequalities.

a) $\frac{x}{3} \le 5$ b) $\frac{x}{7} > 3$ c) $\frac{x}{4} < 9$ d) $\frac{x}{8} \le 12$

e) $\frac{x}{7} \ge 0.4$ f) $\frac{x}{2} < -6$ g) $\frac{x}{11} \ge 4$ h) $\frac{x}{9} < -2.1$

i) $\frac{x}{6} \ge -2.8$ j) $\frac{x}{4} > 2.7$ k) $\frac{2x}{3} \le 8$ l) $\frac{4x}{5} < -12$

4 Solve these inequalities.

a) $3x > 27$ b) $4x \le 36$ c) $5x \ge 80$ d) $7x < 63$

e) $12x \le 84$ f) $4x < 75$ g) $8x < -46$ h) $15x > -78$

5 Solve these inequalities. You'll need to divide by a negative number, so change the direction of the inequality sign in your final answer.

a) $-2x < 45$ b) $-3x \ge 63$ c) $-8x \ge -3.2$ d) $-1.6x \le -1.8$

6 Solve each of the following inequalities.

a) $9 < x + 3 \le 13$ b) $1 \le x - 3 \le 7$ c) $-7 < x + 6 \le 1$

d) $24 < 3x < 33$ e) $25 \le 5x < 60$ f) $-42 \le -6x < 18$

Investigate — Inequalities

Here is the graph of the equation $y = x$.
On a copy of the graph:

a) mark with dots 5 points where $y < x$.

b) mark with crosses 5 points where $y > x$.

c) shade an area on your grid to represent everywhere where $y > x$.

d) On a separate grid, draw these lines:

$y = x$ $y = 4$ $x = 3$

e) Now, use your lines to shade the area where ALL of these inequalities are true:

$y < x$ $y < 4$ $x < 3$

f) On a separate grid, shade the area where ALL of these are true:

$y < x + 2$ $y > 1$ $y < 5 - x$

Section 10 — Formulas

10.1 Writing Formulas

A <u>formula</u> is like a set of instructions for working something out.

For example, $d = 2e + 5$ is a formula for d.
It tells you how to find d if you know the value of e.

The part after the = is an algebraic <u>expression</u>.

You can sometimes write a formula to <u>model</u> a real-life situation.

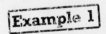 **The total cost of calling out a plumber is made up of:**
i) a cost of £12 for each hour,
plus ii) a fixed cost of £18

Write a formula for £C, the total cost of calling out a plumber for h hours.

1. Multiply h by 12 to find an expression for the total hourly cost.
   Cost (in pounds) for h hours:
   $h \times 12 = 12h$

2. Then add on the fixed cost of £18.
   $12h + 18$

3. The formula should start with '$C =$'.
   So $C = 12h + 18$

Exercise 1

1   Karting costs £25 per hour, plus £20 for insurance.
    Write a formula for K, the cost in pounds of going karting for t hours.

2   Lauren buys a car for £10 000. Every year the value goes down by £500.
    Write a formula for V, the value of the car after y years.

3   Christopher weighed 7 lbs when he was born. Every month he gained 1 lb in
    weight. Write a formula for W, the amount that Christopher weighed after m
    months.

4   Linda buys a flat. She pays a deposit of £25 000, and then pays £500
    a month. Write a formula for M, the amount Linda has paid after e months.

5   Kirstie, a professional curler, joins a new curling team. She is paid £2000 to join
    the new team, and £500 every month after that. Write a formula for P, the amount
    in pounds that Kirstie has earned after x months.

6   Joel is building a model tower. The base needs 45 bricks, and for every floor he uses 20 bricks.
Write a formula for b, the number of bricks Joel needs to build a tower f floors tall.

7   A cafe sells tea and coffee. A cup of tea costs £1.50. A cup of coffee costs £2.
Write down a formula for the cost, £C, of x cups of tea and y cups of coffee.

8   A box has a mass of b grams. The box is packed with x books, each with a mass of y grams. Write a formula for m, the total mass of the packed box in grams.

9   A cake has a mass of c grams. The cake is cut into n equal slices.
Write a formula for s, the mass of each slice in grams.

10 Today there are 364 days until my next birthday. Write a formula for B, the number of days until my birthday after w weeks from today.

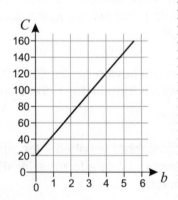

Investigate — Formulas and Graphs

Situations that can be modelled as formulas can also be modelled as graphs.

This graph shows the data from Question 1:

a) Try drawing graphs using the formulas from the other questions in this exercise.

b) Which of the formulas are more useful when modelled as graphs?
Which ones can't be modelled as straight line graphs?

10.2 Substituting into Formulas

Substituting numbers into a <u>formula</u> means replacing letters with numbers.

<u>Formulas</u> are used lots in maths and science:

area of triangle $= \frac{1}{2} \times$ base $\times$ height

Force = mass $\times$ acceleration

$F = ma$

$a^2 + b^2 = h^2$

area of trapezium

$= \frac{1}{2} \times (a + b) \times h$

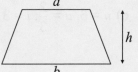

Example 1 Q is found using the formula $Q = \dfrac{2p}{r+7}$.

Find Q when $p = 6.5$ and $r = -2$.

1. Put the numbers for p and r into the formula.

$$Q = \frac{2 \times 6.5}{-2 + 7}$$

2. Work out the top and bottom of the fraction separately.

$$Q = \frac{13}{5}$$

3. Write your answer as a decimal.

$$Q = 2.6$$

Exercise 1

In this exercise, give your answers as decimals where necessary, unless asked otherwise.

1 What is the volume, V, of a cuboid with width $w = 2$ cm, height $h = 4$ cm and length $l = 5$ cm? Use $V = whl$, giving your answer in cm³.

2 Work out F, where $F = ma$, $m = 6.5$ and $a = 0.1$.

3 Work out p, where $p = \dfrac{F}{A}$, $F = 19$ and $A = 0.95$.

4 What is the area, A, of a trapezium with $a = 4$ cm, $b = 7$ cm and $h = 2$ cm?
   Use $A = \dfrac{1}{2}(a + b)h$, giving your answer in cm².

5 Use the formula $C = \frac{5}{9}(F - 32)$ to convert the following temperatures in degrees Fahrenheit (F) to degrees Celsius (C).

a) 113 °F **b)** 95 °F **c)** 140 °F

6 $v = u + at$ is a formula used to find velocity. Work out the velocity, v, if:

a) $u = 5$, $a = 3$, $t = 2$ **b)** $u = \frac{3}{2}$, $a = \frac{3}{4}$, $t = 6$ **c)** $u = 6.5$, $a = 5$, $t = 7$

d) $u = 6$, $a = \frac{2}{3}$, $t = 3$ **e)** $u = 7$, $a = 0.5$, $t = 16$ **f)** $u = 4.5$, $a = 6$, $t = 4$

7 Use the formula $A = \frac{1}{2b - 7}$ to find A using the given values of b.
Leave your answers as **fractions**.

a) $b = 5$ **b)** $b = 5.5$ **c)** $b = 6$

d) $b = 53.5$ **e)** $b = -4.5$ **f)** $b = 1$

8 Use the formula $y = \frac{x + 3}{-2z}$ to find y using the given values of x and z.

a) $x = 0$, $z = -3$ **b)** $x = 5$, $z = -4$ **c)** $x = 13$, $z = 2$

d) $x = -5$, $z = 1$ **e)** $x = 27$, $z = -3$ **f)** $x = -15$, $z = -2$

9 $s = ut + \frac{1}{2}at^2$ is a formula used to work out distance.
Use the given values of u, t and a to work out the distance, s.

a) $u = t = a = 1$ **b)** $u = 5$, $t = 10$, $a = 2$

c) $u = 25$, $t = 5$, $a = 9.8$ **d)** $u = 36$, $t = 1$, $a = 9.8$

10 $v^2 = u^2 + 2as$ is a formula used to find velocity. Work out the velocity, v, if:

a) $u = 8$, $a = 3$, $s = 6$ **b)** $u = 10$, $a = 11$, $s = 2$

c) $u = 5$, $a = 7$, $s = 4$ **d)** $u = 7$, $a = 9$, $s = 4$

e) $u = 8$, $a = \frac{3}{2}$, $s = 12$ **f)** $u = 12$, $a = 5$, $s = \frac{5}{2}$

10.3 Rearranging Formulas

Making a letter the <u>subject</u> of a <u>formula</u> means <u>rearranging</u> the formula so that the letter you want is on its own on the left.

It's a bit like solving an <u>equation</u> — you always have to do the same thing to both sides.

Example 1 **Make e the subject of the formula $f = eg$.**

1. Write down the original formula.

2. Divide both sides by g.
   Then e is on its own, since $eg \div g = e$.

3. In your final answer, always write the letter that's on its own on the left-hand side of the formula.
   All the other letters should be on the right-hand side.

$$f = eg$$
$$f \div g = eg \div g$$
$$\frac{f}{g} = e$$
$$e = \frac{f}{g}$$

Exercise 1

1 Make time the subject of this formula: distance = speed × time

2 Make acceleration the subject of this formula: force = mass × acceleration

3 Make force the subject of this formula: pressure = $\dfrac{\text{force}}{\text{area}}$

4 Make s the subject of the following formulas. All your answers should begin "$s =$".

   a) $h = s + 12$ **b)** $p = s - 9$ **c)** $r = s + 80$

   d) $e = s + 64$ **e)** $m = s - 2$ **f)** $g = 10 + s$

5 Make y the subject of the following formulas.

   a) $g = y + w$ **b)** $5p = y + 8q$ **c)** $3k = 14j + y$

6 Make g the subject of the following formulas.

   a) $a = 19g$ **b)** $b = 2g$ **c)** $c = 15g$

   d) $d = 4g$ **e)** $e = 12g$ **f)** $f = 36g$

7 Make x the subject of the following formulas.

    a) $f = \dfrac{x}{4}$ **b)** $l = \dfrac{x}{11}$ **c)** $t = \dfrac{x}{8}$

    d) $q = \dfrac{x}{6}$ **e)** $e = \dfrac{x}{19}$ **f)** $a = \dfrac{x}{20}$

8 Make b the subject of the following formulas.

    a) $s = bt$ **b)** $xyz = 3b$ **c)** $ef + g = 2b$

    d) $3j = kb$ **e)** $5rs = \dfrac{b}{t}$ **f)** $3c + 2 = \dfrac{b}{5}$

9 The formula to find the area of a parallelogram, A, is $A = bh$, where b is the base length and h is the vertical height.

    a) Rearrange the formula to make b the subject.

    b) Find the base length of a parallelogram which has an area of 48 cm² and a height of 8 cm.

Example 2   **Make x the subject of the formula $y = 3 + ax$.**

    $3 + ax$ means "take your value of x and multiply by a then add 3".

    To get x on its own, do the inverse: $y = 3 + ax$

    1. First, subtract 3 from both sides. $y - 3 = 3 + ax - 3$

    2. Then divide both sides by a. $\dfrac{y - 3}{a} = \dfrac{ax}{a}$

    3. Write x on the left-hand side of the formula. $x = \dfrac{y - 3}{a}$

Exercise 2

1 Make x the subject of the following formulas.

    a) $b = 2x + 7$ **b)** $c = 5x - 1$ **c)** $y = \dfrac{x}{3} + 14$

    d) $k = 3 + \dfrac{x}{12}$ **e)** $z = 4(x - 3)$ **f)** $m = 2(5 + x)$

    g) $p = 5x + 3.2$ **h)** $h = 1.5x - 6$ **i)** $t = \dfrac{x - 2}{3}$

    j) $i = \dfrac{3x + 5}{8}$ **k)** $f = 2 + \dfrac{7x}{3}$ **l)** $q = \dfrac{6 - 2.5x}{10}$

2 Make x the subject of the following formulas.

a) $y = mx + c$ **b)** $w = 2(x + a)$ **c)** $y = \dfrac{x - a}{b}$ **d)** $4t = \dfrac{x}{5} - u$

3 **a)** Rearrange the formula $v = u + at$ to make a the subject.

b) Find a if $u = 2$, $v = 12$ and $t = 2$.

4 The area of a triangle is 30 cm² and its height is 4 cm.

a) Rearrange the formula for the area of a triangle $A = \dfrac{1}{2}bh$ to make the base, b, the subject.

b) What is the length of the base?

5 Make t the subject of the following formulas.

a) $x = t^2$ **b)** $s = \sqrt{t}$ **c)** $u = t^2 - 1$

6 **a)** Write a formula for the volume, V, of a cube with side length x.

b) Rearrange the formula to make x the subject.

c) Find x when $V = 216$ cm³.

7 In each of the following: **i)** expand the brackets.
                                    ii) make x the subject of the formula.

a) $y = (x + 4)(x - 4)$ **b)** $s = (x - 2)(x + 2)$ **c)** $r = (x + 10)(x - 10)$

Investigate — Rearranging with Powers

To make x the subject of $y = x^2 + 5$, you first subtract 5 from both sides and then take the square root of both sides to get $x = \sqrt{y - 5}$.

a) How would you make x the subject of $y = x^3 + 8$?
How about $y = x^4 - 1$?

b) Can you make a general rule for rearranging $y = x^p + n$ to make x the subject, where p is a positive whole number and n is any number?

c) What happens when you use this rule to rearrange $y = 2^x$?

Section 11 — Sequences

11.1 Arithmetic Sequences

Generating a Sequence from the nth Term

An <u>arithmetic sequence</u> is a number <u>sequence</u> where the <u>terms</u> increase or decrease by the same amount each time. You can work out terms of a sequence if you know the first term and the term-to-term rule (what you need to add or subtract to get to the next term).

You can also work out each term by using its position. A term's position in a sequence is described by the letter n. For example, the 1st term has $n = 1$, the 2nd term has $n = 2$, the 3rd term has $n = 3$, and so on.

The <u>nth term</u> of an arithmetic sequence is always in the same format:

$$an + b$$

where a and b can be any positive or negative number.

Example 1   The nth term in a sequence is $3n + 8$.

a) Find the 10th term.

     Substitute $n = 10$ into the expression $3n + 8$. $(3 \times 10) + 8 = \textbf{38}$

b) Show that 89 will be a term in the sequence.

1. Set the rule equal to 89. $3n + 8 = 89$

2. Solve for n. $3n = 81$

3. If n is a whole number, then 89 is $n = 27$
   in the sequence.

                                       n **is a whole number, so**
                                       89 is in the sequence.

Exercise 1

1   Find the first **five** terms of each sequence, where the nth terms are given by:

   a) $n + 6$ **b)** $3n + 3$ **c)** $4n - 2$ **d)** $7n + 2$

   e) $3 + 9n$ **f)** $8 + 5n$ **g)** $6n - 3$ **h)** $23 - n$

   i) $8n - 1$ **j)** $51 - 4n$ **k)** $25 - 2n$ **l)** $12 + 7n$

2   The nth term of a sequence is $26 - 4n$. Find the value of:

   a) the first term   **b)** the third term   **c)** the fourth term   **d)** the seventh term

3 Four sequences are generated by these rules:

> **Sequence 1:** First term = 5, rule = 'add 4 to the previous term'
>
> **Sequence 2:** nth term = $5n - 3$
>
> **Sequence 3:** First term = 40, rule = 'subtract 3 from the previous term'
>
> **Sequence 4:** nth term = $47 - 5n$

a) Which sequence begins 2, 7, 12, ... ?

b) The seventh term of which sequence is equal to 22?

c) Which two sequences have the same values for their fifth terms?

d) Which two sequences have the same values for their sixth terms?

4 A sequence has first term 5 and the term-to-term rule is 'add 6'. The nth term of a different sequence is $4n + 11$. Show that the sixth term of both sequences is the same.

5 The nth term in a sequence is $5n + 6$.

a) Find the 8th term.

b) Show that 106 will be a term in the sequence.

6 The nth term in a sequence is $7n - 2$.

a) Find the 23rd term.

b) Show that 72 won't be a term in the sequence.

7 For each of these matchstick sequences:
   i) Find the largest value of n that would give a pattern you could make with 45 matches.
   ii) Then work out how many matches you'd have left over.

a) Matchsticks in nth term: $3n + 2$

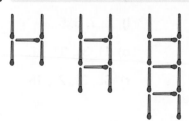

b) Matchsticks in nth term: $2n + 2$

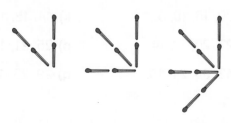

Finding the Rule for the nth Term

You can work out the formula for the nth term by looking at the difference between the terms of a sequence.

Example 2 | Find the nth term of the sequence 11, 9, 7, 5...

1. Find the difference between each term and the next term.

$$11 \quad 9 \quad 7 \quad 5$$
$$-2 \quad -2 \quad -2$$

2. The terms decrease by 2 each time, so the formula for the nth term must include '$-2n$'.

3. List all the values of $-2n$.

$$-2 \quad -4 \quad -6 \quad -8$$

4. Work out what you have to add or subtract to get from $-2n$ to the same term in the sequence.

$$\downarrow +13 \quad \downarrow +13 \quad \downarrow +13 \quad \downarrow +13$$
$$11 \quad 9 \quad 7 \quad 5$$

5. Combine '$-2n$' and '$+13$' to get the expression for the nth term.

$$-2n + 13 \text{ or } 13 - 2n$$

6. Check your formula by using it to find at least one other term.

$$(\text{2nd term is } 13 - (2 \times 2) = 9)$$

Exercise 2

1 Find the difference between each term in the sequence given by the nth term rule:

a) $2n + 8$ **b)** $19 - 3n$ **c)** $84 - 7n$

2 Work out the formula for the nth term for the following sequences.

a) 11, 15, 19, 23...   **b)** 8, 11, 14, 17...   **c)** 10, 19, 28, 37...

d) 3, 7, 11, 15...   **e)** 14, 21, 28, 35...   **f)** 32, 42, 52, 62...

g) 4, 10, 16, 22...   **h)** 6, 15, 24, 33...   **i)** 17, 22, 27, 32...

j) 20, 15, 10, 5...   **k)** 14, 12, 10, 8...   **l)** 8, 7, 6, 5...

m) 23, 20, 17, 14...   **n)** 25, 21, 17, 13...   **o)** 41, 31, 21, 11...

p) 42, 33, 24, 15...   **q)** 29, 23, 17, 11...   **r)** 33, 27, 21, 15...

3 For each of these sequences: **i)** work out the formula for the *n*th term.
                                       ii) use the formula to work out the 8th term.

a) 1, 3, 5, 7...   **b)** 11, 14, 17, 20...   **c)** 18, 20, 22, 24...

d) 41, 46, 51, 56...   **e)** 5, 12, 19, 26...   **f)** 3, 12, 21, 30...

4 For each of these sequences: **i)** work out the formula for the *n*th term.
                                       ii) use the formula to work out the 6th term.

a) 11, 10, 9, 8...   **b)** 39, 35, 31, 27...   **c)** 28, 26, 24, 22...

d) 40, 31, 22, 13...   **e)** 32, 26, 20, 14...   **f)** 45, 38, 31, 24...

5 For the following sequences: **i)** work out the number of matchsticks in the *n*th term.
                                       ii) draw the 7th term in the sequence.

a)

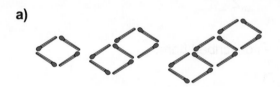

b)

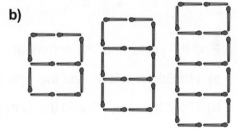

6 The sequence $1\frac{1}{2}$, 2, $2\frac{1}{2}$, 3... increases by $\frac{1}{2}$ each time.

a) List the values of $\frac{1}{2}n$ for the first four terms.

b) What do you need to do to get from $\frac{1}{2}n$ to the corresponding term in the sequence?

c) Use your answers to **a)** and **b)** to write an expression for the *n*th term.

7 Work out the formula for the *n*th term for the following sequences.

a) $2\frac{1}{4}$, $2\frac{1}{2}$, $2\frac{3}{4}$, 3...

b) $3\frac{1}{7}$, $3\frac{2}{7}$, $3\frac{3}{7}$, $3\frac{4}{7}$...

c) $2\frac{1}{2}$, $4\frac{1}{2}$, $6\frac{1}{2}$, $8\frac{1}{2}$...

d) $3\frac{1}{3}$, $6\frac{1}{3}$, $9\frac{1}{3}$, $12\frac{1}{3}$...

e) $4\frac{1}{2}$, $8\frac{1}{2}$, $12\frac{1}{2}$, $16\frac{1}{2}$...

f) $\frac{2}{5}$, $\frac{3}{5}$, $\frac{4}{5}$, 1...

8 The sequence $5\frac{1}{2}$, 5, $4\frac{1}{2}$, 4, $3\frac{1}{2}$... decreases by $\frac{1}{2}$ each time.

a) List the values of $-\frac{1}{2}n$ for the first four terms.

b) What do you need to do to get from $-\frac{1}{2}n$ to the corresponding term in the sequence?

c) Use your answers to **a)** and **b)** to write an expression for the nth term.

9 Work out the formula for the nth term for the following sequences.

a) $3\frac{3}{4}$, $3\frac{1}{2}$, $3\frac{1}{4}$...

b) $1\frac{2}{3}$, $1\frac{1}{3}$, 1, $\frac{2}{3}$...

c) $5\frac{3}{5}$, $5\frac{1}{5}$, $4\frac{4}{5}$, $4\frac{2}{5}$...

d) $-1\frac{1}{2}$, $-3\frac{1}{2}$, $-5\frac{1}{2}$, $-7\frac{1}{2}$...

e) $-\frac{1}{4}$, $-1\frac{1}{4}$, $-2\frac{1}{4}$, $-3\frac{1}{4}$...

f) 0, $-\frac{1}{2}$, -1, $-1\frac{1}{2}$, -2...

10 Find the nth term of the arithmetic sequences described here.

a) The 5th term is 41 and the 10th term is 71.

b) The 7th term is 39 and the 12th term is 69.

c) The 8th term is 10 and the 16th term is 14.

Investigate — The Look-and-Say Sequence

A mathematician called John Conway investigated the look-and-say sequence. It is this sequence of whole numbers:

1, 11, 21, 1211, 111221, 312211, 13112221...

a) Why do you think it is called the 'look-and-say' sequence? Try reading each term out loud, digit by digit, and comparing what you say with the previous term.

b) Write down the next two terms of the sequence.

c) What would happen if you started the sequence with 3? Write down the first seven terms.

d) How about if you started with 22? What do you notice?

e) Look at the end digit in each term of the original sequence. What do you notice? Does the same rule apply for any look-and-say sequences that start from other numbers less than 9?

11.2 Geometric and Other Sequences

Geometric Sequences

A geometric sequence is a number sequence where each term is found by multiplying or dividing the previous term by the same number each time.

> **Example 1**
> A sequence starts 4, 12, 36, 108...
> **Show that this sequence is geometric and find the next term in the sequence.**
>
> 1. Work out what you have to do to get from one term to the next — if you have to multiply by the same number each time it's a geometric sequence.
>
>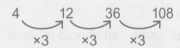
>
>   To get from one term to the next, you multiply by 3, so the sequence is geometric.
>
> 2. To find the next term in the sequence, multiply the previous term (108) by the constant (3).
>
>   108 × 3 = **324**

Exercise 1

1 Write down if each of these sequences is 'arithmetic', 'geometric' or 'other'.

   a) 10, 16, 22, 28, 34...

   b) 1, 2, 4, 8, 16...

   c) 14, 24, 34, 44, 54...

   d) 1, 1, 2, 3, 5...

   e) 10, 100, 1000, 10 000...

   f) $\frac{1}{2}, \frac{1}{4}, \frac{1}{8}, \frac{1}{16}, \frac{1}{32}...$

   g) $\frac{0}{1}, \frac{1}{3}, \frac{1}{2}, \frac{2}{3}, \frac{1}{1}...$

   h) −10, −12, −14, −16, −18...

   i) 1, 3, 6, 10, 15...

2 Find the first four terms of the geometric sequences generated by these rules:

   a) First term = 4, term-to-term rule = 'multiply the previous term by 3'.

   b) First term = 10, term-to-term rule = 'multiply the previous term by 2'.

   c) First term = 12, term-to-term rule = 'divide the previous term by 2'.

   d) First term = 400, term-to-term rule = 'divide the previous term by 10'.

   e) First term = 6, term-to-term rule = 'multiply the previous term by −2'.

3 For each of these geometric sequences,

    i) find the term-to-term rule,

    ii) use the rule to find the next term in the sequence.

    a) 4, 20, 100, 500, 2500...   **b)** 6, 18, 54, 162, 486...

    c) 3, –12, 48, –192, 768...   **d)** 16, –16, 16, –16, 16...

    e) 10 000, 2000, 400, 80, 16...   **f)** 1280, 320, 80, 20, 5...

    g) 6561, –2187, 729, –243, 81...   **h)** –50, 5, –0.5, 0.05, –0.005...

4 Find the terms that should replace the stars (★) in these geometric sequences:

    a) 2, ★, 32, ...

    b) ★, 15, 75, ★...

    c) ★, 60, 30, ★, 7.5...

    d) 8, ★, 18, 27, ★...

    e) 1600, ★, ★, 675...

5 Explain why there are two possible values for the second term in this geometric sequence.

8, ★, 32...

Investigate — Piggy Bank Pennies

Maurice puts 1 penny in his (empty) piggy bank on day 1, 2 pennies on day 2, 4 pennies on day 3 and so on, doubling the amount every day.

a) How many pennies would he put in on day 5? How about day 7?

b) How many pennies will he have in his piggy bank **in total** on day 7?

c) Can you write a formula for the nth term rule for the number of pennies he puts in each day?
It might help to write each number as a power of 2 first.

d) Maurice's piggy bank can hold £30 in pennies.
On what day will he fill it up? How many times will he fill up his piggy bank in one month?

Other Sequences

Some sequences don't follow a standard set of rules, so you'll need to use problem-solving skills to find missing terms.

Exercise 2

1 Find the 100th term in the sequence 1, 4, 9, 16, 25...

2 The Fibonacci sequence describes the sequence of numbers 1, 1, 2, 3, 5...

   a) Write down the next **two** numbers in this sequence.

   b) Describe the relationship between each term.

3 The triangle numbers can be shown in the sequence:

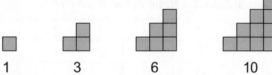

   1   3   6   10

   a) Write down the next **two** numbers in this sequence.

   b) Describe the rule you used to get your answer.

4 Write down the first **five** terms of the sequences given by these nth term rules.

   a) $3n^2$ **b)** n^3 **c)** $2n^3$

5 Write down the next **two** terms in these sequences.

   a) $\dfrac{1}{2}, \dfrac{2}{4}, \dfrac{3}{8}, \dfrac{4}{16}, \dfrac{5}{32}...$

   b) $\dfrac{3}{3}, \dfrac{5}{9}, \dfrac{7}{27}, \dfrac{9}{81}, \dfrac{11}{243}...$

6 Find the nth term rule for the following sequences.

   a) 2, 5, 10, 17, 26...   **b)** 4, 16, 36, 64, 100...

Section 12 — Graphs and Equations

12.1 Plotting Graphs

Linear Graphs

Equations containing x and y describe a connection between x- and y- coordinates.

If you find some coordinate pairs that fit the equation and join them up, you get the graph of that equation. Some equations produce straight line graphs when you do this.

You can draw these graphs by filling in a table of values and plotting points.

Example 1

Complete the table to show the value of $y = 2x - 1$ for values of x from –2 to 2.

Use the table to draw the graph of $y = 2x - 1$ for values of x from –3 to 3.

1. Multiply each x-value by 2 to fill in the second row of the table, and then subtract 1 to fill in the third row.

x	–2	–1	0	1	2
$2x$	–4	–2	0	2	4
$2x - 1$	–5	–3	–1	1	3
Coordinates	(–2, –5)	(–1, –3)	(0, –1)	(1, 1)	(2, 3)

2. Use the completed fourth row of the table to plot coordinates on a grid.

3. Join up the points to plot the graph and extend the line to draw the graph between $x = -3$ and $x = 3$.

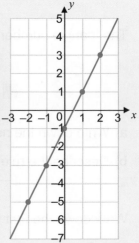

Exercise 1

1 a) Copy and complete the table to show the value of $y = 3x - 2$ for values of x from 0 to 3.

x	0	1	2	3
$3x$	0			
$3x - 2$	–2			
Coordinates	(0, –2)			

b) Copy the grid and plot the coordinates from your table.

c) Join up the points and extend the line to draw the graph of $y = 3x - 2$ for values of x from 0 to 5.

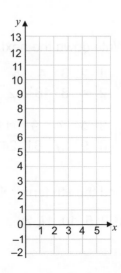

2 **a)** Copy and complete the table to show the value of $y = 5 - 2x$ for values of x from –1 to 2.

b) Draw a set of axes with x-values from –5 to 5 and y-values from –5 to 15 and plot the coordinates from your table.

x	–1	0	1	2
$2x$			2	
$5 - 2x$			3	
Coordinates				

c) Join up the points and extend the line to draw the graph of $y = 5 - 2x$ for values of x from –5 to 5.

3 For each of the following equations:

i) copy and complete the table to show the value of y for values of x from –1 to 2

x	–1	0	1	2
y				
Coordinates				

ii) draw a graph of the equation for values of x from –3 to 3.

a) $y = 2x - 1$ **b)** $y = 3x + 1$ **c)** $y = 4x + 2$

d) $y = 4 - 2x$ **e)** $y = 6 - 3x$ **f)** $y = 3x - 3$

4 Draw a graph of each of the following equations for the given range of x-values.

a) $y = 5x - 3$ for x from 0 to 4

b) $y = 8 - 4x$ for x from 0 to 3

c) $y = -2x + 6$ for x from 0 to 5

5 **a)** Copy and complete the table to show the value of $y = \dfrac{1}{2} - \dfrac{3}{2}x$ for values of x from –2 to 1.

b) Draw a set of axes with x-values from –5 to 5 and y-values from –7 to 8 and plot the coordinates from your table.

x	–2	–1	0	1
$\dfrac{3}{2}x$	–3			
$\dfrac{1}{2} - \dfrac{3}{2}x$	3.5			
Coordinates				

c) Join up the points and extend the line to draw the graph of $y = \dfrac{1}{2} - \dfrac{3}{2}x$ for values of x from –5 to 5.

6 Draw a graph of the following equations for the given range of x-values.

a) $y = \dfrac{1}{3}x - \dfrac{5}{3}$ for x from –4 to 4   **b)** $y = \dfrac{1}{4} - \dfrac{1}{2}x$ for x from –2 to 2

c) $y = \dfrac{(5x + 9)}{2}$ for x from –3 to 3

Quadratic Graphs

Quadratic equations always include an x^2 term (but no higher powers of x, such as x^3, x^4...).

The graph of a quadratic equation is always a smooth curve, with no spikes, lumps or straight lines.

The curve can either be u-shaped or n-shaped and will always be symmetrical.

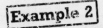 **a) Complete the table to find the value of**
$y = x^2 - 3$ **for values of** x **from −3 to 3.**

b) Draw the graph of $y = x^2 - 3$ **for values of** x **from −3 to 3.**

1. Fill in the table one row at a time. (Remember that the square of a negative number is positive.)

x	−3	−2	−1	0	1	2	3
x^2	9	4	1	0	1	4	9
$x^2 - 3$	6	1	−2	−3	−2	1	6

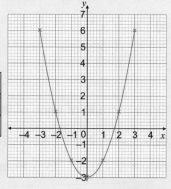

2. Now plot each x-value from the first row against the corresponding y-value from the third row, then join the points with a smooth curve.

Exercise 2

1 **a)** Copy and complete the table to find the value of $y = x^2 + 3$ for values of x from −3 to 3.

x	−3	−2	−1	0	1	2	3
x^2	9		1			4	
$x^2 + 3$	12		4			7	

b) Copy the grid and plot the points from your table.

c) Join up the points to draw the graph of $y = x^2 + 3$ for values of x from −3 to 3.

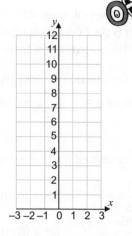

2   For each of the following equations:

    i) copy and complete this table to show the values of y for values of x from -3 to 3.

x	-3	-2	-1	0	1	2	3
y							

    ii) draw a graph of the equation on suitable axes.

    a) $y = x^2 + 1$ **b)** $y = x^2 + 2$ **c)** $y = x^2 - 1$ **d)** $y = x^2 - 5$

    e) $y = x^2 + 4$ **f)** $y = x^2 - 4$ **g)** $y = 2x^2$ **h)** $y = 3x^2$

3   For the equations in parts **a)-c)**:

    i) complete a table to show the values of y for values of x from -3 to 3.

    ii) draw a graph of the equation on suitable axes.

    a) $y = -x^2$ **b)** $y = 10 - x^2$ **c)** $y = 4 - x^2$

    d) How does having a negative x^2 terms affect the shape of the graph?

Example 3 **Draw the graph of $y = -x^2 - 3x + 2$ for values of x from -3 to 3.**

1. Make a table — include separate rows for $-x^2$, $-3x$ and 2.
   The last row should be the sum of the three rows above.

x	-3	-2	-1	0	1	2	3
$-x^2$	-9	-4	-1	0	-1	-4	-9
$-3x$	9	6	3	0	-3	-6	-9
2	2	2	2	2	2	2	2
$-x^2 - 3x + 2$	2	4	4	2	-2	-8	-16

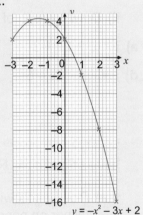

2. Now plot each x-value from the first row against the corresponding y-value from the final row. Join the points with a smooth curve.

$y = -x^2 - 3x + 2$

---

4   **a)** Copy and complete the table to find the value of $y = x^2 + 2x$ for values of x from -4 to 2.

x	-4	-3	-2	-1	0	1	2
x^2	16						4
$2x$	-8						4
$x^2 + 2x$	8						8

    b) Draw a set of axes with x-values from -4 to 2 and y-values from -1 to 8.
   Draw the graph of $y = x^2 + 2x$ on your axes.

5 a) Copy and complete the table to show the value of $y = x^2 - 4x$ for values of x from -1 to 6.

x	-1	0	1	2	3	4	5	6
x^2	1				9			
$-4x$	4				-12			
$x^2 - 4x$	5				-3			

b) Draw the graph of $y = x^2 - 4x$ on your axes for x-values from -1 to 6.

6 For each of the following quadratic equations:

    i) Complete a table to show the value of y for values of x from -3 to 3.

    ii) Draw a graph of the equation on suitable axes.

a) $y = x^2 + x$ **b)** $y = x^2 + 3x$ **c)** $y = x^2 - 2x$

d) $y = x^2 - 5x$ **e)** $y = 2x^2 - 2x$ **f)** $y = 2x^2 + 4x$

7 For each of the following quadratic equations:

    i) Complete a table to show the value of y for values of x from -3 to 3.

    ii) Draw a graph of the equation on suitable axes.

a) $y = x^2 + 2x + 3$ **b)** $y = x^2 + x - 5$ **c)** $y = x^2 - 3x - 1$

d) $y = -x^2 - 4x - 5$ **e)** $y = 2x^2 - 2x - 1$ **f)** $y = 2x^2 - x - 1$

Investigate — Recognising Different Quadratics

    a) Plot the following quadratics on the same set of axes (either on paper or using graphing software):

      $y = x^2$, $y = -x^2$, $y = 2x^2$, $y = x^2 + 1$,
      $y = x^2 + x$, $y = x^2 + 2x$, $y = x^2 + 2x + 1$, $y = x^2 + 4x + 4$.

    b) Use your graphs to come up with rules for how the size of a, b and c in a quadratic $ax^2 + bx + c$ affect the shape of the graph.

    c) What other interesting things do you notice that connect the equations with the graphs?

12.2 Interpreting Linear Graphs

Calculating Gradients

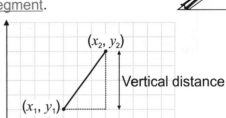

The <u>gradient</u> is the steepness of a line or <u>line segment</u>.

You can calculate the gradient by looking at the <u>coordinates</u> of two points on a line.

The gradient is the <u>vertical</u> distance between them divided by the <u>horizontal</u> distance.

$$\text{Gradient} = \frac{\text{Vertical distance}}{\text{Horizontal distance}} = \frac{y_2 - y_1}{x_2 - x_1}$$

Example 1 — **Find the gradient of this line segment:**

1. Count the squares to find the vertical distance between the ends of the line segment.

2. Do the same for the horizontal distance.

3. Divide the vertical distance by the horizontal distance:

$$\frac{\text{Vertical}}{\text{Horizontal}} = \frac{2}{4} = \frac{1}{2}$$

4. Check if it slopes 'upwards' or 'downwards'.   It slopes downwards so...

5. The gradient is negative if it slopes downwards. $\text{Gradient} = -\frac{1}{2}$

Example 2 — **Find the gradient of the line that passes between points A(1, 1) and B(5, 9).**

1. Call A (x_1, y_1) and B (x_2, y_2).

$$x_1 = 1, y_1 = 1, x_2 = 5, y_2 = 9$$

2. Put the values for x_1, y_1, x_2 and y_2 in the formula.

$$\text{Gradient} = \frac{y_2 - y_1}{x_2 - x_1} = \frac{9 - 1}{5 - 1}$$

3. Calculate the gradient.

$$\text{Gradient} = \frac{8}{4} = 2$$

Exercise 1

1 Find the gradient of each of these line segments:

a)   b)   c)   d)   e)

2 Use the coordinates labelled on the lines to find the gradient of each one:

a)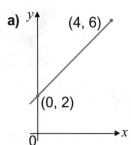

b)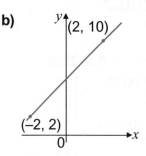

c)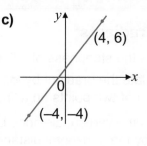

d)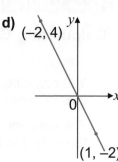

3 For each line, find the coordinates of the labelled points and use them to find the gradient of the line.

a)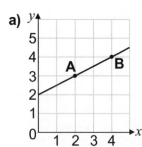

b)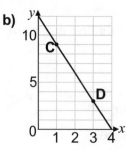

c)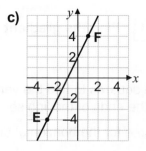

d)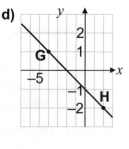

4 a) Plot the points (–3, 2) and (1, 7) on a set of axes and draw a straight line through them.

b) Find the gradient of this line.

5 Find the gradient of each line that passes through points A and B:

a) A:(0, 1) B:(2, 9)   **b)** A:(6, 1) B:(12, 4)   **c)** A:(3, 1) B:(4, –1)   **d)** A:(–2, 7) B:(1, 4)

e) A:(1, 0) B:(5, –8)   **f)** A:(–5, 0) B:(–2, 2)   **g)** A:(–7, 9) B:(1, 7)   **h)** A:(–1, 5) B:(1, –1)

6 Using any two points on each line as a reference, find the gradients of these lines:

a)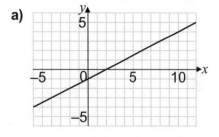

b)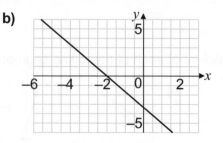

y = mx + c

Equations of straight lines can be written in the form: $y = mx + c$.
m and c are numbers, where:

• **m** is the gradient of the line, and
• **c** tells you the y-intercept — the point where the line crosses the y-axis.

If c is zero (so the equation is $y = mx$) then the graph goes through the origin, (0, 0).
If m is zero (equation $y = c$) then the graph is a horizontal line through c on the y-axis.

You might need to rearrange the equation of a straight line graph
to get it in the form $y = mx + c$.

Example 3 **Give the equation of this straight line graph in the form $y = mx + c$.**

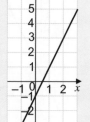

1. First find the gradient, m.
   The line passes through
   coordinates (1, 1) and (2, 3),
   so use the formula.

$$m = \text{gradient} = \frac{y_2 - y_1}{x_2 - x_1}$$

$$m = \frac{3 - 1}{2 - 1} = \frac{2}{1} = 2$$

2. Now find the y-intercept, c.
   The line crosses through −1 on
   the y-axis.

$$c = -1$$

3. Put m and c into the equation.

$$y = 2x + (-1) \quad \text{or} \quad y = 2x - 1$$

Exercise 2

1 For each straight line graph given by these equations, write down:

    i) the gradient,   **ii)** the coordinates of the y-intercept.

a) $y = 2x + 3$ **b)** $y = 6x + 1$ **c)** $y = 3x - 4$ **d)** $y = 5x$ **e)** $y = x + 7$

f) $y = x - 2$ **g)** $y = -2x + 4$ **h)** $y = 2 - 6x$ **i)** $y = 6$ **j)** $y = \frac{x}{2}$

2 Write down a pair of equations from the box whose graphs have the same:

a) gradient.

b) y-intercept.

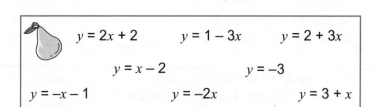

$y = 2x + 2$ $y = 1 - 3x$ $y = 2 + 3x$

$y = x - 2$ $y = -3$

$y = -x - 1$ $y = -2x$ $y = 3 + x$

3 Give an equation, in the form $y = mx + c$, of a graph that has:

    a) gradient 4 and passes through (0, 1).   **b)** gradient 2 and passes through (0, –3).

    c) gradient –2 and passes through (0, 5).   **d)** gradient 1 and passes through the origin.

4 For each of the graphs shown:

    i) Work out the gradient.

    ii) Write down the coordinates of the y-intercept.

    iii) Give the equation of the line in the form $y = mx + c$.

a) 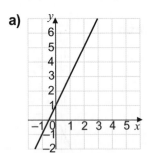   **b)** 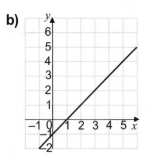   **c)**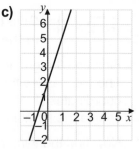

d) 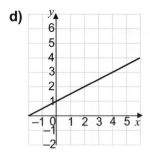   **e)** 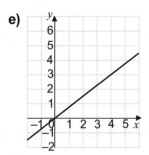   **f)**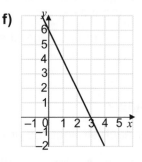

Example 4   **Work out the gradient and the coordinates of the y-intercept of the line $2x + 3y = -6$.**

1. Rearrange the equation into the form $y = mx + c$. Subtract $2x$ from both sides to get the y-term on its own.

$$3y = -2x - 6$$

2. Divide both sides by 3 to get y on its own.

$$y = -\frac{2}{3}x - \frac{6}{3}$$

$$y = -\frac{2}{3}x - 2$$

3. Write down the gradient and the y-intercept from the equation.

$$\text{gradient} = -\frac{2}{3}$$

$$y\text{-intercept} = (0, -2)$$

5 For each of these graphs, find **i)** the gradient and **ii)** the coordinates of the *y*-intercept.

a) $y = 5 + 3x$ **b)** $3y = 3x + 6$ **c)** $3y = 12 - 6x$ **d)** $y - 4 = 3x$

e) $y + x = 7$ **f)** $y - 10 = 5x$ **g)** $x = 9 + 3y$ **h)** $6x + y = 17$

i) $3y - 12x = 18$ **j)** $9x = 3y + 7$ **k)** $15 = x + 5y$ **l)** $3x = 9y - 9$

m) $7x - y = 2$ **n)** $12x - 4y = 16$ **o)** $13 = 9x + 3y$ **p)** $3x + 2y = -6$

q) $y + 5x - 7 = 0$ **r)** $15x - 5y = 10$ **s)** $8x = 8 - 4y$ **t)** $3y - 4x + 9 = 0$

u) $7x - 7y = 3$ **v)** $10x - 2y + 1 = 0$ **w)** $\dfrac{5}{3} = -5x - 3y$ **x)** $-7x = 9y$

6 **a)** Which two of these equations have exactly the same graph?

$2x - 8y = 14$ $x + 4y = 28$ $\dfrac{1}{4}x - y = -\dfrac{7}{4}$ $2x = 14 - 8y$ $x - 7 = 4y$

b) Give the letter of the graph that matches the two equations chosen in part **a)**.

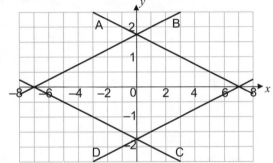

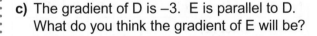

Investigate — Parallel and Perpendicular Lines

The graphs show lines A, B, C, D, E and F.

a) B is parallel to A. Find the gradients of A and B.

b) C is perpendicular (at right angles) to A. Find the gradient of C.

c) The gradient of D is −3. E is parallel to D. What do you think the gradient of E will be?

d) What do your results tell you about the gradients of parallel lines?

e) Find the gradient of F, which is perpendicular to D and E. Can you see a rule linking the gradients of perpendicular lines?

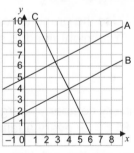

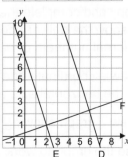

12.3 Modelling Using Graphs

Graphs can be used to show real-life situations.

Describing a real-life situation using a graph (or an equation) is called <u>modelling</u>.
You can model situations using both curved and straight graphs.

Example 1 — A plumber charges customers a fee of £40, plus £30 per hour of work she does.

a) Draw a graph to show how the cost of hiring the plumber varies with the amount of time the job takes.

1. Work out the cost of a few jobs of different lengths of time and put these values in a table.

   A job lasting 1 hour will cost
   £40 + £30 = £70

2. Plot the values on a sheet of graph paper and join the points to draw the graph.

   A job lasting 2 hours will cost
   £40 + (2 × £30) = £100

   A job lasting 3 hours will cost
   £40 + (3 × £30) = £130

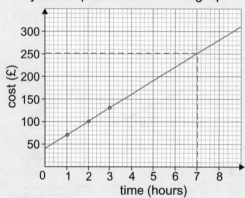

Time (hours)	1	2	3
Cost (£)	70	100	130

b) Use the graph to calculate the cost of a 7 hour job.

Use the graph to read off the cost of the job.
You might need to extend the line.

Cost of a 7 hour job = **£250**

Exercise 1

1 A delivery company charges £6.50 to deliver the first parcel in an order, then £1.50 for every additional parcel in the order after that.

a) Copy and complete the table to show the delivery cost for different numbers of parcels.

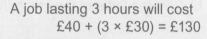

No. of parcels in delivery	1	2	3	4	5
Cost (£)					

b) Draw a coordinate grid on a sheet of graph paper. Plot number of parcels from 0 to 10 on the horizontal axis and cost in pounds from 0 to 20 on the vertical axis.

c) Draw a graph showing how the cost of a delivery varies with the number of parcels.

d) Use the graph to work out the cost of delivering 8 parcels.

2 A short-stay car park charges £3.50 for the first hour, and £1.75 for every hour afterwards.

    a) Copy and complete the table showing the cost of parking for a number of hours.

Hours of parking	1	2	3	4	5
Cost (£)	3.50				

    b) Draw a graph showing how the cost of parking varies with the number of hours parked up to 11 hours.

    c) How much would it cost to park for 11 hours?

    d) The car park offers a deal of 11 hours for £20. How much money does this save?

3 A 'superior' hotel room costs £90 per night for the first 3 nights, then £40 per night for every night after that. A 'luxury' room costs £70 per night, for any number of nights.

    a) Draw a graph showing how the cost of staying in each hotel room varies with the length of stay.

    b) Which room would be cheaper for a 6-night stay and by how much?

4 This table shows how the fuel efficiency of a car in miles per gallon (mpg) varies with the speed of the car in miles per hour (mph).

Speed (mph)	55	60	65	70	75	80
Fuel Efficiency (mpg)	32.3	30.7	28.9	27.0	24.9	22.7

    a) Draw a pair of axes with speed on the horizontal axis and fuel efficiency on the vertical axis. Plot the points from the table on your axes and join them up with a smooth curve.

    b) Use your graph to predict the fuel efficiency of the car when it is travelling at 73 mph.

Exercise 2

1 Match each graph to the most accurate description.

    a) The price of oil rose quickly, and then fell gradually.

    b) The house prices stayed at the same level all year.

    c) The population of rabbits grew more and more quickly.

    d) The interest rate fell at the end of last week, but has been increasing steadily this week.

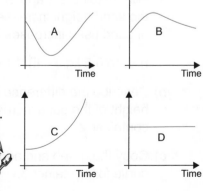

2 The graph shows the sales of a new book over time.

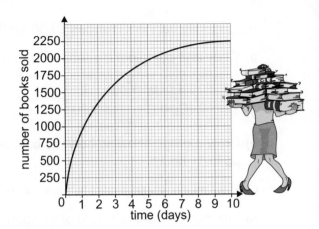

a) Describe how the number of books sold changes during the first 5 days.

b) How many books have been sold after 7 days?

c) How long does it take for the number of books sold to reach 1750?

3 The graph shows how the temperature on the thermometer in Sarah's garden changes over one day.

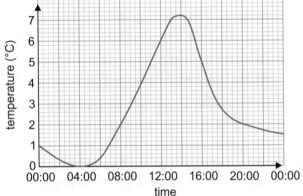

a) Describe how the temperature changed over this time period.

b) At approximately what time was the temperature the greatest?

c) What was the minimum temperature during this period?

d) At approximately what times was the temperature 4 °C?

e) Sarah's patio heater comes on when the temperature is less than 5 °C. How long was Sarah's patio heater on during this time period?

4 Sandy pours sand into different shaped glass containers to make sand patterns. She pours the sand into the containers until they are full. The graph shows how the depth of the sand changes with the amount of sand used.

Container 1   Container 2   Container 3

a) For containers 1 and 2, work out how much the sand height increases when the amount of sand used increases from:

i) 0 to 0.5 kg   **ii)** 1 to 1.5 kg   **iii)** 1.5 to 2 kg

b) Describe the difference between how the height of the sand increases in container 1 and container 2.

c) Copy the graph and add a sketch of the curve for container 3.

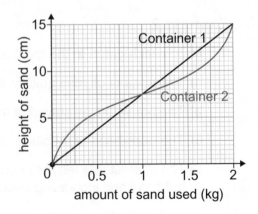

12.4 Solving Equations Using Graphs

Linear and Quadratic Equations

Graphs can be used to solve or estimate solutions to equations.

Example 1 The graphs of $y = 3x - 4$ and $y = 2x + 1$ are shown here. Use them to solve the following equations:

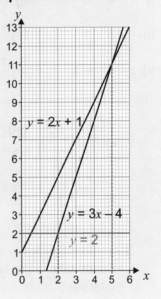

a) $3x - 4 = 2$

1. $3x - 4 = 2$ is true when the graph $y = 3x - 4$ crosses the line $y = 2$.

2. Draw the line $y = 2$.

3. Find the value of x where $y = 2$ meets $y = 3x - 4$. — The solution is $x = 2$.

b) $3x - 4 = 2x + 1$

1. $3x - 4 = 2x + 1$ is true when the line $y = 3x - 4$ crosses the line $y = 2x + 1$.

2. Use the graph to get the value of x at this point. — The solution is $x = 5$.

Exercise 1

This graph shows the lines $y = 3x - 7$ and $y = -2x + 3$. Use the graph to answer questions 1 and 2.

1 Solve the following equations.

a) $3x - 7 = 2$ b) $-2x + 3 = 1$

c) $3x - 7 = -4$ d) $-2x + 3 = -3$

e) $3x - 7 = -1$ f) $-2x + 3 = 3$

2 Find the solution to the equation $3x - 7 = -2x + 3$.

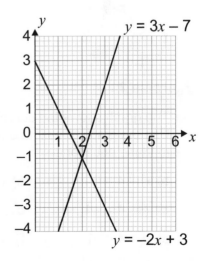

3 The graph shows the lines $y = x - 4$ and $y = \dfrac{1-x}{2}$.
Use the graph to answer these questions.

a) Solve the equation $x - 4 = \dfrac{1-x}{2}$.

b) Solve these equations.

   i) $x - 4 = 0$ ii) $\dfrac{1-x}{2} = 0$

   iii) $x - 4 = 1$ iv) $\dfrac{1-x}{2} = -1$

   v) $x - 4 = -3$ vi) $\dfrac{1-x}{2} = -2$

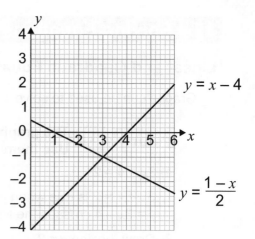

Example 2 **This graph shows the curve $y = x^2 + 2x + 2$.**
Use the graph to find the solutions of $x^2 + 2x + 2 = 5$.

1. $x^2 + 2x + 2 = 5$ is true when the graph
   $y = x^2 + 2x + 2$ crosses the line $y = 5$.

2. So draw the line $y = 5$...

3. ...and write down the x-values of the
   points where the line and the curve
   intersect.

$x = -3$ and $x = 1$

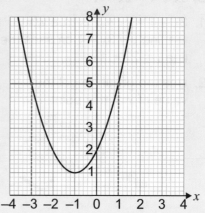

Exercise 2

1 The graph shows the curve $y = x^2 - 4$.
Use the graph to estimate the solutions
to these equations.

a) $x^2 - 4 = 0$ b) $x^2 - 4 = -3$

c) $x^2 - 4 = -4$ d) $x^2 - 4 = -2$

e) $x^2 - 4 = -1$ f) $x^2 - 4 = 1$

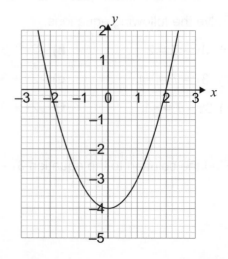

2 The graph shows the curve $y = x^2 + 4x$.
Use the graph to estimate the solutions to these
equations.

a) $x^2 + 4x = -3$ **b)** $x^2 + 4x = -4$

c) $x^2 + 4x = -1$ **d)** $x^2 + 4x = 0$

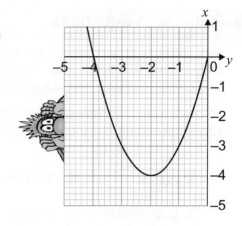

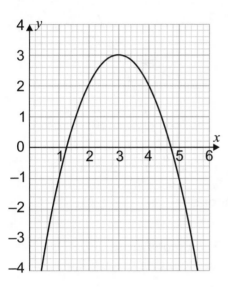

3 The graph shows
the curve $y = -x^2 + 6x - 6$.

Use the graph to solve these equations.

a) $-x^2 + 6x - 6 = 3$ **b)** $-x^2 + 6x - 6 = 2$

c) $-x^2 + 6x - 6 = -1$ **d)** $-x^2 + 6x - 6 = 1$

4 The graph shows the curve $y = x^2 - 4x + 1$ and the
line $y = 1 - x$.

a) Solve the following equations using the graph.

   i) $x^2 - 4x + 1 = -2$

   ii) $1 - x = -1$

   iii) $x^2 - 4x + 1 = 1$

b) Use the graph to solve the equation
$x^2 - 4x + 1 = 1 - x$.

c) Is there a solution to the equation
$x^2 - 4x + 1 = -4$? If so, find it.

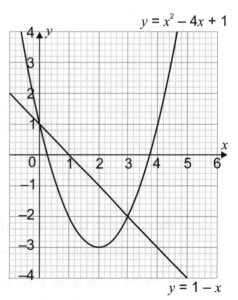

$y = x^2 - 4x + 1$

$y = 1 - x$

Simultaneous Equations

Simultaneous equations are two equations that need to be solved together. They contain two unknowns. To solve them you have to find values for the unknowns that make both equations true.

You can solve simultaneous equations by plotting the graphs of both equations and finding the point(s) where they intersect.

 a) Plot the graphs $2y - x = 12$ and $y - 2x = 3$.

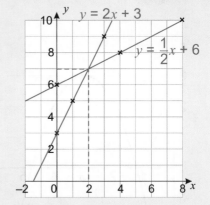

1. Both equations are straight lines
   — they can be written in the form $y = mx + c$,
   as $y = \frac{1}{2}x + 6$ and $y = 2x + 3$.

2. Find three pairs of x- and y-values for each graph and plot them.

$y = \frac{1}{2}x + 6$

x	0	4	8
y	6	8	10

$y = 2x + 3$

x	0	1	3
y	3	5	9

b) Use your graphs to solve the simultaneous equations $2y - x = 12$ and $y - 2x = 3$.

Find the x- and y-values of the point where the graphs intersect.

The graphs cross at (2, 7), so the solution is $x = 2$, $y = 7$.

Exercise 3

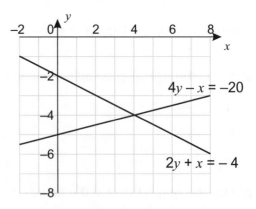

1   The diagram shows the graphs $4y - x = -20$ and $2y + x = -4$.

Use the diagram to find the solution to the simultaneous equations $4y - x = -20$ and $2y + x = -4$.

Draw the graphs in Questions 2–7 for x from –10 to 10 and y from –10 to 10.

2   a) Draw the graph of $y = 2x + 1$.

   b) On the same axes, draw the graph of $y = 7 - x$.

   c) Use your graphs to solve the simultaneous equations $y = 2x + 1$ and $y = 7 - x$.

3 **a)** Rearrange the equations $x + y = -7$ and $y - x = 3$ into the form $y = mx + c$.

b) Draw the graphs of $x + y = -7$ and $y - x = 3$ on the same axes.

c) Use your graphs to solve the simultaneous equations $x + y = -7$ and $y - x = 3$.

4 Solve the following simultaneous equations by drawing graphs.

a) $x + y = -2$ and $y - x = 4$ **b)** $y + x = 10$ and $y - x = -4$

c) $y - x = 2$ and $x + y = 5$ **d)** $x - y = 0$ and $y + x = -3$

5 Solve the following simultaneous equations by drawing graphs.

a) $y - 2x = -3$ and $y + x = 0$ **b)** $2x + y = 9$ and $2y - x = -2$

c) $2y - 4x = -8$ and $2y - x = 4$ **d)** $y + 4x = 0$ and $x - 4y = 0$

6 Solve the following simultaneous equations by drawing graphs.

a) $y + 4x - 1 = 0$ and $4x - 16y + 84 = 0$

b) $4y - x + 12 = 0$ and $y + 4x + 16 = 0$

7 **a)** Draw the graphs of $y - x = 9$ and $x - y = 4$.

b) Explain how this shows that the simultaneous equations $y - x = 9$ and $x - y = 4$ have no solutions.

8 Use these graphs to find a pair of simultaneous equations that have the following solutions:

a) $x = 2$, $y = 2$

b) $x = -2$, $y = 0$

c) $x = 1$, $y = -6$

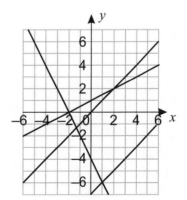

9 Write down a pair of simultaneous equations that have no solutions.

Other Types of Graph

There are many types of graph other than <u>linear</u> and <u>quadratic</u>.

It's often easier to estimate solutions to complicated equations using their graphs. To solve, just read off the graph at a given value of x or y as usual.

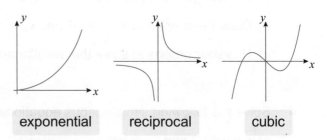

exponential   reciprocal   cubic

Example 4 The graph shows the curve $y = 2^x$.
Use it to estimate a solution to $2^x = 50$.

1. Draw the line $y = 50$...

2. ...and write down the x-value of the point where the line and the curve intersect.

$x = 5.7$

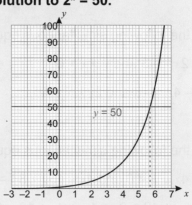

Exercise 4

1 Use the graphs to solve the following equations.

a) $2^x = 16$

b) $x^3 = 1$

c) $\dfrac{1}{x} = 4$

d) $x^3 = 8$

e) $\dfrac{1}{x} = 1$

f) $2^x = 4$

g) $x^3 = -27$

h) $\dfrac{1}{x} = -2$

i) $2^x = 32$

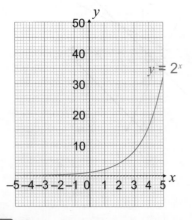

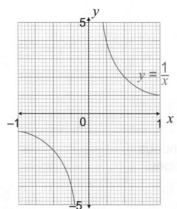

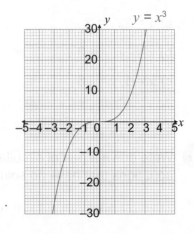

2 Use the graph shown to answer the following questions.

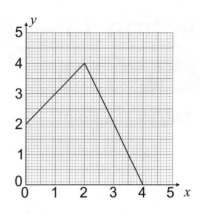

a) **i)** Write down the value(s) of x when $y = 4$.

   ii) Write down the value(s) of x when $y = 3$.

b) Write down the value(s) of y when $x = 0.5$.

c) Write down the range of values of y for which there are 2 values of x.

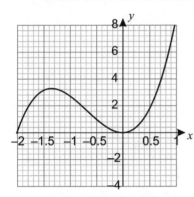

3 Here is the graph of the equation $y = 3x^3 + 6x^2$. Use the graph to answer the following questions.

a) Estimate the solution to $3x^3 + 6x^2 = 6$.

b) Estimate all the solutions to $3x^3 + 6x^2 = 2$.

c) Estimate the range of values of y for which $y = 3x^3 + 6x^2$ has 3 corresponding x-values.

Investigate — Daylight hours

The graph shows the time between sunrise and sunset over time.

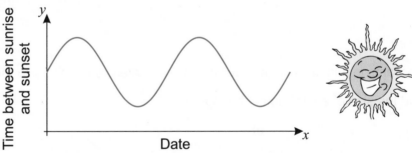

In the Northern hemisphere, the longest day is usually around 21st June, and the shortest is 21st December.

a) Can you use this information to add a scale to the x-axis?

b) Estimate how many hours of daylight you usually have in summer and winter, and add a scale to the y-axis.

c) Use your graph to predict the hours of daylight in:

   i) March   **ii)** September   **iii)** November

d) Describe what happens to the time between sunrise and sunset at key points in the year. Does it always change at a steady rate?

Section 13 — Angles and Shapes

13.1 Angle Rules

Angles at a Point

Angles on a straight line add up to 180°.	Angles around a point add up to 360°.	Angles within a right angle add up to 90°.
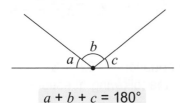 $a + b + c = 180°$	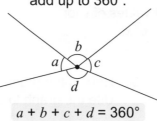 $a + b + c + d = 360°$	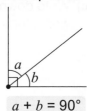 $a + b = 90°$

Example 1   Find the size of angle x.

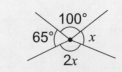

1. Use the fact that angles around a point add up to 360° to write an equation involving x.

2. Simplify the equation.

3. Solve the equation to find x.

$$65° + 100° + 2x + x = 360°$$
$$165° + 3x = 360°$$
$$3x = 360° - 165°$$
$$3x = 195°$$
$$x = \mathbf{65°}$$

Exercise 1

The diagrams in this exercise are **not** drawn accurately, so don't try to measure the angles.

1   Find the size of angle x in each diagram.

a)

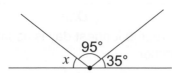

(a) diagram: 40°)

b)

(b) diagram: 95°, x, 35°)

c)

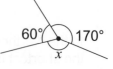

(c) diagram: 60°, 170°, x)

2   Find the size of angle w in each diagram.

a)

(a) diagram: 95°, 50°, 60°, w)

b)

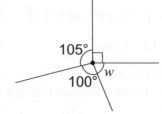

(b) diagram: 105°, 100°, w)

c)

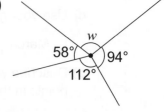

(c) diagram: w, 58°, 94°, 112°)

3 Find the value of the letter in each of the following diagrams.

a)

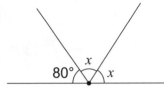

b)

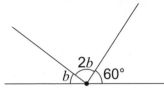

c)

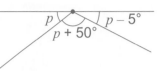

d)

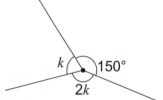

e)

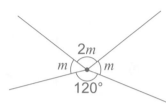

f)

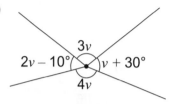

Angles Around Intersecting Lines

Intersecting lines are lines that cross at a point.
At this point, opposite angles are equal —
they're known as vertically opposite angles.

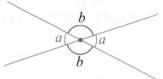

Because they're angles on a straight line, $a + b = 180°$.

Lines that intersect at right angles (90°) are called perpendicular lines.

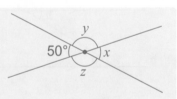

Example 2	**Find the size of angles x, y and z shown in the diagram.**

1. x and the 50° angle are vertically opposite, so they are equal.

   $x = \mathbf{50°}$

2. y and the 50° angle are on a straight line, so they add up to 180°.

   $y + 50° = 180°$
   $y = 180° - 50° = \mathbf{130°}$

3. y and z are vertically opposite, so they are equal.

   $z = y = \mathbf{130°}$

Exercise 2

The diagrams in this exercise are **not** drawn accurately, so don't try to measure the angles.

1 Find the size of the missing angles marked by letters.

a)

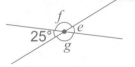

b)

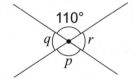

c)

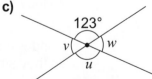

2 Find the value of each letter in the following diagrams.

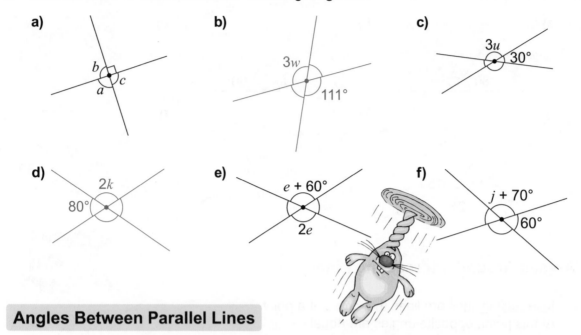

a)

b *c*
a

b)

3*w*

111°

c)

3*u* 30°

d)

2*k*
80°

e)

e + 60°
2*e*

f)

j + 70°
60°

Angles Between Parallel Lines

Parallel lines are lines that are always the same distance apart and never meet.

Here are some special types of angles around parallel lines.

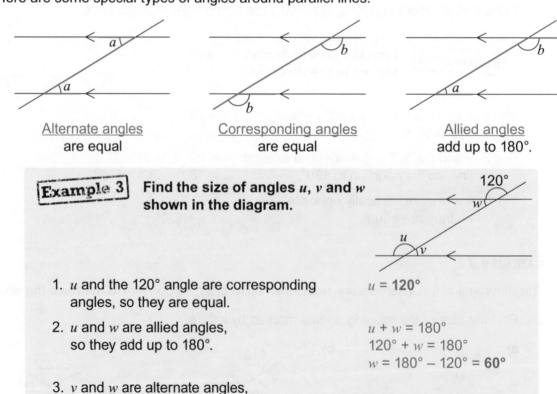

Alternate angles
are equal

Corresponding angles
are equal

Allied angles
add up to 180°.

| Example 3 | Find the size of angles *u*, *v* and *w* shown in the diagram. |

120°
w
u
v

1. *u* and the 120° angle are corresponding angles, so they are equal.

    $u = 120°$

2. *u* and *w* are allied angles, so they add up to 180°.

    $u + w = 180°$
    $120° + w = 180°$
    $w = 180° - 120° = 60°$

3. *v* and *w* are alternate angles, so they are equal.

    $v = w = 60°$

Exercise 3

The diagrams in this exercise are **not** drawn accurately, so don't try to measure the angles.

1 Say whether the angles shown on the diagrams are alternate, corresponding or allied.

a)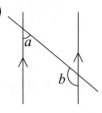

b)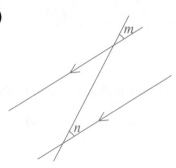

c)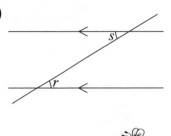

2 Sketch a rough copy of each of these diagrams.

   i) State whether the angles marked are alternate, corresponding or allied.

   ii) Find the size of the missing angles marked by letters.

   iii) Mark on any other angles that are the same size as the angles marked by letters.

a)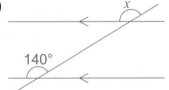

b)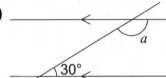

c)

d)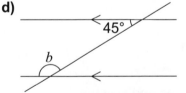

e)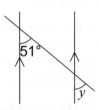

f)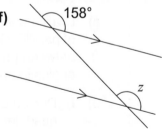

3 Find the size of the missing angles marked by letters and give a reason for each answer.

a)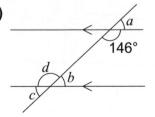

b)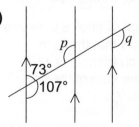

c)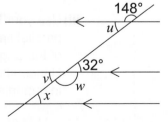

4 Find the size of the missing angles marked by letters.

a)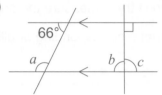

b)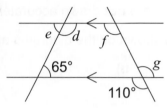

c)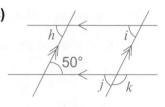

5 Use all the angle rules you know to find the size of the missing angles marked by letters.

a)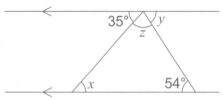

b)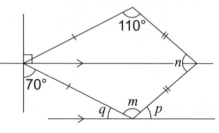

6 Use all the angle rules you know to find the size of the missing angles marked by letters in this diagram.

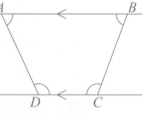

Investigate — Angles in Polygons

a) Draw a quadrilateral *ABCD* with **one pair** of parallel sides. Use your knowledge of angles between parallel lines to show that the sum of the angles in quadrilateral *ABCD* is 360°.

b) i) Draw a quadrilateral *EFGH* with **no** parallel sides and split the quadrilateral into two triangles by drawing the diagonal *EG*.

ii) Draw two lines parallel to *EG*, one going through point *F* and the other through point *H*.

iii) Use your knowledge of angles between parallel lines to show that the sum of the angles in each triangle is 180°. Hence show that the sum of the angles in quadrilateral *EFGH* is 360°.

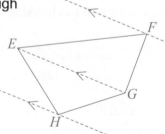

13.2 Polygons

Angles in Polygons

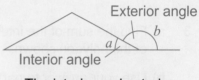

A polygon is an enclosed shape whose sides are all straight.
A regular polygon has sides of equal length and angles that are all equal.

The angles inside a polygon are called interior angles.
The sum of the interior angles depends on
how many sides the polygon has.

The exterior angles are the angles between a
side of the polygon and the line extended from
the next side of the polygon.
The sum of the exterior angles is always **360°**.

Exterior angle

b

a

Interior angle

The interior and exterior
angles lie on a straight line:
$a + b = 180°$

The interior angles of a triangle always add up to **180°**.

The interior angles of a quadrilateral add up to **360°**.

The sum of the interior angles, S, in an n-sided polygon is given by: $S = (n - 2) \times 180°$

Example 1

a) Find the sum of the interior angles of a hexagon.

1. Write out the formula for the sum, S,
   of the interior angles of a polygon.

   $S = (n - 2) \times 180°$

2. A hexagon has 6 sides, so substitute
   $n = 6$ into the formula for S
   and work out the answer.

   $S = (6 - 2) \times 180°$
   $S = 4 \times 180°$
   $S = \mathbf{720°}$

**b) Hence find the size of the 6th angle in a hexagon,
   if the other 5 angles add up to 695°.**

1. Write an equation containing the missing angle, x.

   $695° + x = 720°$

2. Solve your equation to find x.

   $x = 720° - 695°$
   $x = \mathbf{25°}$

Exercise 1

The diagrams in this exercise are **not** drawn accurately, so don't try to measure the angles.

1   Find the sum of the interior angles of:

   a) a pentagon (a 5-sided polygon)

   b) a heptagon (a 7-sided polygon)

   c) a nonagon (a 9-sided polygon)

2 Look at the sketch of the polygon.

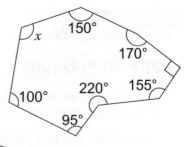

a) Find the sum of the interior angles of the polygon.

b) Use your answer to part **a)** to find the size of the angle marked x.

3 a) Find the sum of the interior angles of the polygon shown.

b) Use your answer to part **a)** to find the size of the angle marked y.

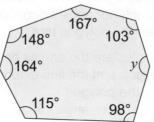

4 A hexagon has two angles measuring 130°, two right angles and one angle measuring 175°. Find the size of the missing angle.

5 Find the size of the missing angles marked by letters in the following shapes:

a)

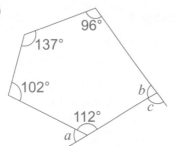

b)

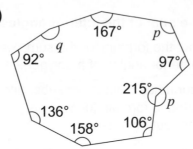

Example 2

a) Find the size of each interior angle of a regular pentagon.

1. A pentagon has five sides — so substitute $n = 5$ into the formula for the sum of the interior angles.

$$S = (n - 2) \times 180°$$
$$S = (5 - 2) \times 180°$$
$$S = 540°$$

2. Angles in a regular polygon are all equal. There are five interior angles in a pentagon, so divide the sum of the interior angles by 5 to find the size of one angle.

Each interior angle
$= 540° \div 5 = \textbf{108°}$

b) Hence find the size of each exterior angle of a regular pentagon.

Interior and exterior angles always lie on a straight line, so subtract the interior angle from 180° to find the exterior angle. $180° - 108° = \textbf{72°}$ (Or use $360° \div 5$, since exterior angles always sum to 360°.)

Exercise 2

1 **a)** Find the sum of the interior angles in a dodecagon (a 12-sided shape).

  b) Use your answer to part **a)** to find the size of one interior angle of a regular dodecagon.

  c) Find the size of one exterior angle of a regular dodecagon.

2 In the following shapes, find the size of: **i)** one exterior angle   **ii)** one interior angle

  a) a regular hexagon   **b)** a regular octagon   **c)** a regular 15-sided polygon

3 Five interior angles in a hexagon are 125° each.
  Is this a regular hexagon? Give a reason for your answer.

4 Eight interior angles in a decagon (a 10-sided shape) are 144° each.

  a) Given that the last two angles are equal to each other, work out their size.

  b) Is this a regular decagon? Give a reason for your answer.

5 Each exterior angle of a regular polygon is 15°. How many sides does the polygon have?

6 Find the number of sides a regular polygon has if it has interior angles of:

  a) 60°   **b)** 90°   **c)** 140°   **d)** 160°

Investigate — Tessellation

A tessellation is a tiling pattern where one or more shapes can be repeated forever with no gaps or overlaps. The angles around the points where the shapes meet must add up to 360° in order for the shapes to tessellate.

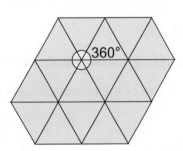

a) Investigate regular polygons with 3 to 10 sides.
   Which ones tessellate? Use what you know about angles to explain why.

b) Will a regular 100-sided shape tessellate?

c) Which combinations of regular shapes will tessellate?

Properties of Polygons

You need to know the different types of <u>triangles</u> and <u>quadrilaterals</u> and their properties.

Triangles

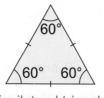   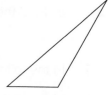

<u>Equilateral triangle</u>   <u>Isosceles triangle</u>   <u>Right-angled triangle</u>   <u>Scalene triangle</u>

Quadrilaterals (four-sided shapes)

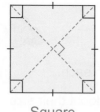 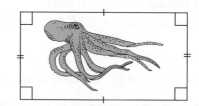 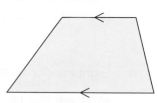

<u>Square</u>   <u>Rectangle</u>   <u>Trapezium</u>

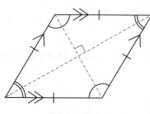 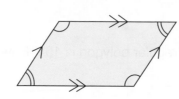 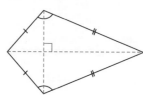

<u>Rhombus</u>   <u>Parallelogram</u>   <u>Kite</u>

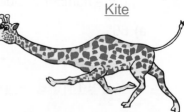

<u>Regular polygons</u> with n sides always have n equal angles, n <u>lines of symmetry</u> and <u>rotational symmetry</u> of order n.

Exercise 3

The diagrams in this exercise are **not** drawn accurately, so don't try to measure the angles.

1   Find the size of the missing angles marked by letters.

a) 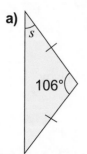   **b)** 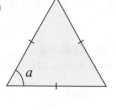   **c)** 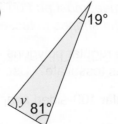   **d)**

2   I am thinking of a shape with four sides. It has two pairs of equal angles and rotational symmetry of order 2. Its diagonals cross at right angles. What is the name of the shape I am thinking of?

3   For each of the following shapes, write down the number of lines of symmetry.

   a) rhombus   **b)** regular hexagon   **c)** trapezium   **d)** square

   e) regular octagon   **f)** parallelogram   **g)** regular pentagon   **h)** kite

4   A parallelogram has an interior angle of 106°.
   List the sizes of the other three interior angles.

5   Sanjay and Eve are looking at the same triangle. Sanjay says, "this triangle is isosceles". Eve says, "this is a right-angled triangle". Can they both be correct? Explain your answer.

6   Write down all the different types of quadrilateral which have:

   a) 2 pairs of parallel sides   **b)** diagonals that cross at right angles

   c) 4 different interior angles   **d)** 4 equal sides

7   A kite has a perimeter of 65 cm. One of its sides is 14 cm long.
   It has two interior angles measuring 63° and 22° each. The other two angles are equal.

   a) What are the lengths of the other three sides?

   b) Work out the size of the other two angles.

8   A quadrilateral has two pairs of equal angles.

   a) Suggest two shapes that the quadrilateral could be.

   b) Name one thing you could observe to say for certain what the quadrilateral was.

9   Use this diagram of a square, along with your knowledge of angle rules, to show that the diagonals cross at a 90° angle.

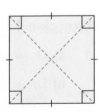

10 Use your knowledge of angle rules to show that
   the diagonals of a rectangle are not lines of symmetry.

Section 14 — Constructions

14.1 Constructions

Perpendicular Lines

The <u>perpendicular</u> from a point to a line:
- passes through the point, and
- meets the line at a <u>right angle</u> (90°).

There are two different perpendicular lines you will need to be able to <u>construct</u>:

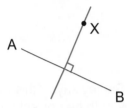

The perpendicular **from** the point X **to** the line AB. (This is the **shortest distance** between X and AB.)

The perpendicular **at** the point X **on** the line AB.

Example 1	Construct the perpendicular from a point X to a horizontal line using only a ruler and a compass.

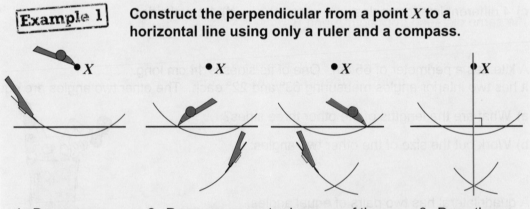

1. Draw an arc centred on X cutting the line twice.

2. Draw an arc centred on one of the points where your arc meets the line. Do the same for the other point, keeping the radius the same.

3. Draw the perpendicular to where the arcs cross.

Exercise 1

1 **a)** Draw two points P and Q. Draw a long straight line passing through them.

   b) Draw another point R (not on the line PQ).
   Construct the perpendicular from R to line PQ.

2 **a)** On squared paper, draw axes with *x*-values and *y*-values from –5 to 5.

b) Plot the points *A*(–5, –1), *B*(3, 3) and *C*(4, –4). Join points *A* and *B* with a straight line.

c) Construct a line to show the shortest distance from point *C* to the line *AB*.

d) Give the coordinates of the point where the line you drew in **c)** meets *AB*.

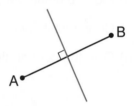

3 Draw an equilateral triangle using a ruler and a protractor.
Construct a perpendicular from each of the triangle's corners to the opposite side.
What do you notice about these lines?

4 Draw a straight line and label either end of the line *A* and *B*.
Mark a point *C* on the line. Construct the perpendicular to the line *AB* through point *C*.

Perpendicular Bisectors

The <u>perpendicular bisector</u> of a line between points A and B:
- is at <u>right angles</u> to the line AB
- cuts the line AB in half.

All points on the perpendicular bisector are
the same distance from both A and B.

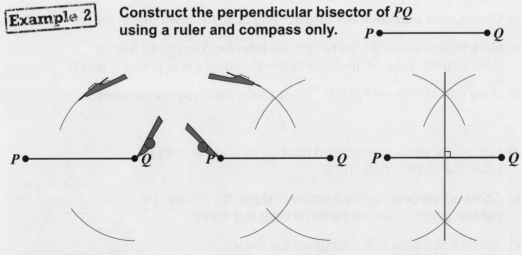

Example 2 | **Construct the perpendicular bisector of *PQ* using a ruler and compass only.**

1. Place the compass point at *Q*, with the radius more than half of the length *PQ*. Draw two arcs as shown.

2. Keep the radius the same and put the compass point at *P*. Draw two more arcs.

3. Use a ruler to draw a straight line through the points where the arcs meet. This is the perpendicular bisector.

Exercise 2

1 a) Draw a horizontal line AB 8 cm long.

 b) Construct its perpendicular bisector using a ruler and compass only.

2 a) Draw a vertical line XY 12 cm long.

 b) Construct its perpendicular bisector using a ruler and compass only.

3 a) Draw a slanting line XY 70 mm long.

 b) Construct the perpendicular to XY that cuts XY 35 mm from point X.

4 a) On squared paper, draw axes with x-values and y-values from 0 to 10.

 b) Plot the points $A(0, 4)$ and $B(8, 8)$ and join them to make the straight line AB.

 c) Construct its perpendicular bisector using a ruler and compass only.

 d) Give the coordinates of the point where the line you drew in **c)** cuts the x-axis.

5 a) Draw a horizontal line EF 10 cm long.

 b) Construct its perpendicular bisector and label the point where the two lines cross D.

 c) Mark two points on the perpendicular bisector, 5 cm away from D
   (one above the line EF and one below it). Label these points G and H.

 d) Draw the quadrilateral $EGFH$. What shape have you constructed?

6 a) Use a ruler and a protractor to draw an equilateral triangle.
   Label the corners P, Q and R.

 b) Construct perpendicular bisectors of sides PQ, QR and PR.
   Label the point S, where the three bisectors cross.

 c) Set your compass to the length of the line PS.
   Draw a circle with centre S.

 d) What do you notice about the circle?

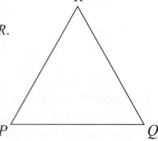

Angle Bisectors

An <u>angle bisector</u> cuts an angle exactly in half, leaving two equal angles.

Every point on the angle bisector is exactly the same distance away from the two original lines.

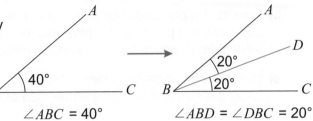

$\angle ABC = 40°$ $\angle ABD = \angle DBC = 20°$

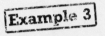 **Construct the bisector of an 80° angle.**

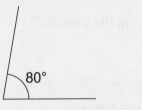 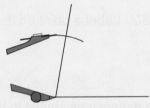 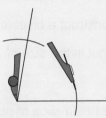

1. Place the point of the compass on the angle and draw arcs crossing both lines — using the same radius.

 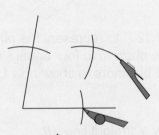 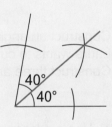

2. Now place the point of the compass where your arcs cross the lines, and draw two more arcs — using the same radius.

3. Use a ruler to draw the angle bisector.

Exercise 3

1   Draw the following angles using a protractor.
    For each angle, construct the angle bisector using a ruler and compass.

a) 30°   b) 64°   c) 90°   d) 130°

e) 54°   f) 108°   g) 38°   h) 180°

Check each of your angle bisectors with a protractor.

2 a) Draw a straight line and label the end points A and B.

b) Construct a perpendicular bisector of the line AB.
Label the end points of the perpendicular bisector C and D and label point E, where lines AB and CD cross.

c) Construct an angle bisector of $\angle BED$.
Label the size of the angles either side of this line.

3 a) Use a protractor to draw an angle RST of 100°.

b) Construct a bisector of $\angle RST$. Label a point on the angle bisector U.

c) Construct a bisector of $\angle RSU$. Label a point on this angle bisector V.

d) What is the size of $\angle RSV$?

4 Laura has a slice of pizza with dimensions shown in this diagram:

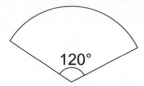

Construct an angle of 120° to represent the pizza.
Laura wants to cut the pizza in to four equal slices.
Construct three angle bisectors to show how Laura should cut the pizza up.

5 a) Use a ruler to draw a straight line AB.

b) Using only angle bisectors, draw an angle of 22.5° accurately.

> ## Investigate — Why Do Constructions Work?
>
> **a)** Follow the steps to draw an angle bisector, but each time you draw a construction arc, draw a full circle instead. (You should end up with 3 circles.)
>
> **b)** All three of the circles will have the same radius.
> Mark every place that the circles intersect with a dot. Draw 4 lines of the same length to make a quadrilateral by joining up the 4 dots.
>
> **c)** Can you use the properties of this quadrilateral to show how the angle bisector construction works?
>
> **d)** Do the same when constructing the perpendicular bisector of a line.

Triangles

When you are given all three side lengths of a triangle there is only one possible triangle you can construct.

Two constructions of the same triangle might look different (they could be a rotation or reflection of one another), but they will have the same shape and size. We say the two triangles are congruent.

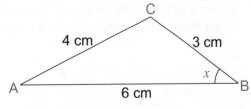

AB = 6 cm, BC = 3 cm and AC = 4 cm

$x = \angle ABC$

Always label the corners of your triangle so you can describe the line that connects them and the angle between the two sides.

Example 4 **Draw triangle *ABC*, where *AB* is 4 cm, *BC* is 2 cm and *AC* is 3.5 cm.**

1. Start by sketching and labelling the triangle so you know roughly what is needed.

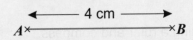

2. Draw and label the 4 cm side using a ruler.

3. Set your compass to 2 cm. Draw an arc 2 cm from *B*.

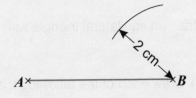

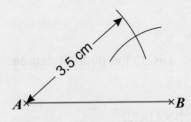

4. Set your compass to 3.5 cm. Draw an arc 3.5 cm from *A*.

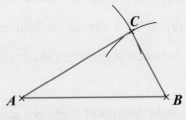

5. Label point *C* where the two arcs cross and use a ruler to draw the other two sides of the triangle.

Exercise 4

1 These triangles are not drawn accurately.
Draw them accurately with the measurements given using a ruler and compass.

a)

3 cm   4 cm

5 cm

b)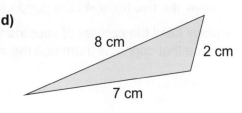

12 cm   5 cm

9 cm

c)

9 cm

4.5 cm   7.5 cm

d)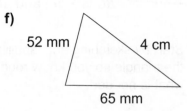

8 cm   2 cm

7 cm

e)

60 mm

40 mm

55 mm

f)

52 mm   4 cm

65 mm

2 Draw an equilateral triangle with side lengths of 5 cm using a ruler and compass.

3 a) Draw each of the following triangles ABC using a ruler and compass.

    i) AB is 5 cm, BC is 11 cm, AC is 11 cm.

    ii) AB is 8.5 cm, BC is 4 cm, AC is 6.5 cm.

    iii) AB is 2.6 cm, BC is 4.4 cm, AC is 5.3 cm.

    iv) AB is 63 mm, BC is 38 mm, AC is 81 mm.

  b) For each of the triangles in part a) measure $\angle ABC$ to the nearest degree.

4 Amanda, Beth and Carla are standing on the school field.
- Amanda is 45 metres from Beth,
- Beth is 20 metres away from Carla, and
- Amanda is 35 metres away from Carla.

Using a scale of 1 cm : 10 metres, construct a triangle to show their positions.
Measure and label all of the angles (to the nearest degree) in your triangle construction.

14.2 Loci and Bearings

Loci

A <u>locus</u> (plural = 'loci') is a set of points which satisfy a particular condition.

The locus of points 1 cm from a point P is a circle with radius 1 cm centred on P.

1 cm

P

The locus of points 1 cm from a line AB is a 'sausage shape'.

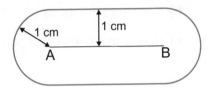

1 cm

1 cm

A   B

The locus of points <u>equidistant</u> (the same distance) from points A and B is the <u>perpendicular bisector</u> of AB.

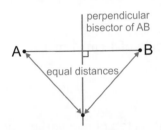

perpendicular bisector of AB

A   B

equal distances

The locus of points equidistant from two lines is their <u>angle bisector</u>.

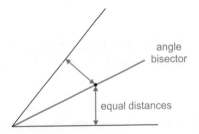

angle bisector

equal distances

Example 1

The diagram shows a field containing two fences, A and B, along with a post, X, in the corner.
Shade the points that are both closer to B than A, <u>and</u> more than 30 m from X. Use a scale of 1 cm : 10 m.

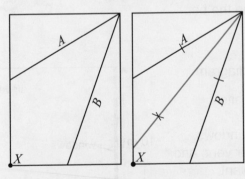

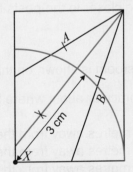

1. Construct an angle bisector between fences A and B. Anything to the right of this line is closer to fence B than fence A.

2. Draw a locus of points 30 m from post X using the scale 1 cm : 10 m.

3. Shade the area that's over 3 cm from point X and closer to fence B than fence A.

Exercise 1

1 a) Draw a horizontal line 6 cm long and label the end points A and B.

b) Construct the locus of all the points that are equidistant from points A and B.

2 a) Draw a line 4 cm long and label the end points P and Q.

b) Construct the locus of all the points 3 cm from the line.

c) Shade the locus of all points that are less than 3 cm from the line PQ.

3 a) Draw a pair of perpendicular axes with the same scale on each, ranging from 0 to 10. Label the axes x and y.

b) Construct the locus of the points which are closer to the y-axis than the x-axis.

4 A horse is tethered to a post by a 7 m rope. Use a scale of 1 cm : 1 m to construct a locus to show where the horse can move.

5 A 5-a-side football goal is made up of a horizontal bar on top of two vertical posts. The bar is 3 m long and the posts are 2 m tall.

a) Make a scale drawing of the goal using the scale 1 cm : 0.5 m.

b) By constructing two angle bisectors, show all the points in the goal that are closer to the posts than the bar.

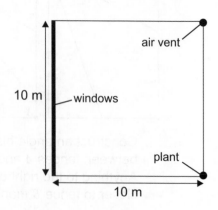

6 The plan of a classroom is shown on this diagram.

Sheldon is very particular about where he sits.
He must sit:
- more than 5 metres away from the windows,
- more than 6 metres away from the air vent, and
- more than 5 metres away from the plant.

Show, on an accurate scale drawing, the area of the classroom where Sheldon could sit.
Use the scale 1 cm : 1 m.

air vent

10 m   windows

plant

10 m

Bearings

A <u>bearing</u> tells you the direction of one point from another.

Bearings are always given as three-figure angles, measured clockwise from north.
(So an angle of 50° measured clockwise from north is written as 050°.)

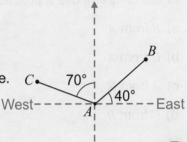

Example 2 Use this diagram to find the bearing of:

a) *B* from *A*.
 1. Find the clockwise angle from north.
    The dotted lines are perpendicular, so the
    bearing makes a right angle with the 40° angle.
    90° − 40° = 50°
 2. Give the bearing as three figures: **050°**

b) *C* from *A*.
 1. Find the clockwise angle from north
    — subtract the anticlockwise angle from 360°.
 2. Give the bearing as three figures. 360° − 70° = **290°**

Exercise 2

1 Give the bearings of these compass directions.

 a) North   **b)** East   **c)** South   **d)** West

 e) Northeast   **f)** Southeast   **g)** Southwest   **h)** Northwest

2 Find the bearing of *B* from *A* in the following diagrams.
(The dotted lines are perpendicular.)

a)
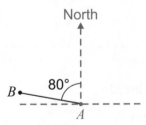

b)
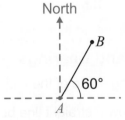

c)
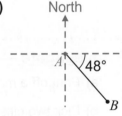

d)
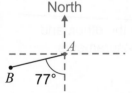

e)
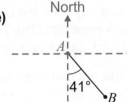

f)
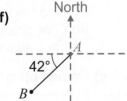

3 Mark a point A and draw in a north line from the point.
Use a protractor to help you draw the points **a)** to **f)** with the following bearings from A.

a) 063°   **b)** 171°   **c)** 340°

d) 222°   **e)** 302°   **f)** 009°

4 In this diagram, use a protractor to help you find the bearing of:

a) B from A

b) C from A

c) A from B

d) C from B

e) A from C

f) B from C

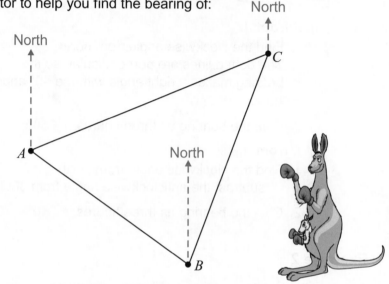

5 Use angle properties of parallel lines to find the bearing of B from A in these diagrams:

a) 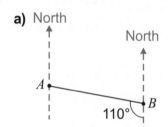   **b)** 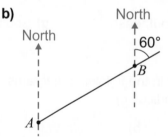   **c)**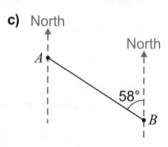

Investigate — Maps and Bearings

a) Print off a map showing some of the major cities in the UK.

b) Pick two cities and draw a straight line between them.
  i) Use the map scale to find the actual distance between the two cities.
  ii) Find the bearing of one city from the other.
  iii) Give directions (as the crow flies) from one city to the other, and back again, using your distance and bearings measurements.

c) Do part **b)** again for a different pair of cities.

Section 15 — Perimeter, Area and Volume

15.1 Perimeter and Area

Triangles

The <u>formula</u> for the <u>area</u> of a rectangle is **length × width**.

If you cut a rectangle in half along its diagonal, you get two <u>triangles</u> that are the same size.

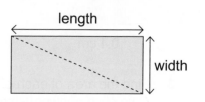

So the area of a triangle is half of the area of the rectangle.

The formula is: **Area = $\dfrac{\textbf{base} \times \textbf{height}}{\textbf{2}}$** or $A = \dfrac{1}{2}bh$

The base of the triangle is the length of the rectangle and the height of the triangle is the width of the rectangle.

The height of the triangle in this formula is not the sloping height. The base and height of a triangle are always at <u>right angles</u> to each other.

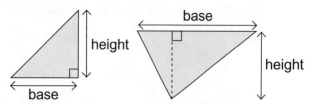

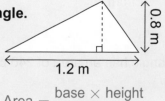

Example 1 Calculate the area of this triangle.

1. The base of the triangle is 1.2 m. The height of the triangle is 0.8 m.

2. Put these numbers into the formula to work out the area.

3. Remember to include units in your answer. Area is measured in square units.

$$\text{Area} = \frac{\text{base} \times \text{height}}{2}$$

$$= \frac{1.2 \times 0.8}{2}$$

$$= 0.48 \text{ m}^2$$

Exercise 1

The diagrams in this exercise are **not** drawn accurately.

1 Find the area of each of these triangles.

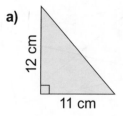

a) 12 cm, 11 cm

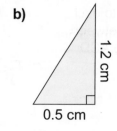

b) 1.2 cm, 0.5 cm

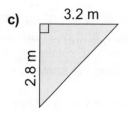

c) 3.2 m, 2.8 m

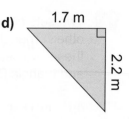

d) 1.7 m, 2.2 m

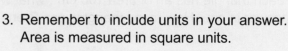

$11 \times 12 = \dfrac{132}{2}$

2 Find the area of each of these triangles.

a)

0.7 cm

0.4 cm

b)

0.9 m

1.9 m

c)

7.2 m

9.8 m

d)

18.6 m

21.3 m

3 Find the area of each of these triangles, given their base (b) and height (h).
Give each answer using the same units as the base.

a) $b = 82$ cm, $h = 2$ m

b) $b = 17$ mm, $h = 4$ cm

c) $b = 1.3$ m, $h = 80$ cm

d) $b = 29$ mm, $h = 1.4$ cm

e) $b = 9$ cm, $h = 30$ mm

f) $b = 57$ cm, $h = 1.2$ m

g) $b = 31$ mm, $h = 2.2$ cm

h) $b = 34$ cm, $h = 1.82$ m

i) $b = 24$ mm, $h = 1.1$ cm

4 Find the area of each of these triangles.

a)

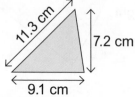

11.3 cm

7.2 cm

9.1 cm

b)

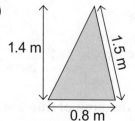

1.4 m

1.5 m

0.8 m

c)

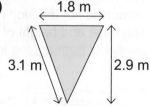

1.8 m

3.1 m

2.9 m

5 A triangle has an area of 240 cm² and a height of 15 cm. What is the length of its base?

6 Brenda is making triangular flags from a rectangular strip of fabric with a width of 20 cm and a length of 6 m. Given that each triangle has an of area 100 cm², what will the base of each triangle be? Give your answer in cm. How many triangles can Brenda make?

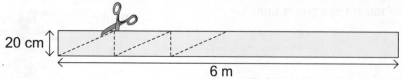

20 cm

6 m

7 Two sets of parallel lines are at right angles to each other. Triangles ACD and BCD are drawn between these two sets of lines. Explain why triangle ACD and triangle BCD have the same area.

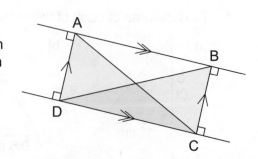

A

B

D

C

Parallelograms

Parallelograms have two pairs of parallel sides
(opposite sides are the same length).
Parallel sides are shown with sets of matching arrows.

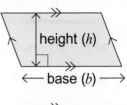

A parallelogram can be rearranged to make a rectangle with
height h and base b. The area of this rectangle is $b \times h$.

So the area of a parallelogram is given by the formula: $A = bh$

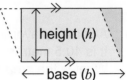

Here, h is the perpendicular height, not the sloping height.
It makes a right angle with the base.

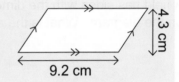

Example 2 **Calculate the area of this parallelogram.**

1. The base of the parallelogram is 9.2 cm.
   The height of the parallelogram is 4.3 cm.

2. Put these numbers into the formula to work out the area.

   $A = bh$
   $A = 9.2 \times 4.3$

3. Don't forget the units.

   $A = \textbf{39.56 cm}^2$

Exercise 2

The diagrams in this exercise are **not** drawn accurately.

1   Find the area of each parallelogram.

a)
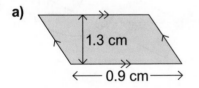

b)
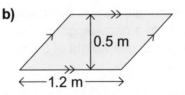

c)
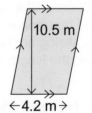

d)
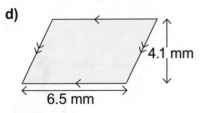

e)
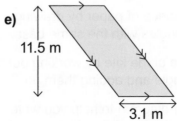

f)
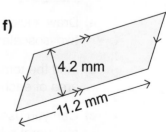

2 Work out the area of each of these parallelograms from the base (*b*) and height (*h*) given. Give each answer using the same units as the height.

a) *b* = 6.1 cm, *h* = 11 mm

b) *b* = 9 cm, *h* = 17 mm

c) *b* = 83 cm, *h* = 2 m

d) *b* = 3.7 cm, *h* = 15 mm

e) *b* = 1.78 m, *h* = 78 cm

f) *b* = 30 cm, *h* = 2.85 m

3 A school playground is the shape of a parallelogram. It is 40.5 metres long and 21.5 metres wide. What is the area of the playground?

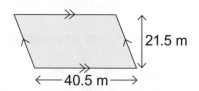

4 A field has sides with the dimensions shown on the diagram. What is the area of the field?

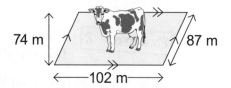

5 A toy is made up of two parallelograms which have exactly the same dimensions. Use the diagram to work out the area of the toy.

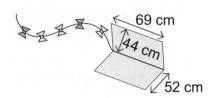

6 A parallelogram has an area of 720 cm² and a height of 15 cm. What is the length of its base?

7 Doris has a rectangular piece of card with an area of 112 cm². She cuts the rectangle up into two triangles and rearranges them to form a parallelogram. The parallelogram has a perpendicular height of 8 cm. Find the length of its base.

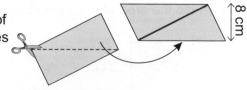

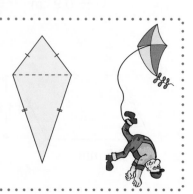

> ### Investigate — Area of a Kite
>
> a) Draw a kite on a piece of paper by drawing two isosceles triangles with the same base.
>
> b) Find the total area of the kite by working out the area of each triangle and adding them up.
>
> c) Can you use your diagram to help you write a general rule for the area of a kite?

Trapeziums

Trapeziums have one pair of parallel sides.

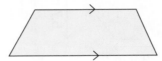

The area of a trapezium comes from the area of a parallelogram, made up of two trapeziums with the same dimensions.

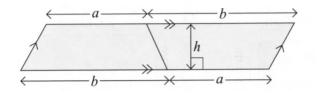

The area (A) of this parallelogram is:

$$A = (a + b) \times h$$

The area of one trapezium is equal to half of this.

$$A = \frac{1}{2}(a + b) \times h$$

a and b are the lengths of the parallel sides, and h is the perpendicular height.

Example 3   **Calculate the area of this trapezium.**

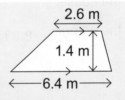

1. Write down the formula for the area of a trapezium.

$$A = \frac{1}{2}(a + b) \times h$$

2. Substitute in the values of a, b and h.

$$= \frac{1}{2}(2.6 + 6.4) \times 1.4$$

3. Give your answer with the correct units.

$$= 6.3 \, m^2$$

Exercise 3

The diagrams in this exercise are **not** drawn accurately.

1   Calculate the area of each of these trapeziums.

a)

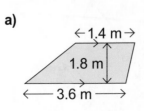

b)

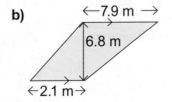

c)

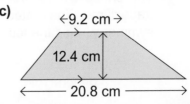

2 Calculate the area of each of these trapeziums.

a)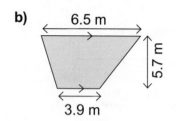

4.2 m
14.9 m
8.6 m

b)

6.5 m
5.7 m
3.9 m

c)

11.8 cm
8.8 cm
19.3 cm

3 Calculate the area of each of these trapeziums. Give your answers in cm².

a)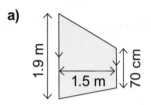

1.9 m
1.5 m
70 cm

b)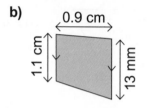

0.9 cm
1.1 cm
13 mm

c)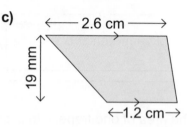

2.6 cm
19 mm
1.2 cm

4 Find the area of:

a) the side of the house.

b) the side of the garage.

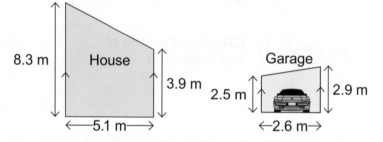

8.3 m   House   3.9 m
5.1 m

Garage
2.5 m   2.9 m
2.6 m

5 A trapezium-shaped paddling pool has a base with parallel sides of 1.9 m and 2.1 m, which are 1.4 m apart. What is the area of the base of the paddling pool?

6 A trapezium-shaped field has parallel sides of 280 m and 640 m, which are 0.4 km apart. What is the area of the field in km²?

7 A trapezium has an area of 149.1 cm² and its two parallel sides measure 12.6 cm and 8.4 cm. What is its perpendicular height?

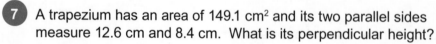

8 This shape is made from two identical trapeziums. The dotted line is a line of symmetry. Find the total area of the shape.

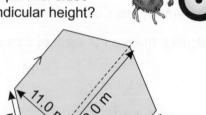

8.2 m
11.0 m
22.0 m
6.4 m

Circumference and Area of Circles

The <u>diameter</u> of a circle is the length across the circle, going through the centre.

The <u>radius</u> is the distance from the centre to the edge of the circle.

The diameter of a circle is always twice as long as the radius:

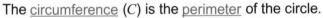

Diameter (*d*) = 2 × Radius (*r*) or $d = 2r$

The <u>circumference</u> (*C*) is the <u>perimeter</u> of the circle.
The perimeter of a shape is just the distance around the outside of it.

The circumference of a circle can be found using the formula:

Circumference (*C*) = π × Diameter (*d*) or $C = \pi d = 2\pi r$

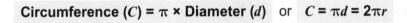

This symbol (called "<u>pi</u>") stands for the number 3.14159265...
Pi is an <u>irrational number</u>. There's a button for it on your calculator.

The area (*A*) of a circle is given by the formula: $A = \pi r^2$

A <u>sector</u> is a wedge-shaped area cut right from the centre of a circle.

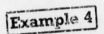

sector

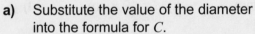

Look at this circle. Find:
a) its circumference
b) its area

Give your answers to 2 decimal places.

18 cm

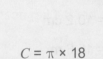

a) Substitute the value of the diameter into the formula for *C*.

$C = \pi \times 18$
= **56.55 cm**

b) 1. Halve the diameter of the circle to find the radius.

$r = 18 \div 2$
= 9 cm

2. Substitute the value of *r* into the formula for *A*. Include the units in your answer — area always has square units.

$A = \pi \times 9^2$
= $\pi \times 81$
= **254.47 cm²**

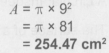

Exercise 4

For this exercise, give your answers to 2 decimal places.

1   For each of these circles, calculate **i)** the circumference and **ii)** the area.

a)
9 cm

b)
6.5 m

c)
4.1 mm

d)
8.8 cm

2   For each of these circles, calculate **i)** the circumference and **ii)** the area.

a)
18.2 cm

b)
6.3 m

c)
20.6 cm

d)
22.7 mm

3   For each of these circles, calculate **i)** the circumference and **ii)** the area.

a)
11.1 mm

b)
5.8 cm

c)
19.9 m

d)
21.2 m

4   Find **i)** the circumference and **ii)** the area of each
of these circles with the given diameter (*d*) or radius (*r*).

a) $r = 2.8$ mm   **b)** $r = 6.5$ cm   **c)** $r = 10.3$ m   **d)** $r = 12.9$ m

e) $d = 10.2$ cm   **f)** $d = 4.3$ cm   **g)** $d = 12.4$ mm   **h)** $d = 16.5$ m

i) $d = 15.6$ m   **j)** $r = 14.7$ mm   **k)** $d = 19.8$ cm   **l)** $r = 23.9$ cm

5   Find **i)** the circumference and **ii)** the area of each of the following:

a) The floor of a circular pool with a radius of 11.3 metres.

b) A circular frisbee with a diameter of 27.4 centimetres.

c) The surface of a circular trampoline with a diameter of 4.8 metres.

6 Work out the area of each of these circles, given their circumference (C).
Give each answer as a multiple of π.

a) $C = 8\pi$ cm
b) $C = 16\pi$ mm
c) $C = 2\pi$ m

d) $C = 28\pi$ mm
e) $C = 10\pi$ cm
f) $C = 56\pi$ cm

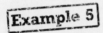 **Look at this semicircle. Find:**
a) its perimeter and b) its area.
Give your answers to 2 decimal places.

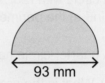

93 mm

a) 1. Find the circumference of the whole
circle by substituting the value of the
diameter into the formula for C.

$C = \pi \times 93$
   $= 292.16...$ mm

2. Halve C to find the length of the
curved side of the semicircle.

Length of curved side
$= 292.16... \div 2$
$= 146.08...$ mm

3. Add the length of the curved side to
the diameter to find the perimeter of
the semicircle.

Perimeter of semicircle
$= 146.08... + 93$
$= \mathbf{239.08}$ **mm**

b) 1. Halve the diameter of the circle
to find the radius.

$r = 93 \div 2$
  $= 46.5$ mm

2. Substitute the value of r into the formula
for A to find the area of the whole circle.

$A = \pi \times 46.5^2$
   $= 6792.90...$ mm^2

3. Divide by 2 to find the area
of the semicircle.

Area of semicircle
$= 6792.90... \div 2$
$= \mathbf{3396.45}$ **mm**^{2}

Exercise 5

For this exercise, give your answers to 2 decimal places.

1 Find **i)** the perimeter and **ii)** the area of each of these semicircles.

a)
14 cm

b)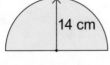
6 m

c)
11 mm

d)
19 mm

e)
0.9 cm

f)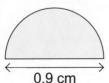
14.2 mm

g)
13.8 m

h)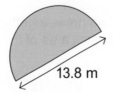
17.4 cm

2 Find **i)** the perimeter and **ii)** the area of each of these quarter-circles.

a)
4.2 m

b)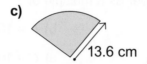
5.8 m

c)
13.6 cm

d)
21.3 m

3 A circle with radius 14.5 cm is split into three identical sectors.
Find **a)** the perimeter and **b)** the area of one sector.

4 A quarter-circle has an area of 59 mm².

    a) What is the area of the whole circle?

    b) What is the radius of the circle?

Composite Shapes

A composite shape is a shape made up of two or more simple shapes.
To work out the area of a composite shape, you work out the areas of
the individual shapes, then add the areas together.

Example 6	**Work out the area of this shape.**
	Give your answer to 2 decimal places.

1. This shape is made up of a semicircle with
    radius 2 cm, and a triangle with a height of 5 cm,
    and a base of double the radius, $2 \times 2 = 4$ cm.

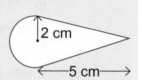
2 cm
5 cm

2. Work out the area of a circle
    with $r = 2$ using the formula:

    Area of circle $= \pi r^2$

$$= \pi \times 2^2$$
$$= 12.56... \text{ cm}^2$$

3. Halve the answer to find the area
    of half of a circle.

    Area of semicircle $= 12.56... \div 2$

$$= 6.28... \text{ cm}^2$$

4. Work out the area of the triangle
    using the formula:

    Area of triangle $= \dfrac{b \times h}{2}$

$$= \dfrac{4 \times 5}{2}$$
$$= 10 \text{ cm}^2$$

5. Add the two areas together to
    find the overall area of the shape.

    Total area $= 10 + 6.28...$

$$= \mathbf{16.28 \text{ cm}^2}$$

Exercise 6

The diagrams in this exercise are **not** drawn accurately.

1 Calculate **i)** the perimeter and **ii)** the area of each of these shapes.

a)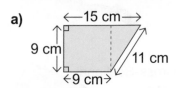

b)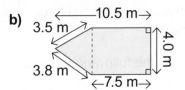

c)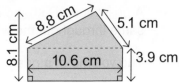

2 Calculate **i)** the perimeter and **ii)** the area of each of these shapes.

a)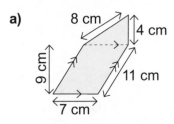

b)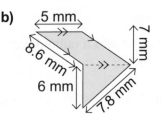

c)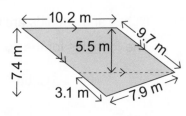

3 Calculate **i)** the perimeter and **ii)** the area of each of these shapes.
Give your answers to 2 decimal places.

a)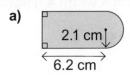

b)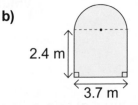

c)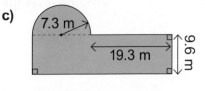

4 Calculate **i)** the perimeter and **ii)** the area of each of these shapes.
Give your answers to 2 decimal places. The dotted lines are lines of symmetry.

a)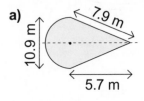

b)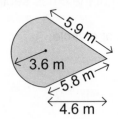

c)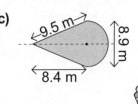

5 Calculate **i)** the perimeter and **ii)** the area of each of these shapes.
Give your answers to 2 decimal places.

a)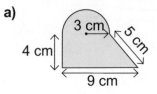

b)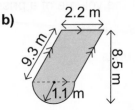

c)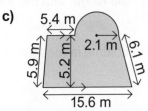

15.2 Volume and Surface Area

Volume of a Prism

A prism is a 3D shape where the cross-section is the same throughout the whole shape.

The volume of a prism is given by the following formula:

> **Volume = cross-sectional area × length**

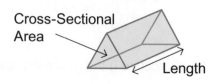

Cubes and cuboids are types of prism.

The formulas for the volume of a cube and a cuboid are:

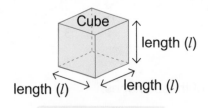

Volume = length³

$$V = l^3$$

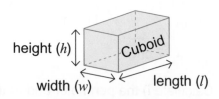

Volume = length × width × height

$$V = l \times w \times h$$

Example 1   **Calculate the volume of this cylinder. Give your answer to 2 decimal places.**

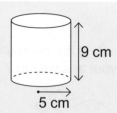

1. Start by working out the area of the cross-section, which is a circle.
   Use the formula for the area of a circle, and substitute in the value for r.

   $A = \pi r^2$

   $A = \pi \times 5^2$

   $\quad = \pi \times 25$

   $\quad = 78.539...\ \text{cm}^2$

2. Substitute the values for the cross-sectional area and the length into the formula for the volume of a prism.

   Volume = cross-sectional area × length   Volume = 78.539... × 9

   Volume is measured in cubic units. $= 706.86\ \text{cm}^3$

Exercise 1

The diagrams in this exercise are **not** drawn accurately.

1 Calculate the volumes of these cubes and cuboids,
given their width (w), length (l) and height (h).

   a) w = 5 cm, l = 5 cm, h = 11 cm   **b)** w = 12 mm, l = 12 mm, h = 12 mm

   c) w = 9 m, l = 11 m, h = 7 m   **d)** w = 14 m, l = 10 m, h = 15 m

   e) w = 3 cm, l = 14 cm, h = 18 cm   **f)** w = 13 mm, l = 13 mm, h = 13 mm

2 Calculate the volume of each of these prisms from their lengths and cross-sectional areas.

   a) Area = 5 cm², length = 12 cm   **b)** Area = 9 m², length = 8 m

   c) Area = 14 mm², length = 6 mm   **d)** Area = 22 m², length = 5 m

   e) Area = 18 cm², length = 11 cm   **f)** Area = 19 mm², length = 21 mm

3 Calculate the volume of each of these prisms.

   a) Area = 16 cm²   **b)** Area = 23 m²   **c)** Area = 31 m²

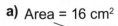

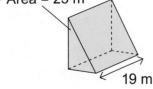

11 cm   19 m   20 m

4 Calculate the volume of these cubes and cuboids.

   a)   **b)**   **c)**

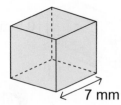
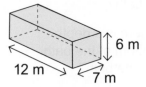
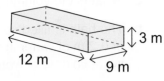

                              6 m   3 m

                 7 mm   12 m   7 m   12 m   9 m

   d)   **e)**   **f)**

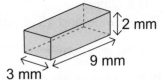
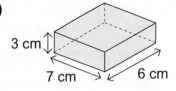

    11 cm   2 mm   3 cm

                          9 mm   6 cm

                      3 mm   7 cm

5 Calculate the volume of the following prisms. Give your answers to 2 decimal places where appropriate. The prisms in parts **j)** to **l)** have a trapezium-shaped cross-section.

a)
4 cm
7 cm
10 cm

b)
6 cm
12 cm
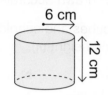

c)
18 m
11 m
8 m

d)
14 m
19 m

e)
11 mm
14 mm
28 mm
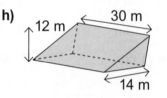

f)
4 cm
26 cm
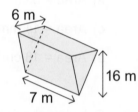

g)
15 mm
4 mm

h)
30 m
12 m
14 m
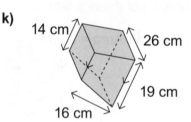

i)
6 m
16 m
7 m
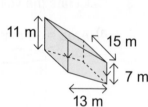

j)
12 cm
9 cm
5 cm
11 cm

k)
14 cm
26 cm
19 cm
16 cm

l)
11 m
15 m
7 m
13 m

6 A bath can be modelled as a cuboid with dimensions 1.7 m × 0.8 m × 0.5 m.

  a) What is the volume of the bath?

  b) The bath is filled so that there is a depth of 0.2 m of water in the bottom of the bath. What volume of water is in the bath?

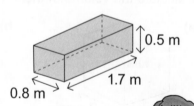
0.5 m
1.7 m
0.8 m

7 A sand pit can be modelled as a cuboid.
The sand pit is 1.2 m long, 80 cm wide and 45 cm deep.

  a) What is the volume of the sand pit in cm³?

  b) The sand pit is filled so that the top of the sand is 10 cm away from the top of the pit. What is the volume of sand in the sand pit?

8 An attic is the shape of a triangular prism.
The height of the attic at its highest point is 2.2 metres
and the width of the attic is 5.7 metres.
The attic is 6.5 metres long.
What is the volume of the attic?

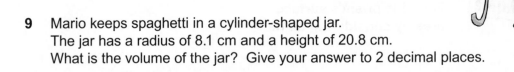

9 Mario keeps spaghetti in a cylinder-shaped jar.
The jar has a radius of 8.1 cm and a height of 20.8 cm.
What is the volume of the jar? Give your answer to 2 decimal places.

10 Albert has a telescope that is shaped like a cylinder.
His telescope has a diameter of 42 mm and is 27.2 cm long.
What is the volume of his telescope? Give your answer in mm³ to 3 significant figures.

11 A cylindrical glass has a diameter of 6.8 cm and is 14.1 cm tall.
The glass is filled with water so that the water is 3.2 cm below the top of the glass.
What is the volume of water in the glass? Give your answer to 2 decimal places.

12 A greenhouse is shaped like a
triangular prism placed on top
of a cuboid. What is the total
volume of the greenhouse?

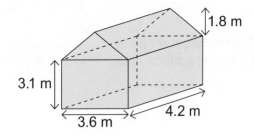

13 A cube has a volume of 4913 mm³. What is the length of one side of this cube?

14 A triangular prism has a volume of 11 475 cm³. It is 85 cm long, and the base of the
triangular face is 15 cm. Work out the perpendicular height of this prism.

15 Lana is filling buckets of water from a water tank.
The water tank is a cuboid with dimensions 1.2 m × 1.5 m × 0.8 m.
Each bucket is a cylinder with a radius of 20 cm and a height of 40 cm.

a) What is the volume of the water tank?

b) What is the volume of the bucket? Give your answer in m³ to 2 decimal places.

c) If the water tank is full, how many whole buckets of water can Lana fill?

Surface Area

You can find the <u>surface area</u> of a <u>3D shape</u> by adding together the areas of all its <u>faces</u>.

Drawing a <u>net</u> of the shape can help when working out surface area.

Example 2 | **Find this prism's surface area by considering its net.**

1. Draw the net of the triangular prism — the flat shape that would fold together to make the 3D prism.

2. Find the area of each face.

   Area of 1 triangular face = $\frac{1}{2}$ × 10 × 12 = 60 cm²

   Area of 'base' rectangle = 10 × 15 = 150 cm²

   Area of 1 'slanted' rectangle = 13 × 15 = 195 cm²

3. Add the different areas to find the total surface area.

   Total surface area of triangular prism
   = (2 × 60) + 150 + (2 × 195) = **660 cm²**

Exercise 2

The diagrams in this exercise are **not** drawn accurately.

1 Find the surface area of each of the following prisms.
You might find it useful to sketch out the net for each prism first.

a)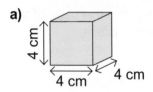

b)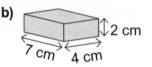

c)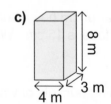

d)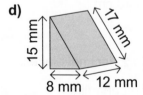

e)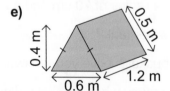

f)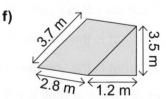

2 Find the surface area of each of the following prisms.
You can sketch out the net of the prism if you need to.

a) A cube with edges of length 9 m.

b) A cube with edges of length 8 mm.

c) A 4 m × 6 m × 11 m cuboid.

d) A 3.5 m × 8.5 m × 2.9 m cuboid.

e) A prism of length 12 m whose cross-section is an
isosceles triangle of height 4 m, slant edges 5 m and base 6 m.

3 Chris is waterproofing a tent, including the base.

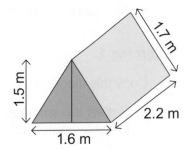

a) Find the surface area of the outside of the
tent by drawing a net.

b) How many tins of waterproofing spray will he
need to buy to cover the outside of the tent,
if each tin covers an area of 4 m²?

4 The net of a cylinder has been drawn here.
Give your answers to 2 decimal places.

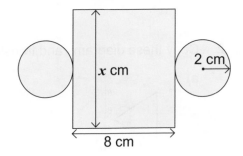

a) What is the value of the length marked x?

b) Use your answer to part **a)** to find the surface
area of the curved surface of the cylinder.

c) What is the total surface area of the cylinder?

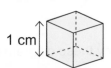

> ## Investigate — Enlarging Prisms
>
> a) Here is a cube with sides of length 1 cm.
> What is the volume and the surface area of this cube?
>
> b) The cube is enlarged by a factor of 2 so the side length is now 2 cm.
> What happens to the volume? What happens to the surface area?
>
> c) Repeat for cubes of side length 3 cm and 4 cm. Can you find a pattern?
>
> d) Now try with a cuboid. Increase all the lengths by the same scale factor
> and see what happens to the volume and surface area.
>
> e) Can you write any general rules for working out volume and surface area
> when enlarging cuboids? Do they work with other types of prism?

Section 16 — Transformations

16.1 Reflection, Rotation and Translation

Single Transformations

There are three ways to transform a shape to produce another congruent shape — reflection, rotation and translation.

- To describe a reflection you need to give the equation of the mirror line.

- To describe a rotation you need to give the angle of rotation, the direction of rotation and the centre of rotation.

- To describe a translation you need to give the translation vector.

Exercise 1

1 Copy this diagram.

a) Reflect the shape in the y-axis.
   Label the reflection of point A with A_1.

b) Write down the coordinates of the point A_1.

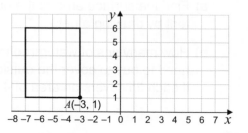

2 Copy these diagrams and translate each shape by the vector $\begin{pmatrix} 6 \\ -2 \end{pmatrix}$

a)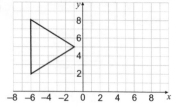

b)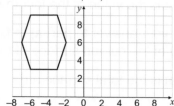

3 Copy these diagrams, and rotate each shape 180° about the origin.

a)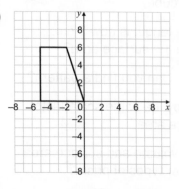

b)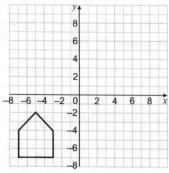

4 Use this diagram to give the vector that translates:

a) shape P onto shape Q

b) shape R onto shape S

c) shape T onto shape U

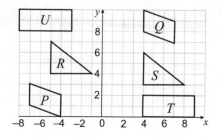

5 Copy this diagram.

a) Reflect shape A in the line $y = -x$.

b) Rotate shape B 270° anticlockwise about $(-1, 0)$.

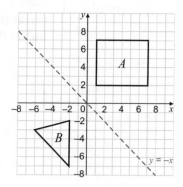

6 Use this diagram to give the equation of the mirror line that reflects:

a) $ABCD$ onto $A_1B_1C_1D_1$

b) $ABCD$ onto $A_2B_2C_2D_2$

c) $ABCD$ onto $A_3B_3C_3D_3$

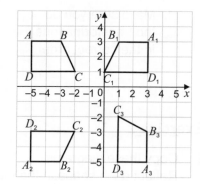

Investigate — Centres of Rotation

a) Find three different centres of rotation that will transform square A onto square B.

b) Draw another grid containing two congruent squares. Label one square 'A' and the other 'B' and repeat part a).

c) Do you notice anything about the three centres of rotation?

d) Are there any other shapes that have more than one centre of rotation?

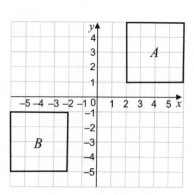

Combining Transformations

Transformations can be combined by performing them one after another.

The order in which you combine them is important — a reflection then a translation won't necessarily give the same result as the translation followed by the reflection.

Example 1
Reflect shape A in the x-axis and then rotate the reflected shape 90° clockwise about the origin. Label the final shape B.

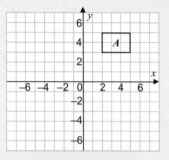 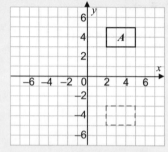 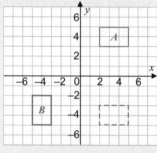

1. Make sure you do the transformations in the correct order.

2. First, reflect shape A in the x-axis.

3. Then rotate the reflected shape 90° clockwise about the origin. Label this shape B.

Exercise 2

1 Copy these diagrams.
Reflect each shape in the y-axis, and then rotate each reflection 180° about the origin. Label each final shape A_1.

a)

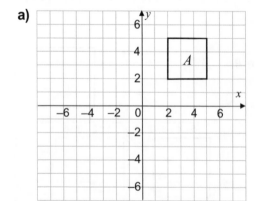

b)

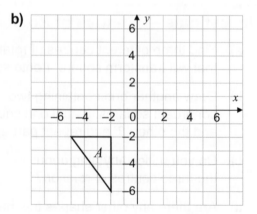

2 Copy this diagram.

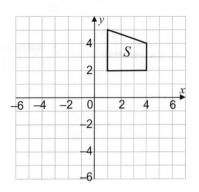

  a) Translate shape S by the vector $\begin{pmatrix} 2 \\ -7 \end{pmatrix}$.
     Label this shape S_1.

  b) Rotate shape S_1 90° clockwise about (1, 1).
     Label this shape S_2.

  c) Reflect shape S_2 in the line $y = 1$.
     Label this shape S_3.

3 Make two copies of this diagram.

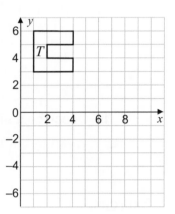

  a) i) On the first copy, translate shape T by the vector $\begin{pmatrix} 3 \\ -1 \end{pmatrix}$.

     ii) Reflect the translated shape in the x-axis.

  b) i) On the second copy, reflect shape T in the x-axis.

     ii) Translate the reflected shape by the vector $\begin{pmatrix} 3 \\ -1 \end{pmatrix}$.

  c) Does the order of the transformations
     matter in this case?

4 Copy this diagram.

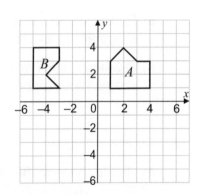

  a) Reflect shape A in the line $x = -1$ and rotate the
     reflected shape 180° about point (−1, 0).
     Label the final shape A_1.

  b) Rotate shape B 90° anticlockwise about point (−1, −1)
     and then reflect the rotated shape in the line $x = -1$.
     Label the final shape B_1.

  c) A_1 and B_1 combine to make a shape.
     What shape do they make?

5 **a)** Draw a pair of axes with the x-axis and y-axis ranging from −8 to 8.

  b) Draw pentagon $ABCDE$ with corners at A(4, 2), B(3, 4), C(5, 5), D(7, 4) and E(6, 2).

  c) Reflect $ABCDE$ in the y-axis and then rotate the reflected shape 180° about (−1, −1).
     Label the transformed shape $A_1B_1C_1D_1E_1$.

  d) Write down the coordinates of the corners of the transformed shape.

Example 2   a) **Rotate shape A by 180° about the origin and then reflect the rotated shape in the x-axis. Label this shape B.**

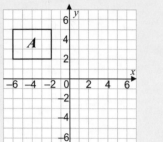 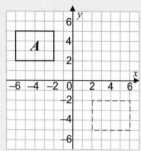 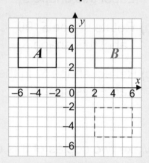

              1. First rotate the shape   2. Then reflect the rotated
                  180° about the origin.   shape in the x-axis.
                                           Label this shape B.

   b) **Describe a single reflection that would transform shape A onto shape B.**

      A reflection in the y-axis will transform shape A onto shape B.

Exercise 3

1   Copy this diagram.

   a) Reflect shape S in the y-axis, then rotate the reflected
       shape 90° clockwise about (2, 0). Label this shape S_1.

   b) Give the single translation vector that transforms
       shape S onto shape S_1.

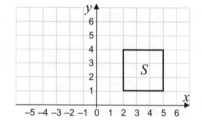

2   Copy this diagram.

   a) Rotate shape R 180° about (1, 1), then reflect the
       rotated shape in the line $y = 3$. Label this shape R_1.

   b) Describe two different single transformations
       that would take shape R onto shape R_1.

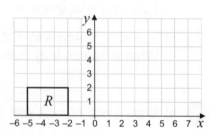

3   **a)** Draw a pair of axes with the x-axis and y-axis ranging from –8 to 8.
        Plot points $A(-3, -5)$, $B(-7, -5)$ and $C(-7, -1)$. Join these points to make triangle T.

   b) Translate triangle T by the vector $\begin{pmatrix} 8 \\ 0 \end{pmatrix}$ and reflect the translated shape in the line $y = 1$.
       Label the final shape T_1.

   c) Describe a single rotation that would transform triangle T onto triangle T_1.

16.2 Enlargement

Positive Scale Factors

When an object is enlarged, its size changes but its shape stays the same.
Two objects that are the same shape but different sizes are <u>similar</u>.

<u>Enlargements</u> are described using
scale factors and centres of enlargement.

- The <u>scale factor</u> tells you how the lengths of the sides change.
  A scale factor between 0 and 1 will make the new shape smaller than the original.

- The <u>centre of enlargement</u> tells you where the enlargement is measured from.

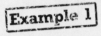

**Enlarge this rectangle by scale factor 2
with centre of enlargement (1, 3).**

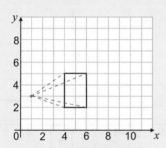

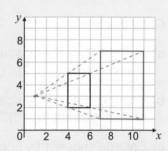

1. Draw a line from the centre of enlargement (1, 3) to each corner of the shape.

2. The scale factor is 2, so extend each line until it is 2 times as long as before.

3. Join up the ends of the extended lines to draw the enlarged shape.

Exercise 1

1 Copy these diagrams.
Enlarge each shape by scale factor 2 with centre of enlargement (1, 1).

a)

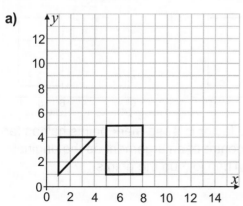

b)

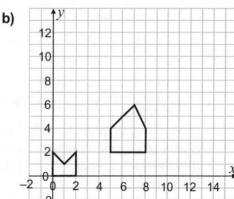

2 Copy these diagrams.
   Enlarge each shape by scale factor 3 with centre of enlargement (–2, 0).

a)

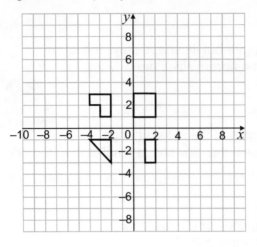

b)

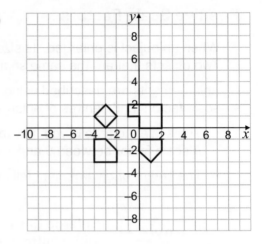

3 Copy this diagram.

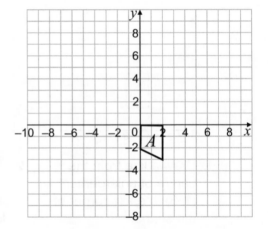

   a) Enlarge shape A by scale factor 2 with centre of enlargement (8, 2). Label this shape B.

   b) Enlarge shape A by scale factor 2 with centre of enlargement (6, –6). Label this shape C.

   c) Enlarge shape A by scale factor 3 with centre of enlargement (–1, –4). Label this shape D.

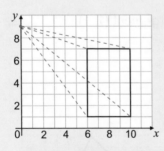 **Example 2** Enlarge this rectangle by scale factor $\frac{1}{2}$ with centre of enlargement (0, 9).

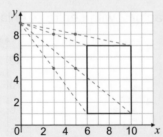 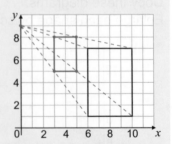

1. Draw a line from the centre of enlargement (0, 9) to each corner of the shape.

2. The scale factor is $\frac{1}{2}$, so mark points half as far from the centre of enlargement as the original corners. Then join up the points.

Exercise 2

1 Copy these diagrams.
Enlarge each shape by the scale factor given, with centre of enlargement (0, 0).

a) Scale factor $\frac{1}{2}$

b) Scale factor $\frac{1}{3}$

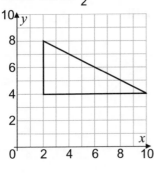 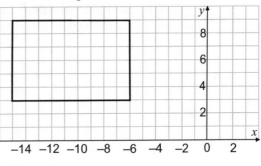

2 Copy these diagrams.
Enlarge all the shapes by the given scale factor and centre of enlargement.

a) Scale factor $\frac{1}{2}$ with centre (−2, −2)

b) Scale factor $\frac{1}{3}$ with centre (−1, 1)

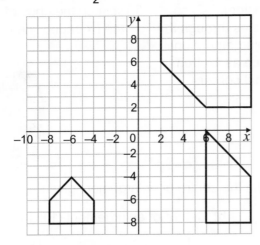 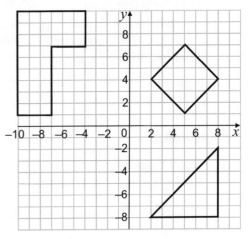

3 For each of these diagrams, describe the enlargement that maps:
   i) shape A onto shape B **ii)** shape B onto shape A.

a) 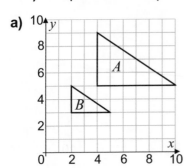   **b)** 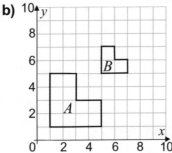   **c)**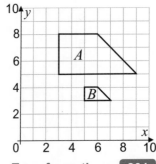

Negative Scale Factors

When a shape is <u>enlarged</u> by a negative <u>scale factor</u>, the enlarged shape
will be on the opposite side of the <u>centre of enlargement</u>, and will be 'upside down'.

Example 3 Enlarge shape P by scale factor −2 with
centre of enlargement (3, 2).

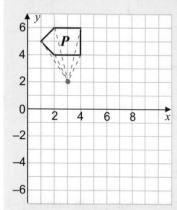

1. Draw a line from each corner of the shape to the centre of enlargement (3, 2).

2. The scale factor is −2, so extend the lines through the centre of enlargement until they are twice as far from it as the original corners.

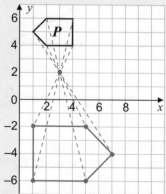

3. Join up the ends of the extended lines.

Exercise 3

1 Copy these diagrams.
Enlarge each shape by scale factor −2, with the centre of enlargement given.

a) Centre of enlargement (5, 4)

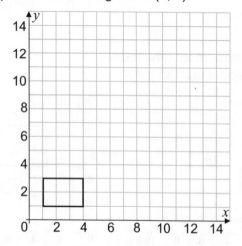

b) Centre of enlargement (10, 10)

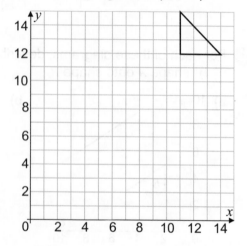

2 Copy these diagrams.
Enlarge each shape by scale factor –3, with the centre of enlargement given.

a) Centre of enlargement (8, 3)

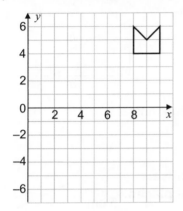

b) Centre of enlargement (–4, 7)

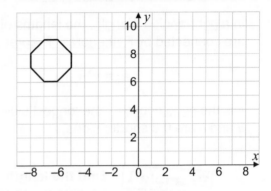

3 Copy this diagram.

a) Enlarge shape A by scale factor –2, with centre of enlargement (3, 6).

b) Enlarge shape B by scale factor –2, with centre of enlargement (–2, –3).

c) Enlarge shape C by scale factor –3, with centre of enlargement (–5, 4).

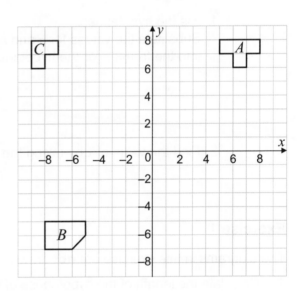

Investigate — Enlargements

a) Shape A has been enlarged by a scale factor of –2, with centre of enlargement (0, 0) to give shape B. What combination of positive enlargement and another transformation would transform shape A onto shape B?

b) Does this combination work for other negative enlargements?

c) What about the transformation from shape B to shape A?

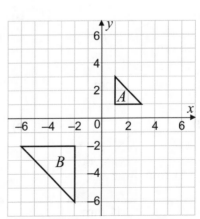

Section 17 — Geometric Relationships

17.1 Pythagoras' Theorem

In a <u>right-angled triangle</u>, the lengths of the sides
are connected by <u>Pythagoras' Theorem</u>:

$$h^2 = a^2 + b^2$$

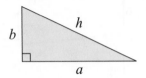

h is the <u>hypotenuse</u> — the longest side, opposite the right angle.
a and b are the shorter sides.

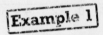 **Find the length of the hypotenuse.
Give your answer to 2 decimal places.**

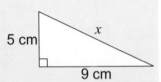

1. x is the hypotenuse.
   Substitute the values for a and b
   into the formula for the hypotenuse.

$$h^2 = a^2 + b^2$$
$$x^2 = 5^2 + 9^2$$
$$x^2 = 25 + 81$$
$$x^2 = 106$$

2. Find the value of x by taking the square root.

$$x = 10.2956...$$
$$x = \textbf{10.30 cm (to 2 d.p.)}$$

Exercise 1

The diagrams in this exercise are **not** drawn accurately.

1 Calculate the length of the hypotenuse of the following triangles.
Give your answers to 2 decimal places.

a)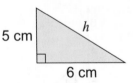

b)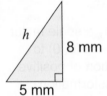

c)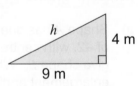

d)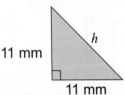

e)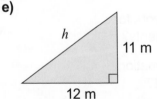

f)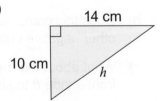

2 Work out the length of the ladder.
Give your answer to 1 decimal place.

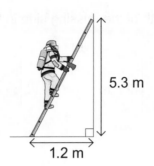

5.3 m

1.2 m

3 The size of a TV screen is found by measuring the length of the diagonal.
Find the size of a rectangular TV screen that is 67 cm wide and 48 cm tall.
Give your answer to the nearest cm.

4 Darius swims diagonally across a swimming pool with
a width of 25 metres and a length of 33 metres.
What distance does Darius swim, to the nearest metre?

Example 2 **Find the length of the missing side, x.**
Give your answer to 2 decimal places.

7 cm x

5 cm

1. x is one of the shorter sides.
   Substitute the values of $h = 7$ cm and $b = 5$ cm
   into the formula for Pythagoras' theorem.

   $h^2 = a^2 + b^2$
   $7^2 = x^2 + 5^2$

2. Rearrange the equation so that x^2 is on its own.

   $x^2 = 7^2 - 5^2$
   $x^2 = 49 - 25$
   $x^2 = 24$

3. Solve to find x.

   $x = \sqrt{24} = 4.8989...$
   $x = \mathbf{4.90}$ **cm (to 2 d.p.)**

Exercise 2

The diagrams in this exercise are **not** drawn accurately.

1 Calculate the length of side x in the following triangles.
Give your answers to 2 decimal places.

a)

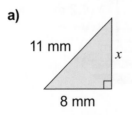

11 mm x

8 mm

b)

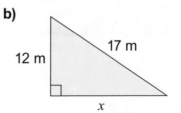

12 m   17 m

x

c)

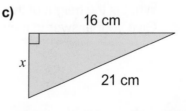

16 cm

x

21 cm

2 Calculate the length of the missing side in the following triangles, to 1 decimal place.

a)

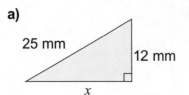

25 mm

12 mm

x

b)

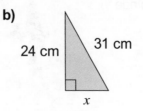

24 cm

31 cm

x

c)

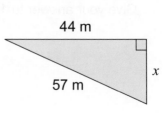

44 m

57 m

x

3 Calculate the length of the missing side in the following triangles, to 2 decimal places.

a)

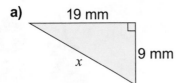

19 mm

x

9 mm

b)

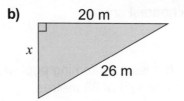

20 m

x

26 m

c)

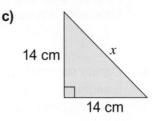

14 cm

x

14 cm

d)

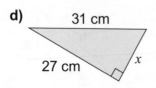

31 cm

27 cm

x

e)

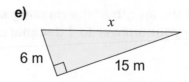

x

6 m

15 m

f)

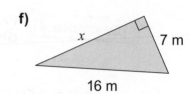

x

7 m

16 m

4 When placed diagonally, a pencil measuring 23 cm long
fits exactly into a pencil tin that is 8 cm wide.
What is the length of the pencil tin, to the nearest cm?

8 cm

23 cm

5 The bottom of a ladder is 1.3 metres away from the bottom of
a wall and the top of the ladder is resting against the top of the wall.
If the ladder is 4.1 metres long, how high is the wall? Give your answer in metres to 1 d.p.

6 A boat has a triangular sail, as shown.
What is the height of the sail?
Give your answer in metres to 2 decimal places.

4.2 m

4.2 m

2.8 m

7 A tent flap is made from 2 identical right-angled triangles, as shown.
What is the width of the tent flap?
Give your answer in metres to 1 d.p.

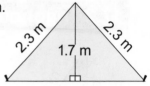

8 State whether each of these triangles is right-angled or not right-angled.
Explain your answers.

a)

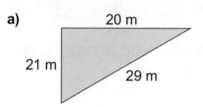

20 m

21 m

29 m

b)

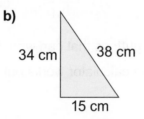

34 cm   38 cm

15 cm

c)

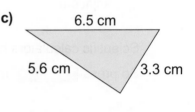

6.5 cm

5.6 cm   3.3 cm

9 Calculate the length of side x in these diagrams. Give your answers to 2 d.p.

a)

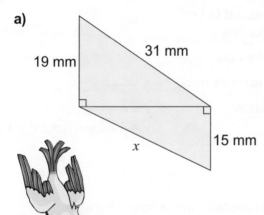

31 mm

19 mm

x

15 mm

b)

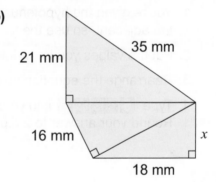

35 mm

21 mm

16 mm

x

18 mm

Investigate — 3D Pythagoras

Here is a drawing of a cuboid.
Each vertex is labelled with a letter A-H.

How could you use Pythagoras' Theorem
to work out the length of the diagonal DF?

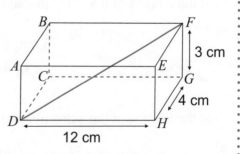

3 cm

4 cm

12 cm

(Hint: you'll need to find the length of the diagonal of one of the faces first.)

17.2 Trigonometry

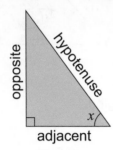

In a right-angled triangle, the side opposite the right angle is called the hypotenuse, the side opposite a particular angle is called the opposite, and the side next to that angle is called the adjacent.

The sine, cosine and tangent of that angle, x, can be calculated using the length of the sides:

$$\sin x = \frac{\text{opp}}{\text{hyp}} \qquad \cos x = \frac{\text{adj}}{\text{hyp}} \qquad \tan x = \frac{\text{opp}}{\text{adj}}$$

Scientific calculators have buttons that can work out trigonometric functions: [sin] [cos] [tan]

So press [sin] [3] [0] and the calculator works out $\sin 30° = 0.5$.

| Example 1 | Find the length of the missing side, y. Give your answer to 2 decimal places. |

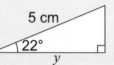

1. You're given the hypotenuse and asked to find the adjacent, so use the formula for cos x.

$$\cos x = \frac{\text{adj}}{\text{hyp}}$$

2. Put the values you know into the formula.

$$\cos 22° = \frac{y}{5}$$

3. Rearrange the equation so that y is on its own.

$$5 \times \cos 22° = y$$

4. Type [5] [cos] [2] [2] into your calculator. Round your answer to 2 d.p.

$$y = 4.6359...$$
$$y = 4.64 \text{ cm (to 2 d.p.)}$$

Exercise 1

For this exercise, give your answers to **2 decimal places**, unless told otherwise.
The diagrams in this exercise are **not** drawn accurately.

1 Find the lengths of the sides marked with letters using the sine formula.

a) 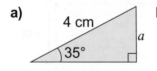 b) 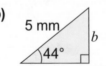 c) 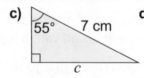 d)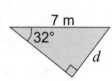

2 Find the lengths of the sides marked with letters using the cosine formula.

a) 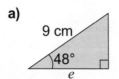 b) 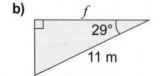 c) 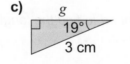 d)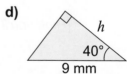

3 Find the lengths of the sides marked with letters using the tangent formula.

a)

b)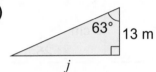

c)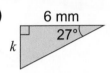

d)

4 Find the lengths of the sides marked with letters using the appropriate trig formulas.

a)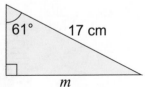

b)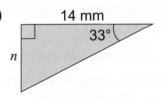

c)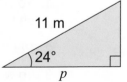

d)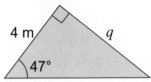

e)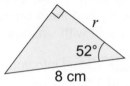

f)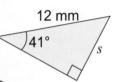

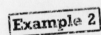

Example 2	**Find the length of the missing side, a.**
	Give your answer to 2 decimal places.

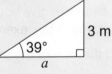

1. You're given the opposite and asked to find the adjacent, so use the formula for $\tan x$.

$$\tan x = \frac{\text{opp}}{\text{adj}}$$

2. Put the values you know into the formula.

$$\tan 39° = \frac{3}{a}$$

3. Rearrange the equation so that a is on its own.

$$a = \frac{3}{\tan 39°}$$

4. Type ③ ÷ tan ③ ⑨ into your calculator. Round your answer to 2 d.p.

$$a = 3.7046... \text{ m}$$
$$a = \textbf{3.70 m (to 2 d.p.)}$$

5 Find the lengths of the sides marked with letters using the appropriate trig formulas.

a)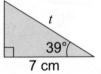

b)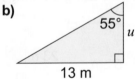

c)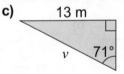

d)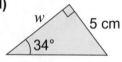

6 Find x, the base of this triangle. Give your answer, in cm, to 3 significant figures.

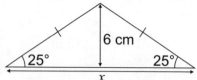

Example 3 Find the missing angle, x. Give your answer to 1 decimal place.

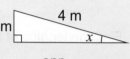

1. You're given the opposite and hypotenuse, so use the formula for sin x.

$$\sin x = \frac{\text{opp}}{\text{hyp}}$$

2. Put the values you know into the formula.

$$\sin x = \frac{1}{4}$$

3. To work out a missing angle, you need to find the <u>inverse</u> of the trig function. The inverse trig functions are $\sin^{-1}$, $\cos^{-1}$ and $\tan^{-1}$. You usually find them on your calculator by using shift with sin, cos or tan.

$$x = \sin^{-1}\left(\frac{1}{4}\right)$$

4. Type $\boxed{\text{SHIFT}}$ $\overset{\sin^{-1}}{\boxed{\text{sin}}}$ $\boxed{(}$ $\boxed{1}$ $\boxed{\div}$ $\boxed{4}$ $\boxed{)}$ into your calculator. Round the answer to 1 d.p.

$x = 14.4775...$
$x = \mathbf{14.5°}$ (to 1 d.p.)

Exercise 2

For this exercise, give your answers to **1 decimal place**, unless told otherwise. The diagrams in this exercise are **not** drawn accurately.

1 Find the size of the angles marked with letters using the sine formula.

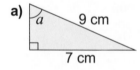

a) a, 9 cm, 7 cm   b) 5 m, b, 2 m   c) 7 m, c, 5.5 m   d) 5 mm, d, 3.5 mm

2 Find the size of the angles marked with letters using the cosine formula.

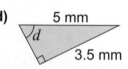

a) 8 cm, e, 11 cm   b) 27 m, f, 33 m   c) 5.5 cm, g, 8 cm   d) 52 m, h, 81 m

3 Find the size of the angles marked with letters using the tangent formula.

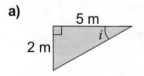 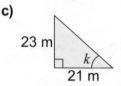

a) 5 m, i, 2 m   b) j, 11 cm, 6 cm   c) 23 m, k, 21 m   d) 15 m, l, 11 m

4 Find the sizes of the angles marked with letters.

a)

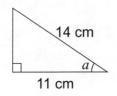
14 cm
11 cm
a

b)

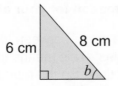
6 cm
8 cm
b

c)

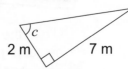
c
2 m
7 m

d)

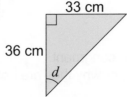
33 cm
36 cm
d

e)

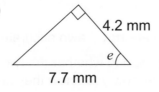
4.2 mm
7.7 mm
e

f)

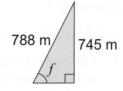
788 m
745 m
f

5 Use trigonometry twice to find *y*. Give your answer to 3 significant figures.

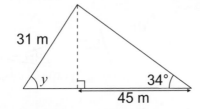
31 m
y
34°
45 m

17.3 Geometric Relationships

Congruent Triangles

Congruent shapes are exactly the same shape and size.
Two triangles are congruent if they satisfy one of the following 'congruence conditions'.
If they satisfy one condition then they satisfy them all.

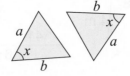

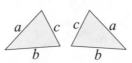

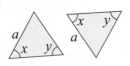

Side Angle Side:
Two sides and the angle between them on one triangle are the same as two sides and the angle between them on the other triangle.

Side Side Side:
The three sides on one triangle are the same as the three sides on the other triangle.

Angle Angle Side:
Two angles and a side on one triangle are the same as two angles and the corresponding side on the other triangle.

Example 1 Are these two triangles congruent? Give a reason for your answer.

Two of the sides and the angle between them are the same on both triangles. This means they satisfy the 'Side Angle Side' condition. So the triangles **are congruent**.

Exercise 1

The diagrams in this exercise are **not** drawn accurately.

1   For each of the following, decide whether the two triangles are congruent. In each case explain either how you know they are congruent, or why they are not.

a)

b)

c)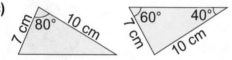

d)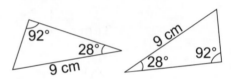

e)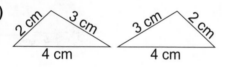

f)

2   For each of the following, the two triangles are congruent. Find the size of all the angles and side lengths marked with letters.

a)

b)

c)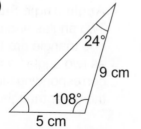

d)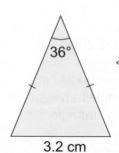

Similar Shapes

Two shapes are <u>similar</u> if they are the same shape but different sizes.
Their angles must be identical and their sides must be in the same ratio (so if you double the length of one side, you double the lengths of all the sides).

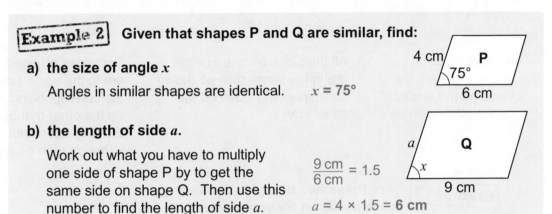

Example 2 **Given that shapes P and Q are similar, find:**

a) **the size of angle x**

   Angles in similar shapes are identical. $x = 75°$

b) **the length of side a.**

   Work out what you have to multiply one side of shape P by to get the same side on shape Q. Then use this number to find the length of side a.

   $\dfrac{9 \text{ cm}}{6 \text{ cm}} = 1.5$

   $a = 4 × 1.5 = 6 \text{ cm}$

Exercise 2

The diagrams in this exercise are **not** drawn accurately.

1   In each of the following, decide whether the two shapes are similar or not.
    In each case explain either how you know they are similar, or why they are not.

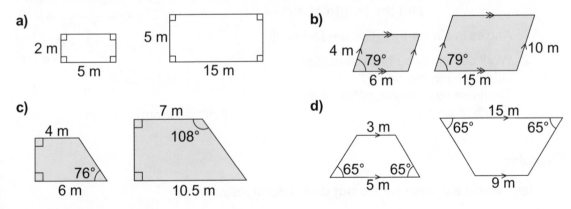

2   All three of the shapes below are similar. Find the size of the angles and lengths marked with letters.

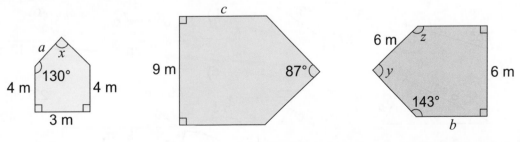

Similar Triangles

Two triangles are similar if they satisfy any one of the following 'similarity conditions'.
If they satisfy one condition then they satisfy them all.

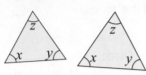

All the angles on one triangle are the same as the angles on the other triangle.

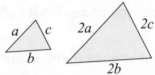

All the sides on one triangle are in the same ratio as the corresponding sides on the other triangle.

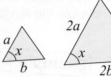

Two sides on one triangle are in the same ratio as the corresponding sides on the other triangle, and the angle between is the same on both triangles.

Example 3 **Are these two triangles similar? Give a reason for your answer.**

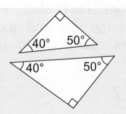

All the angles in one triangle are the same as the angles in the other triangle, so the triangles must be **similar**.

Example 4 **This diagram shows two similar triangles, *ABC* and *DEF*. Find the size of angle *x* and the length of side *a*.**

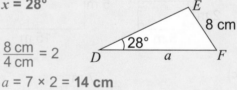

1. Angles in similar triangles are identical. $x = 28°$

2. Work out what you have to multiply side *CB* by to get side *EF*.
   Then use this number to find the length of side *a*.

   $\frac{8 \text{ cm}}{4 \text{ cm}} = 2$

   $a = 7 × 2 = \textbf{14 cm}$

Exercise 3

The diagrams in this exercise are **not** drawn accurately.

1   For each of the following, decide whether the two triangles are similar or not.
    In each case explain either how you know they are similar, or why they are not.

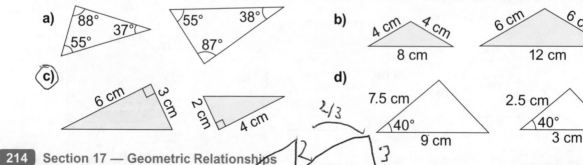

2 In each of these pairs of similar triangles, find the size of the angles and lengths marked with letters.

a)

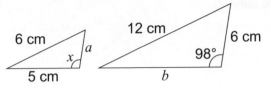

b)

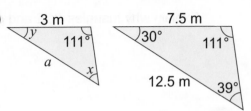

c)

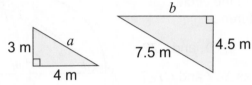

d)

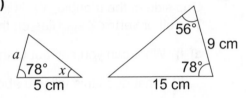

e)

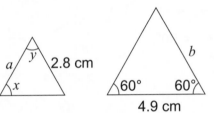

f)

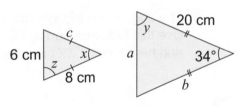

3 This diagram shows two triangles, ADE and ABC.

a) Explain why triangles ADE and ABC are similar.

b) Calculate the length of AB.

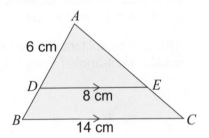

Deriving Geometric Relationships

You can use known or given facts about shapes and angles to <u>derive</u> or <u>prove</u> other geometric relationships.

Exercise 4

The diagrams in this exercise are **not** drawn accurately.

1 This diagram shows a parallelogram, $ABCD$, with the diagonal AC drawn in.

Are the two triangles ABC and ADC congruent? Explain your answer.

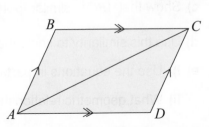

2 This diagram shows two triangles, *PQR* and *QSU*, inside a bigger triangle *PST*.

Explain why triangles *PQR* and *QSU* are similar.

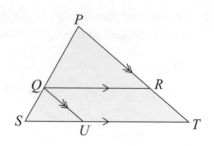

3 Triangle *XYZ* lies inside a circle with centre *C*.
One side of the triangle, *XY*, is a diameter of the circle.
The other vertex *Z* also lies on the circumference.

a) i) What can you say about the lengths *CX*, *CY*, and *CZ*?

ii) What does this tell you about triangles *XCZ* and *CYZ*?

iii) How does this show that *d* = *e*, and *n* = *p*?

b) The angles in a triangle add up to 180°.
Use this fact, and part **a) iii)**, to show that *e* + *p* = 90°,
and hence that ∠*XZY* is always a right angle.

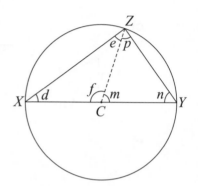

4 Look at the diagram of the triangle *ABC*.
Each side has been labelled, so that
a = *BC*, *b* = *AC* and *h* = *AB* = *AH* + *BH*.

ABC can be split into these two
smaller right-angled triangles:

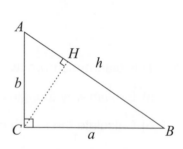

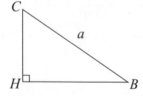 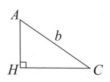

a) Show that *ABC* is similar to *CBH*.
(Hint: ∠*ABC* is the same as ∠*CBH*.)

b) Use this similarity to show that $\dfrac{a}{h} = \dfrac{BH}{a}$.

c) Show that *ABC* is similar to *ACH*.

d) Use this similarity to show that $\dfrac{b}{h} = \dfrac{AH}{b}$.

e) i) Use the equations in parts **b)** and **d)** to show that $a^2 + b^2 = h^2$.

ii) What geometric relationship have you now derived?

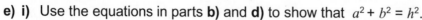

Section 18 — Probability

18.1 Probability Experiments

Estimating Probabilities

You can <u>estimate</u> probabilities using the results of an experiment or what you know has already happened. Your estimate is called an <u>experimental probability</u> (or a <u>relative frequency</u>). Work out experimental probability using this formula:

$$\text{Experimental probability} = \frac{\text{Number of times the result has happened}}{\text{Number of times the experiment has been carried out}}$$

The more times you carry out an experiment, the more reliable your estimate will be.

Example 1 A biased dice is rolled 100 times and the results are shown in this table. Estimate the probability of rolling a 4.

1. Find the number of times 4 was rolled.
2. Divide by the total number of rolls.

Score	1	2	3	4	5	6
Frequency	14	13	26	23	13	11

4 was rolled 23 times out of 100. So probability = $\dfrac{23}{100}$ = 0.23 = 23%

Exercise 1

1 Abigail rolls a dice and records the number that it lands on each time. Her results are shown in the table.

Number	1	2	3	4	5	6
Frequency	26	21	18	31	19	15

Estimate the probability of rolling each number. Give your answers as simplified fractions.

2 Ben and Dave each toss the same coin and record the number of times it lands on heads and tails. Their results are shown in this table.

	Ben	Dave
Number of heads	6	47
Number of tails	14	53

a) Find the relative frequencies of the coin landing on a head for each person. Give your answers as decimals.

b) The relative frequencies are estimates of the probability of tossing a head. Whose estimate is more reliable? Explain your answer.

3 After 40 attempts on a coconut shy, Jack works out that his relative frequency of winning a coconut is 0.15. How many coconuts did he win?

Expected Frequency

You can estimate the number of times an event will happen by working out its expected frequency.

Expected frequency of an event = probability of the event × number of trials

Here, 'trial' just means an action that could lead to the event happening — for example, a toss of a coin or a roll of a dice.

> 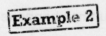 **The probability that a biased dice lands on 6 is 0.4. How many times would you expect to roll a 6 if you rolled the dice 40 times?**
>
> Multiply the probability of rolling a 6 by the number of rolls.   0.4 × 40 = **16**

Exercise 2

1   The probability that a biased dice lands on 5 is 0.6.
    How many times would you expect the dice to land on 5 if it's rolled:

   a) 10 times?   **b)** 60 times?   **c)** 100 times?   **d)** 1000 times?

2   A fair, six-sided dice numbered 1-6 is rolled 180 times.
    How many times would you expect to roll:

   a) a 2?   **b)** a 5?   **c)** an odd number?   **d)** higher than 2?

3   This spinner has 3 equal sections.
    How many times would you expect to spin 'penguin' in:

   a) 90 spins?   **b)** 150 spins?   **c)** 540 spins?

4   Rob and Paul are footballers. The probability that Rob's team win a match is 0.6.
    The probability that Paul's team win a match is 0.4. Rob's team played 30 matches and
    Paul's team played 35 matches. How many more matches did Rob win than Paul?

Fair or Biased?

Things like dice are fair if the probability of landing on each side is the same,
otherwise we say they're biased. You can do an experiment to check for bias.

If you rolled a fair six-sided dice 100 times, you'd expect it to land on 6 about $\frac{1}{6}$ of the time
(about 17 times). But if $\frac{1}{2}$ of the rolls (50) were 6, you'd say the dice was biased.

Naveena thinks her dice is biased. She rolls it 50 times and records the results in the table shown.

Work out the relative frequencies of each score.

Score	1	2	3	4	5	6
Frequency	10	2	8	8	12	10

1. For each score, work out frequency ÷ total number of rolls.

2. Write the probabilities as decimals so they're easier to compare.

1: $\frac{10}{50}$ = 0.2   3: $\frac{8}{50}$ = 0.16   5: $\frac{12}{50}$ = 0.24

2: $\frac{2}{50}$ = 0.04   4: $\frac{8}{50}$ = 0.16   6: $\frac{10}{50}$ = 0.2

Do you think the dice is fair or biased? Explain your answer.

Compare the relative frequencies to the theoretical probability of $\frac{1}{6}$ = 0.17 for each score.

The relative frequency of a score of 2 is very different from the theoretical probability, so the experiment suggests that the dice is **biased**.

Exercise 3

1 This table shows the results when a four-sided spinner is spun 100 times.

Number	1	2	3	4
Frequency	25	19	20	36

a) Work out the relative frequencies (as decimals) of the four numbers on the spinner.

b) Write down the theoretical probability (as a decimal) of getting each of the numbers, assuming the spinner is fair.

c) Explain whether you think the spinner is fair or biased.

2 An eight-sided dice numbered 1-8 is rolled 160 times. The number 2 comes up 36 times.

a) How many times would you expect 2 to come up in 160 rolls if the dice is fair?

b) Use your answer to part **a)** to explain whether you think the dice is fair or biased.

c) What could you do to improve the reliability of the experiment?

Investigate — Probability Experiments

a) Find a friend, and play 10 games of 'rock, paper, scissors'.
Record in a table the number of times you win, lose and draw.

b) Calculate the relative frequencies of winning, losing and drawing.
Use these relative frequencies to decide which is more likely to happen.

c) Keep playing, and after every 10 games repeat part **b)** using all the results you've recorded so far. What do you notice about the relative frequencies?

18.2 Theoretical Probabilities

Calculating Probabilities

You can work out the probability of an <u>event</u> happening using this <u>formula</u>:

$$\text{Probability of an event} = \frac{\text{Number of ways event can happen}}{\text{Total number of possible outcomes}}$$

You can only use this formula if each possible <u>outcome</u> is equally likely to happen —
e.g. throwing a dice or picking a ball from a bag containing balls of the same size.

The probabilities of all the possible outcomes add up to 1.

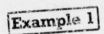 **A bag contains 15 counters. 6 are black and the rest are
either yellow or white. One counter is picked at random.**

a) Find the probability of picking a black counter at random out the bag.

Put the numbers into the formula and simplify.

$$\text{Probability of picking black} = \frac{\text{number of black counters}}{\text{total number of counters}} = \frac{6}{15} = \frac{2}{5}$$

**b) Work out how many white counters there are in the bag,
given that the probability of picking yellow is $\frac{1}{3}$.**

1. Subtract the probabilities of picking
a black or yellow counter from 1 to find
the probability of picking a white counter.

$$1 - \frac{2}{5} - \frac{1}{3} = \frac{15}{15} - \frac{6}{15} - \frac{5}{15}$$
$$= \frac{4}{15}$$

2. Multiply the probability of picking a white
counter by the total number of counters
to find the number of white counters.

$$\frac{4}{15} \times 15 = \textbf{4 white counters}$$

Exercise 1

1 Use this spinner to find the probability of these events.
Give your answers as fractions in their simplest form.

a) Spinning a 3   **b)** Spinning a 2   **c)** Spinning an even number

2 Make a copy of this spinner. Shade the spinner so that:

- It is certain to land on either red, blue or green.
- The probability of it landing on red is 0.5.
- It is twice as likely to land on blue than on green.

3   A standard pack of 52 playing cards is shuffled and one card is selected at random.
    Find the probability of selecting each of the following.
    Give your answers as fractions in their simplest form.

    a) A red card   **b)** A king   **c)** A red king   **d)** A card that isn't a red king

4   There are 100 pupils in Year 9. 52 pupils are boys, 40 pupils wear glasses and
    24 boys wear glasses. Find the probability that a randomly selected pupil:

    a) isn't a boy   **b)** doesn't wear glasses   **c)** is a boy who doesn't wear glasses

    Give your answers as decimals.

5   A fair ten-sided spinner has three sides numbered 1.
    The other sides are numbered either 2 or 3.

    a) What is the probability of spinning a 1? Give your answer as a fraction.

    b) The probability of spinning a 3 is 0.5. How many sides are numbered 2?

6   A bag contains only red, green, yellow and blue balls.
    There are 20 balls in total and 6 of them are red.

    a) What is the probability of picking a ball that isn't red? Give your answer as a decimal.

    b) The probability of picking a green ball is 0.4 and there are
        half as many yellow balls as green balls. How many blue balls are there?

7   Sophia has a biased dice. This table shows the probabilities of each score.

Score	1	2	3	4	5	6
Probability	0.2	0.25	0.15	0.1		0.25

    Work out the probability of scoring:

    a) a 5   **b)** an odd number   **c)** a number less than 4

8   Ripu's spinner has red, yellow, green and blue sections. The probability of the spinner
    landing on some of the sections is shown in the table. The spinner is equally likely to land
    on green or blue. Find the probability that the spinner lands on green.

Colour	Red	Yellow	Green	Blue
Probability	0.32	0.26		

9 Ali ordered a new compass from The Compass Emporium.
The probability that she will receive the compass today is 0.5.
The probability that she will receive the compass tomorrow is 0.4.

a) What is the probability that Ali won't receive the compass today?
Give your answer as a decimal.

b) Why don't the probabilities that the compass arrives today or tomorrow add up to 1?

10 Greg is playing a game of chess. The probability that he wins
the game is 0.31 and the probability that he loses the game is 0.64.
Find the probability that he does not win the game and explain why
your answer is different to the probability of losing the game.

Sample Spaces

A <u>sample space diagram</u> can be used to list all the possible <u>outcomes</u> from a combination
of two <u>trials</u>. This is just a table with the outcomes of one trial down the side and the
outcomes of the second trial along the top.

The sample space diagram for
tossing two coins looks like this:

		Second coin	
		Heads	Tails
First coin	Heads	HH	HT
	Tails	TH	TT

Example 2 | **Two fair spinners are spun and their scores added together.**
Spinner A is divided into three sections numbered 1-3 and
spinner B is divided into three sections numbered 4-6.

a) Draw a sample space to show all the possible outcomes.

1. Draw a table with the outcomes
from spinner A down the side
and the outcomes from spinner B
along the top.

2. Fill in each box by adding
together the numbers from the
left-hand column and the top row.

		Spinner B		
		4	5	6
Spinner A	1	5	6	7
	2	6	7	8
	3	7	8	9

b) Find the probability of scoring at least 7.

1. Divide the number of outcomes that are
7 or more by the total number of outcomes.

There are 9 possible outcomes,
and 6 of them are 7 or more.

2. Give your answer in its simplest form.

$$P(\text{at least } 7) = \frac{6}{9} = \frac{2}{3}$$

Exercise 2

In this exercise, give all probabilities as fractions in their simplest form.

1 Two fair spinners are spun and their scores added together.
Spinner A is divided into three sections numbered 1-3 and
spinner B is divided into four sections numbered 1-4.

  a) Draw a sample space to show all the possible outcomes.

  b) Find the probability of scoring a total of:

   i) 4   **ii)** 6 or more   **iii)** an odd number

  c) Is the total score more likely to be an odd number or a prime number?
  Explain your answer.

2 A coin is tossed and a fair six-sided dice is rolled.

  a) Copy and complete the sample space diagram to show all the possible outcomes.

	1	2	3	4	5	6
Heads	H1					
Tails						

  b) Find the probability of getting:

   i) a 5 and a head   **ii)** a number less than 3 and a tail

3 Two fair, six-sided dice, each numbered 1-6, are rolled and the scores multiplied together.

  a) Draw a sample space diagram to show all the possible outcomes.

  b) What is the most likely outcome?

  c) Find the probability of rolling numbers with:

   i) a product of 8   **ii)** a product of 4   **iii)** a product that is less than 20

4 Two fair, six-sided dice, each numbered 1-6, are rolled and their scores added together.

  a) Draw a sample space diagram to show all the possible outcomes.

  b) Find the probability of scoring a total of:

   i) 7   **ii)** 11 or more   **iii)** less than 4

  c) Find the total scores which are most and least likely to occur.

5 A bag contains five counters coloured red, red, blue, green and yellow.
A counter is taken from the bag and then replaced.
A second counter is then taken.

a) Complete the sample space diagram to show the possible colour combinations of the counters.

b) Work out the probability of taking:

    i) two green counters

    ii) at least one red counter

    iii) two counters of the same colour.

Second counter

	R	R	B	G	Y
R	RR	RR	RB		
R	RR				
B	BR				
G					
Y					

First counter

6 Jenny is at a Mexican restaurant.

There are three different options: burritos, tacos or fajitas.
Each option has a choice of four different fillings:
chicken, beef, pork or vegetable.

Jenny decides that she is going to select her meal at random
from these options.

a) What is the probability that she will get a burrito with a meat filling?

b) What is the probability that she will **not** have either a pork filling or beef tacos?

c) Jenny goes back to the restaurant a second time and does the same thing again.
What is the probability that she will have the same thing twice in a row?

Investigate — Tree Diagrams

Tree diagrams can be used to show the outcomes from a combination of trials.

This tree diagram shows the possible outcomes
when a card is picked at random from a pack,
then **replaced** before another is picked at random.
Each 'branch' is labelled with the probability of
that individual outcome occurring.

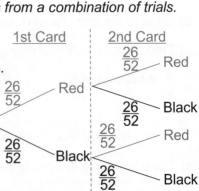

1st Card   2nd Card

a) Draw another tree diagram to show the
possible outcomes and probabilities
if two cards are picked at random
without replacing the first one.

b) Extend your tree diagram to show the possible outcomes and probabilities
if a **third card** is picked at random (without replacing the other two).
What do you notice about the probabilities after each card is picked?

18.3 Sets

Sets

A <u>set</u> is a collection of items or numbers. They are shown by curly brackets { }. The things in a set are called <u>elements</u>. Here are some examples of sets:

A = {odd numbers}, B = {days of the week}, C = {apples, pears, oranges}, D = {1, 2, 3, 4}.

n(A) means 'the number of elements in set A'.

ξ is the <u>universal set</u> — the group of things that the elements of a set are selected from.

The <u>union</u> of sets A and B (A $\cup$ B) contains all the elements that are in either set.

The <u>intersection</u> of sets A and B (A $\cap$ B) contains all the elements that are in both sets.

The <u>complement</u> of a set A (A') is all the elements of the universal set that aren't in set A.

The <u>empty set</u> {} is a set with no elements in it.

Example 1 ξ = {whole numbers from 1-20}, A = {even numbers} and B = {prime numbers}. List the elements of each set.

1. For the universal set, just list all the numbers from 1-20.

ξ = {1, 2, 3, 4, 5, 6, 7, 8, 9, 10, 11, 12, 13, 14, 15, 16, 17, 18, 19, 20}

2. Set A is the even numbers, but they must be taken from the universal set, so it's just the even numbers up to 20.

A = {2, 4, 6, 8, 10, 12, 14, 16, 18, 20}

3. Similarly, set B is prime numbers up to 20.

B = {2, 3, 5, 7, 11, 13, 17, 19}

Exercise 1

1 For each of the following sets:
   i) list the elements of the set, and
   ii) find the number of elements in the set.

a) A = {months of the year beginning with J}   **b)** B = {days of the weekend}

c) C = {planets beginning with an M}   **d)** D = {colours of the rainbow}

e) E = {editors of this book with the initials S.H.} (see credits page)

2 For each of the following sets:
   i) list the elements of the set, and
   ii) find the number of elements in the set.

a) A = {factors of 24}   **b)** B = {multiples of 9 up to 70}

c) C = {cube numbers up to 130}   **d)** D = {prime numbers between 10 and 30}

3 List the elements of the following sets, given that ξ = {whole numbers from 1-40}.

    a) A = {multiples of 7}   **b)** B = {factors of 100}

    c) C = {multiples of both 3 and 5}   **d)** D = {multiples of both 5 and 9}

4 List the elements of the following sets, given that ξ = {whole numbers from 40-80}.

    a) A = {multiples of 6}   **b)** B = {factors of 240}

    c) C = {factors of 30}   **d)** D = {square numbers}

5 ξ = {whole numbers from 1-100}, A = {square numbers} and B = {cube numbers}.

    a) Write out the elements of set A.

    b) Write out the elements of set B.

    c) C = A $\cup$ B. Write out the elements of set C and find n(C).

    d) D = A $\cap$ B. Write out the elements of set D and find n(D).

6 ξ = {whole numbers from 1-10}   A = {multiples of 2}   B = {factors of 24}
Write out the elements of the following sets:

    a) C = A $\cup$ B   **b)** D = A $\cap$ B   **c)** E = A'   **d)** F = B'

    e) G = A $\cup$ B'   **f)** H = B $\cup$ A'   **g)** I = A $\cap$ B'   **h)** J = B $\cap$ A'

Investigate — Subsets

B is a subset of A if every element of B is also an element of A.
E.g. the subsets of {1, 2} are {1, 2}, {1}, {2} and {} (the empty set).

    a) If A = {3, 4}, write down all the subsets of A.

    b) Choose another set with two elements and write down all the subsets.
        How many subsets of any two-element set are there?

    c) If A = {1, 2, 3}, write down all the subsets of A.

    d) Choose some more sets with three elements and write down all the subsets.
        How many subsets of any three-element set are there?

    e) Investigate the number of subsets for sets with four or more elements.

Venn Diagrams

Venn diagrams are used to display sets and to show when they overlap.

Each set is represented by a circle, and the universal set is a rectangle that goes round the outside of the circles.

If there are elements that belong to both sets, the circles overlap and these elements go in the overlap, which is called the intersection.

Any element inside either circle is in the union of the sets.

Venn diagrams can show the actual elements, or just the number of elements that belong in each bit of the diagram.

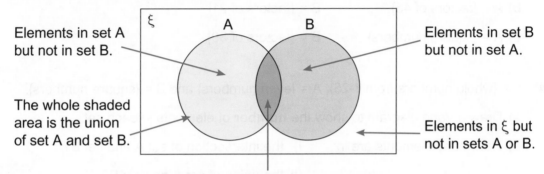

Elements in set A but not in set B.

The whole shaded area is the union of set A and set B.

Elements in set B but not in set A.

Elements in ξ but not in sets A or B.

The intersection of set A and set B contains elements that are in both sets.

Example 2   ξ = {whole numbers from 1-10}, A = {odd numbers} and B = {factors of 6}.
Show this information on a Venn diagram.

1. Write out sets A and B:
   A = {1, 3, 5, 7, 9}
   B = {1, 2, 3, 6}

2. 1 and 3 are in both sets, so they go in the overlap. The other elements of A and B go in the circles for A and B, but not in the overlap.

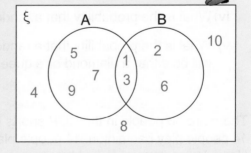

3. The elements of ξ that aren't in A or B go outside the circles (but inside the rectangle).

Exercise 2

1   ξ = {Manchester, Munich, Newcastle, London, Paris, Madrid, Moscow, Barcelona},
A = {cities beginning with M} and B = {cities in England}.
Show this information on a Venn diagram.

2 The Venn diagram shows sets A and B for ξ = {whole numbers from 10-20}.

    a) Give a possible description of sets A and B.

    b) List the elements in the following sets:

        i) A ∪ B   **ii)** A ∩ B   **iii)** A'   **iv)** A' ∩ B'

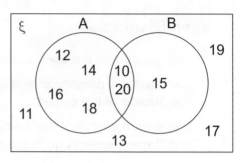

3 For ξ = {odd numbers from 1-20}, draw Venn diagrams to show the following sets:

    a) A = {multiples of 3}   B = {prime numbers}

    b) A = {factors of 45}   B = {factors of 21}

    c) A = {square numbers}   B = {factors of 39}

4 ξ = {whole numbers from 1-25}, A = {even numbers} and B = {square numbers}.

    a) Draw a Venn diagram to show the **number** of elements in each set.

    b) How many elements are in: **i)** the intersection of set A and set B?

                                    ii) the union of set A and set B?

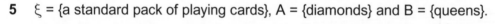

5 ξ = {a standard pack of playing cards}, A = {diamonds} and B = {queens}.

    a) Draw a Venn diagram showing the **number** of elements in each set.

    b) Use your Venn diagram to answer the following questions:
       How many elements are there in:

       i) set A?   **ii)** the union of set A and set B?   **iii)** the intersection of set A and set B?

       iv) What is the probability that a randomly selected card will be the queen of diamonds?

       v) What is the probability that a randomly selected card will be either a diamond or a queen?

6 There are 38 people in the CGP sports club. 16 people play football and 14 people play badminton. 14 people play don't play badminton or football. Use a Venn diagram to find how many people play both badminton and football.

7 In a group of 20 friends, 8 people like Italian food and 12 people like Chinese food. These people include 6 people who like both Italian and Chinese food. Use a Venn diagram to find how many people don't like either Italian or Chinese food.

Section 19 — Statistics

19.1 Frequency Diagrams

Bar Charts and Pictograms

Bar charts (and bar-line charts) show how many items fall into
different categories. The number in each category is the frequency.
A dual bar chart shows the same categories for two different people or things.

Pictograms show frequency using symbols or pictures instead of bars.
They always have a key to tell you what each symbol represents.

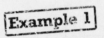

The dual bar chart shows how many cups of tea Sophie and Dave drank at work each day for a week.
In its simplest form, what fraction of the total cups of tea did Dave drink?

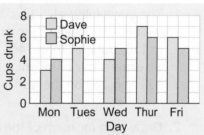

1. Calculate the total cups drunk by Dave
    and the total cups of tea drunk altogether.

    $3 + 5 + 4 + 7 + 6 = 25$

    $25 + 4 + 5 + 6 + 5 = 45$

2. Write these numbers as a fraction,
    with Dave's total as the numerator.
    Simplify the fraction as much as possible.

    $\dfrac{25}{45} = \dfrac{5}{9}$

Exercise 1

1 Will asked everyone in his class how they get to school.
He recorded his results in this bar chart.
To the nearest whole number, work out what percentage
of people use the most popular transport.

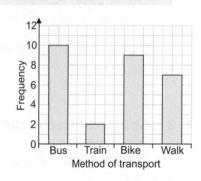

2 Some students were asked to name their favourite sport.
The results were recorded in this pictogram.
Use the pictogram to create a bar-line chart
to show the students' favourite sports.

Tennis	⬡⬡
Football	⬡⬡⬡
Rugby	⬡⬡
Key: ⬡ = 6 people	Athletics	⬡

3 The table shows the test scores of the boys
and girls in a class. Draw a dual bar chart to
show this information and describe what the
shape of the graph tells you about the boys'
scores compared to the girls' scores.

Marks	0-10	11-20	21-30	31-40	41-50
Girls	0	4	6	7	8
Boys	1	2	9	7	6

Frequency Bar Charts and Frequency Polygons

Frequency bar charts and frequency polygons are used to show continuous data (data that is measured rather than counted). Instead of a label under each bar, there's a continuous scale on the x-axis, divided into a number of classes.

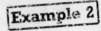 **This frequency table shows some information about the heights of 30 children. Draw a frequency bar chart to represent the information.**

Height (h) in cm	Frequency
130 ≤ h < 140	4
140 ≤ h < 150	9
150 ≤ h < 160	11
160 ≤ h < 170	4
170 ≤ h < 180	2

1. The class interval "130 ≤ h < 140" means h is greater than or equal to 130, but less than 140.
   So draw a bar of height 4 between 130 and 140 on the horizontal axis.

2. Draw bars for each of the other class intervals in the same way with the correct frequencies.

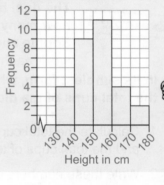

Exercise 2

1 The grouped frequency table on the right shows how many seconds (s) it took 22 children to complete a puzzle.

Draw a frequency bar chart to represent this information.

Seconds (s)	Frequency
10 ≤ s < 20	5
20 ≤ s < 30	7
30 ≤ s < 40	8
40 ≤ s < 50	2

2 Children at a tennis club were asked to see how many seconds they could keep a rally going for.
This frequency table shows their results.

Draw a frequency bar chart to represent this information.

Time (t) in seconds	Frequency
0 ≤ t < 4	9
4 ≤ t < 8	12
8 ≤ t < 12	27
12 ≤ t < 16	3
16 ≤ t < 20	1

3 Some pupils were asked the length of their journey to school. This frequency bar chart shows their responses.

a) How many pupils had a journey of 5 km or less?

b) How many pupils had a journey of 6 km or longer?

c) What is the modal class of this data?

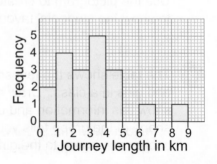

A frequency polygon is a line graph joining the midpoints of each of the classes.

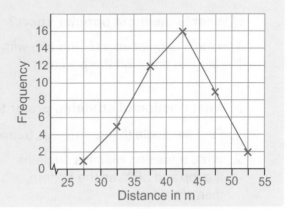

Example 3 Fatima records the distances, in metres, that her friends can throw a ball.

The results are shown in the grouped frequency table. Draw a frequency polygon to represent this information.

Distance (d) in m	Frequency
$25 \le d < 30$	1
$30 \le d < 35$	5
$35 \le d < 40$	12
$40 \le d < 45$	16
$45 \le d < 50$	9
$50 \le d < 55$	2

1. Find the midpoint of each interval by adding the endpoints, and dividing by 2:

   First midpoint = $\dfrac{25 + 30}{2}$ = 27.5

2. Then plot the frequency at each of these midpoints.

3. Join your points with lines.

Exercise 3

1 The weights, in kilograms, of some marrows at a vegetable competition were recorded.
This frequency table shows the results.

Draw a frequency polygon to represent this information.

Weight (w) in kg	Frequency
$40 \le w < 50$	1
$50 \le w < 60$	11
$60 \le w < 70$	13
$70 \le w < 80$	9
$80 \le w < 90$	4

2 Some students recorded the total area of some fields near their school.
Their results are shown in the table.

Draw a frequency polygon to show this information.

Area (a) in thousands of square feet	Frequency
$12 \le a < 13$	3
$13 \le a < 14$	7
$14 \le a < 15$	5
$15 \le a < 16$	2

3 A train company recorded the delay in minutes of all of its trains one day, using class intervals 5 minutes wide.
Their results are shown in this frequency polygon.

a) How many trains had a delay of 40 minutes or longer?

b) What is the modal class for this data?

c) In total, how many trains did this train company have that day?

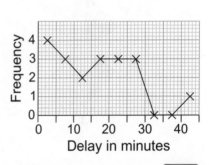

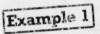

19.2 Pie Charts

Interpreting Pie Charts

In a pie chart, the size of the angle of each sector represents frequency.
So to work out frequencies from a pie chart, you need to know the sizes of the angles.

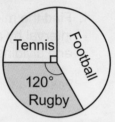

> **Example 1** A student carries out a survey to find out which sport
> 150 students prefer to play. This pie chart shows the results.
>
> **a) What is the most popular sport?**
>
> The most popular sport is the one with   **Football**
> the biggest angle on the pie chart.
>
> **b) What fraction of students prefer tennis?**
>
> 1. Find the angle that represents tennis.   The angle for 'Tennis' is 90°
>
> 2. Write a fraction with this angle as
>   the top and 360° as the bottom,   Fraction who prefer tennis $= \frac{90°}{360°} = \frac{1}{4}$
>   then simplify.
>
> **c) How many students prefer rugby?**
>
> 1. Find the fraction who prefer rugby   Fraction who prefer rugby $= \frac{120°}{360°} = \frac{1}{3}$
>   using the angle, as before.
>
> 2. Then multiply this fraction by $\frac{1}{3} \times 150 = (1 \times 150) \div 3 = \textbf{50 students}$
>   the total number of students.

Exercise 1

1   Match each of the pie charts, P to S, with the correct data set.

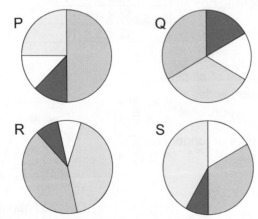

Data Set 1	A	B	C	D
Frequency	12	12	6	6

Data Set 2	A	B	C	D
Frequency	24	12	6	6

Data Set 3	A	B	C	D
Frequency	30	24	12	6

Data Set 4	A	B	C	D
Frequency	30	30	6	6

2 This pie chart shows the proportions of Ryan's class that have different pets.
No one in his class has more than one pet.

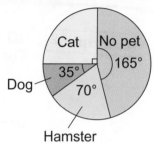

a) What is the most common pet?

b) Which pet is half as common as a hamster?

c) What fraction of the class don't have a pet?
Give your answer in its simplest form.

d) Can you tell from the pie chart how many people in
Ryan's class have a cat? Explain your answer.

3 Marco asks 180 people to choose their favourite type of cake.
The results are shown in this pie chart.

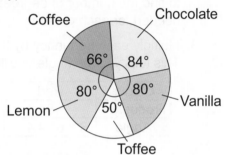

a) What fraction of people chose coffee
or chocolate cake as their favourite?

b) How many people chose lemon
or vanilla cake as their favourite?

c) How many people chose a cake
other than toffee as their favourite?

4 James carries out a survey in a city. He asks people "What is your
favourite type of restaurant?" and draws a pie chart of his results.

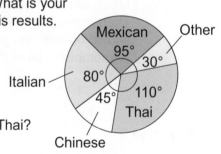

a) 320 people chose Italian. Using this information,
work out how many people chose:

　i) Chinese　　　　**ii)** Thai.

b) What percentage of people chose either Mexican or Thai?
Give your answer to the nearest whole number.

5 Andy and Beth recorded the amount of time they spent doing Maths, English and Science
homework during one term. Andy spent a total of 120 hours on his homework, and Beth
spent a total of 90 hours on her homework. Their data is displayed in the pie charts.

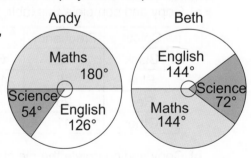

a) Andy says: "I spent 11 less hours doing my
Science homework than my English homework."
Is he correct?

b) Beth says: "I spent 18 hours more doing
my Maths homework than doing my
Science homework." Is she correct?

c) Which subject's homework did Beth and Andy
spend the same amount of time on?

Constructing Pie Charts

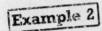

Example 2 Jill asks everyone in Year 8 their favourite colour.
The frequency table shows her results.

Colour	Red	Green	Blue	Pink
Frequency	8	16	28	8

Draw a pie chart to show this data.

1. Calculate the total frequency — this is
   the number of people in Year 8.

   Total Frequency = 8 + 16 + 28 + 8
   = 60

2. Divide 360° by the total frequency
   to find the number of degrees
   needed for each person.

   Each person represented by:
   360° ÷ 60 = 6°

3. Multiply each frequency by the number of degrees for each person.
   This tells you the angle you'll need in the pie chart for each colour.

Colour	Red	Green	Blue	Pink
Frequency	8	16	28	8
Angle	8 × 6° = 48°	16 × 6° = 96°	28 × 6° = 168°	8 × 6° = 48°

4. Draw the pie chart:
   First draw a circle, then draw a start line from the centre.
   Measure the 48° angle from here and draw another line.
   Then measure the 96° angle from this line,
   and so on until you get back to the start line.
   Remember to label the sectors on the chart.

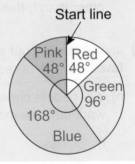

Exercise 2

1 Boris recorded the colours of 60 cars at a car show.
The results are shown in this frequency table.

Colour	Frequency
Black	6
Blue	18
Red	25
Other	11

a) Find how many degrees represent each car.

b) Copy and complete this table to find the angle for each colour.

Colour	Frequency	Angle
Black	6	6 × ...... = 36°
Blue	18	18 × ...... = ...
Red	25	
Other	11	

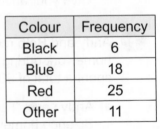

c) Copy and complete the pie chart to show this data.

2 A library surveyed some of its members to find out their favourite type of book.
Their results are shown in this table.

a) Find the total number of people the library asked.

b) Find how many degrees represent each person.

c) Calculate the angle for each type of book.

d) Draw a pie chart showing the results.

Type of Book	Frequency
Crime	18
Adventure	24
Thriller	22
Sci-fi	26

3 Ollie carried out a survey to find out how many pets
the pupils in his year group have.
He recorded his data in this table.

a) Find the total frequency.

b) Calculate the angle for each number of pets.

c) Draw a pie chart showing the data.

Number of Pets	Frequency
0	46
1	42
2	20
3 or more	12

4 Charlotte carried out a survey to find out
which country people would prefer to visit.
Her results are in this table.
Draw a pie chart showing Charlotte's results.

Country	Frequency
America	15
France	25
Greece	17
Spain	23

5 Hasan recorded the instruments that students at his school play
as their main instrument. Half of the students played the piano.
60% of the remaining students played the trumpet.
The others all played the violin. Draw a pie chart showing the data.

Investigate — Pie Charts

a) Take a survey of your class mates — you could ask them about their
favourite colour for example, or their shoe size, or how they get to school.

b) Record the results of your survey in a frequency table, and then present
your data in a pie chart.

c) Label your pie chart and swap it with a friend.
Draw as many different conclusions from each pie chart as you can.

19.3 Scatter Graphs

Scatter Graphs and Correlation

A scatter graph shows two things plotted against each other.
Scatter graphs can be used to show whether two things are related to each other.

If the points on a scatter graph lie close to a straight line, the data shows correlation
— the two things are related.

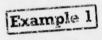 **For each of these scatter graphs, decide if it shows positive, negative or no correlation, and what that correlation means.**

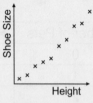

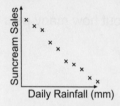

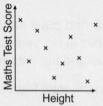

The points lie close to a straight line, and as x increases, so does y.
Positive correlation — people who are taller generally have bigger feet.

The points lie close to a straight line, and as x increases, y decreases.
Negative correlation — when daily rainfall is higher, less suncream is sold.

The points are all spread out — there's no pattern here.
No correlation — there is no relation between someone's height and their test score.

Exercise 1

1   For each of these scatter graphs, say if they show positive, negative or no correlation, and explain what that correlation means.

a)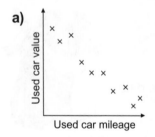

b)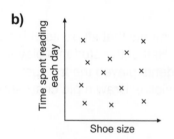

c)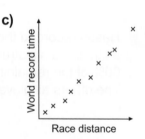

2   What correlation would you expect between each of these pairs of variables? Explain your answers.

   a) Shoe size and glove size.

   b) Outside temperature and visitors to a theme park.

   c) Daily wind speed and sales of newspapers.

   d) Hours watching TV per evening and hours doing homework per evening.

Lines of Best Fit

If a scatter graph shows correlation, then you can draw a line of best fit.
This is a straight line which lies as close as possible to as many points as possible.

Example 2 The scatter graph shows the marks scored by pupils in a maths test and in a science test.

a) Draw a line of best fit for the data.

Draw a line that lies as close to the group of points as possible. It doesn't have to actually touch any of the points.

b) Jimmy scored 34 on his science test, but missed the maths test. Use the scatter graph to predict the score he would have achieved.

Follow the grid up from 34 on the 'Science' axis until you reach the line of best fit, then follow the grid across to find the mark on the 'Maths' axis.

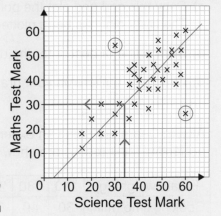

Predicted maths
mark for Jimmy = **30**

c) Circle any outliers on the graph.

An outlier is a data point that is much higher or much lower than the rest of the data. Look for any points that don't lie near the line of best fit.

Exercise 2

1   In an experiment, people were asked how many hours a week they spent exercising, and their BMI (body mass index) was recorded. The results are shown on the scatter graph. A line of best fit has been drawn.

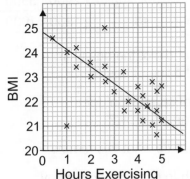

a) What type of correlation is shown by the scatter graph?

b) Frank spends 4 hours a week exercising. Use the line of best fit to predict his BMI.

c) Give the value of the BMI and the hours spent exercising for any outliers.

2   A lemonade stall records the temperature and the number of glasses of lemonade sold over a period of 8 days. The results are shown in the table.

Temperature (°C)	27	24	25	26	23	21	28	22
Glasses of lemonade sold	9	6	10	8	7	6	10	5

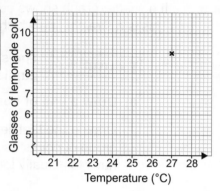

a) Copy this grid and plot the points from the table. The first point has been plotted for you.

b) Draw a line of best fit for the data.

c) Circle any outliers on your graph.

3   Ali and Ceara are doing an experiment to find out how long different potatoes take to bake perfectly. Their results are shown in this table:

Potato weight (g)	150	180	250	200	330	280	220
Cooking time (min)	30	40	70	45	110	85	55

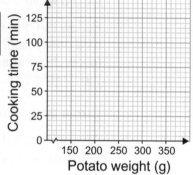

a) Copy this grid and use it to plot the points from the table.

b) Draw a line of best fit for the data.

c) Use your line of best fit to estimate how long a 300 g potato will take to bake.

4   This table shows the number of supporters at eight different football matches and the number of pies sold in the stadium during each match.

Supporters at a football match	2500	3500	5000	4500	3000	6000	4000	3500
Number of pies sold	1300	1900	2500	2200	1600	3100	2300	2000

a) Copy the grid and plot the points from the table. Add a line of best fit.

b) i) What type of correlation does the scatter graph show?

ii) Explain in words what this means.

c) Use your graph to estimate how many supporters would be at a football match where 2900 pies are sold.

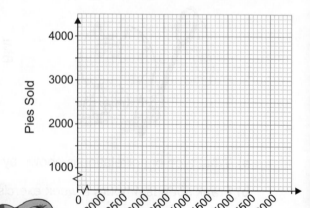

19.4 Average and Range

Mode, Median, Mean and Range

An <u>average</u> is a way of representing a whole set of data using just one number. The <u>mode</u>, <u>median</u> and <u>mean</u> are three different types of average.

Mode (or modal value) = the most common value

Median = the middle value once the items have been put in size order

Mean = the total of all the values ÷ the number of values

The <u>range</u> tells you how spread out the values are: Range = largest value – smallest value

---

Example 1   **20 people were asked how many text messages they had sent on that day. Their answers are shown in the box.**

Find the median, the mode, the mean and the range.

4	11	4	9	2	1	6	7	9	0
3	5	4	7	7	3	2	7	8	6

1. Put the numbers in order from smallest to largest.

   0, 1, 2, 2, 3, 3, 4, 4, 4, 5, 6, 6, 7, 7, 7, 7, 8, 9, 9, 11

2. The median is the middle value. If the list has an even number of values, the median will be halfway between the two middle values.

   There are 20 values, so the median is between the 10th and 11th values.

   Median = $\dfrac{5 + 6}{2}$ = **5.5 messages**

3. The mode is the value that appears the most times in the list.

   Mode = **7 messages**

4. To find the mean, add all the values together, then divide the total by the number of values.

   0 + 1 + 2 + 2 + 3 + 3 + 4 + 4 + 4 + 5 + 6 + 6 + 7 + 7 + 7 + 7 + 8 + 9 + 9 + 11 = 105

   Mean = $\dfrac{105}{20}$ = **5.25 messages**

5. To find the range, subtract the smallest value from the largest value.

   Range = 11 – 0 = **11 messages**

Exercise 1

1   For the following sets of data, find: **i)** the mode   **ii)** the range

   a) 7, 8, 2, 9, 9, 2, 9   **b)** 18, 22, 19, 27, 32, 16, 22

   c) 31, 28, 44, 37, 31, 33, 40   **d)** 7.6, 9.1, 9.3, 8.2, 8.0, 9.2, 8.2, 9.6, 7.1

2 For the following sets of data, find: **i)** the median   **ii)** the mean

    a) 2, 6, 1, 3, 5, 8, 3   **b)** 9, 10, 8, 7, 19, 13, 11   **c)** 21, 23, 20, 19, 17, 21, 27, 32

3 Ten pupils rated a film from 1 to 10. Here are their scores: 7, 4, 8, 5, 2, 10, 8, 6, 1, 9

    Find: **a)** the median score   **b)** the modal score

4 The times, to the nearest 0.1 of a second, that it took some children to finish a puzzle are:

    23.8, 19.7, 17.2, 28.7, 23.8, 18.5, 27.5, 21.2, 16.3, 28.3, 21.4, 19.4.

    Find: **a)** the mode   **b)** the range

              c) the median   **d)** the mean

5 The mean age of the seven members of a club is 49.
A new member, who is 27 years old, joins the club.
Work out the new mean age of the club members.

Investigate — What's the Best Average?

a) Which average do you think would be the best to use to:

    i)   find the average number of words a group of children can type in a minute.

    ii) find the average height of a class of children.

    iii) find the average annual salary of an entire company.

    iv) find the average shoe size of a group of adults.

    Explain your choice in each case.

b) Copy and complete the table with any advantages and disadvantages of using each average that you can think of.

	Advantages	Disadvantages
Mode		
Median		
Mean		

Comparing Averages and Range

Averages, such as the mean, median and mode, can be used to compare sets of data.

The range can be used to compare the spread of two or more sets of data.

A large range means that the data is more spread out.
It can sometimes indicate an outlier.

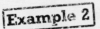 **Example 2** Use the following information to draw some conclusions about the heights of the girls and boys in Class 1.

The boys in Class 1 have a mean height of 175.3 cm,
a median height of 177 cm and a range in height of 33 cm.

The girls in Class 1 have a mean height of 155.1 cm,
a median height of 147 cm and a range in height of 53 cm.

1. Compare the mean heights.

   The mean height for the boys is larger than the mean height for the girls.
   This means that, in general, the **boys are taller than the girls**.

2. Compare the median heights.

   The median height for the boys is larger than the median height for the girls.
   This again suggests that the **boys are taller than the girls**.

3. Compare the range of heights.

   The range of boys' heights is smaller than the range of girls' heights.
   This means that the **boys' heights are more consistent**.
   The girls' range is large, which could suggest that there is an **outlier**
   in the data. If so, the outlier is probably larger than the rest
   of the data as it makes the mean height greater than the median height.

Exercise 2

1 Alice weighs 20 dogs and 20 cats.
The mean weight for the dogs is 32 kg and the mean weight for the cats is 4 kg.
The range in weights for the dogs is 45 kg and the range in weights for the cats is 0.5 kg.
State **two** conclusions that you can draw from this information.

2 A ferry company is comparing the number of passengers carried per day on
two of its routes. Route 1 carries a median of 36 passengers per day with a range of 12.
Route 2 carries a median of 56 passengers with a range of 51.
State **two** conclusions that you can draw from this information.

3 Two classes sit an exam. Their marks are recorded as percentages.
Class X had a mean score of 80%, a median score of 76% and a range of 12%.
Class Y had a mean score of 72%, a median score of 74% and a range of 14%.
State **two** conclusions that you can draw from this information.

4 An audience watched two films and gave each film a score between 1 and 100.
Film 1 had a mean score of 75, a median score of 76 and a range of 22.
Film 2 had a mean score of 49, a median score of 63 and a range of 51.
State **three** conclusions that you can draw from this information.

19.5 Averages and Range from Tables

Mode and Range

Frequency tables are a better way to record data than lists if you've got a lot of data.

For example, 30 people were asked to rate their local park on a scale of 1 to 5. Here are their answers in a list:

| 3 | 2 | 2 | 3 | 1 | 4 | 5 | 1 | 1 | 2 | 5 | 5 | 1 | 3 | 3 |
| 4 | 2 | 2 | 2 | 4 | 1 | 1 | 1 | 4 | 3 | 1 | 2 | 1 | 1 | 3 |

It's hard to make sense of this data at a glance.
Here are their answers in a frequency table:

Score	1	2	3	4	5
Frequency	10	7	6	4	3

You can now see straight away that most people gave the park a low score.

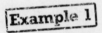
Example 1 The frequency table shows the number of cars owned by a group of people.

Number of cars	0	1	2	3
Frequency	6	10	2	1

a) Find the modal number of cars.
This is the number with the highest frequency.

Modal number of cars owned = **1 car**

b) What is the range of the number of cars owned?

Range = largest value – smallest value
= 3 – 0 = **3 cars**

Exercise 1

1 This frequency table shows the number of siblings the students in a class have.

Number of siblings	0	1	2	3	4
Frequency	5	11	4	1	1

What is the modal number of siblings?

2 This frequency table shows the number of biscuits the people in a company eat one day:

Number of biscuits	2	3	4	5	6	7
Frequency	4	7	3	2	1	1

a) What was the modal number of biscuits eaten that day?

b) Work out the range of the data.

Example 2 The grouped frequency table shows the number of people in the audience at a cinema, over 70 days.

Find: a) the modal group   b) the largest possible range

Size of audience	11 – 30	31 – 50	51 – 70	71 – 90	91 – 110	111 – 130
Frequency	4	11	19	20	12	4

1. The mode is the most common value, but in grouped data tables, you only know the **group** with the highest frequency, and not the actual mode itself.

Modal group = **71 – 90 people**

2. You can't know the actual range for grouped data tables, so just give the **largest range possible** by subtracting the smallest possible value from the largest possible value.

Range = 130 – 11
= **119 people**

---

3. This frequency table shows the weight, w, in kilograms, of some dogs at a kennels. What is the modal group?

Weight (kg)	$10 \leq w < 20$	$20 \leq w < 30$	$30 \leq w < 40$	$40 \leq w < 50$	$50 \leq w < 60$
Frequency	6	21	18	7	4

4. This frequency table shows the percentage marks that some children got in a test. Work out: **a)** the modal group   **b)** the largest possible range

Mark (%)	1 – 20	21 – 40	41 – 60	61 – 80	81 – 100
Frequency	16	12	27	22	11

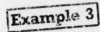

Median

To find the <u>median</u>, imagine all of the data in the table written out in order. The median will be halfway through the list of data. In a grouped frequency table, you can only say which group the median lies in, and not the actual value.

Example 3 The frequency table shows the number of books read in a month by a group of people.

What is the median number of books read?

Number of books	0	1	2	3
Frequency	2	9	5	4

The frequencies tell you that the list of all the individual data values would be:
0, 0, 1, 1, 1, 1, 1, 1, 1, 1, 1, 2, 2, 2, 2, 2, 3, 3, 3, 3

There are 20 values (2 + 9 + 5 + 4), so the median is halfway between the 10th and the 11th values.

To find the median position in the table, add the frequencies across the table.

The 11th position (2 + 9) is at the end of the '1' group. So the median position (between the 10th and 11th) is also in the '1' group.

Median = **1 book**

Exercise 2

1 This frequency table shows the number of pairs of trainers owned by 21 of Phil's friends:

Number of pairs of trainers	1	2	3	4
Frequency	5	11	4	1

a) What is the position of the median friend?

b) Work out the number of pairs of trainers the median friend owns.

2 Kamal recorded the temperature every day on his holiday:

Temperature (°C)	20	21	22	23	24	25
Frequency	2	3	3	4	2	1

What was the median temperature on Kamal's holiday?

3 Gary asked the members of a swimming team how many times they train each week. Work out the median of the data from this frequency table:

Number of times	1	2	3	4	5	6	7
Frequency	1	3	6	4	2	1	1

4 Katherine records the length of time, in minutes, it takes some of her colleagues to get to work. Her data is shown in this frequency table.

Time (minutes)	1 – 5	6 – 10	11 – 15	16 – 20	21 – 25	26 – 30	31 – 35
Frequency	3	4	2	11	12	4	15

In which group does the median time taken to get to work lie?

5 Mary asked some people how much they spent at the supermarket in the last week. She recorded their answers, a, in pounds, in this frequency table.

Amount (£)	$8 \leq a < 12$	$12 \leq a < 16$	$16 \leq a < 20$	$20 \leq a < 24$	$24 \leq a < 28$	$28 \leq a < 32$
Frequency	11	6	15	26	22	14

a) Find the group containing the median.

b) Can you be sure what the exact median value is? Explain your answer.

Mean

You can use frequency tables to find the <u>mean</u> of a set of data, but you have to do a bit of extra calculation first. For grouped data, you can only estimate the mean.

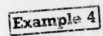

This is a frequency table showing the number of people in each house on a street.

Find the mean number of people in each house.

People	Frequency
1	7
2	12
3	13
4	8

1. Add an extra row and an extra column to the table.

2. In the extra column, multiply the number of people by the frequency.

3. In the extra row, add up all the numbers in the frequency column to find the **total number of houses**...

4. ...and add up all the numbers in the 'People × Frequency' column to find the **total number of people**.

5. Divide the total number of people by the total number of houses to find the mean.

People	Freq.	People × Freq.
1	7	1 × 7 = 7
2	12	2 × 12 = 24
3	13	3 × 13 = 39
4	8	4 × 8 = 32
Total	40	102

$$\text{Mean} = \frac{\text{Total number of people}}{\text{Total number of houses}}$$

$$= 102 \div 40 = \textbf{2.55 people}$$

Exercise 3

1 This table shows the number of glasses of lemonade drunk by people at a party.

Glasses	Frequency
1	3
2	7
3	3
4	1

a) Copy the table and add a 'Glasses × Frequency' column and a 'Total' row.

b) Complete the table by filling in the column and row you've added.

c) Use your table to find the mean number of glasses of lemonade drunk by the people at the party. Give your answer to 1 decimal place.

2 Florence is taking part in a bird-spotting survey. She records the number of blackbirds she sees each day, and puts the results into a frequency table.

Use the table to find the mean number of blackbirds seen by Florence each day.

No. of blackbirds seen each day	Frequency
0	7
1	6
2	4
3	5
4	3

Example 5 This is a frequency table showing the number of pages in some books in a library.

No. of pages	51 – 100	101 – 150	151 – 200	201 – 250
Frequency	11	19	32	12

Estimate the mean number of pages in the library books, to 1 d.p.

1. Add a new row to the table. Find the midpoint for each group by adding together the highest and lowest values of the group, and then dividing by 2.

No. of pages	51 – 100	101 – 150	151 – 200	201 – 250
Frequency	11	19	32	12
Midpoint	$\frac{51 + 100}{2} = 75.5$	$\frac{101 + 150}{2} = 125.5$	$\frac{151 + 200}{2} = 175.5$	$\frac{201 + 250}{2} = 225.5$

2. Add another row to the table. In this row, multiply each midpoint by the frequency for that group.

Frequency × Midpoint	11 × 75.5 = 830.5	19 × 125.5 = 2384.5	32 × 175.5 = 5616	12 × 225.5 = 2706

3. Find the total of the values in this row, and divide the result by the total frequency. $\frac{11\ 537}{74} = $ **155.9 pages (to 1 d.p.)**

Exercise 4

1 The number of cupcakes sold by a bakery each day for 60 days is shown in this grouped frequency table. By adding two rows to the table,

Cupcakes Sold	1 - 5	6 - 10	11 - 15	16 - 20
Frequency	9	11	24	16

a) find the midpoint of each group.

b) multiply the midpoint of each group by the frequency for the group.

c) use your answer to b) to estimate the mean to 2 decimal places.

2 Gabriel collected some information about the length of time, to the nearest hour, some students spent studying during one week. By adding two columns to the table,

a) find the midpoint of each group.

b) use your answer to a) and the rest of the table to find an estimate for the mean to 1 decimal place.

Time (hours)	Frequency
1 – 3	3
4 – 6	11
7 – 9	5
10 – 12	7
13 – 15	2

3 Martha records how many tickets were sold for each showing of a musical.
She puts the data in this frequency table.

Tickets sold	1 – 30	31 – 60	61 – 90	91 – 120	121 – 150	151 – 180	181 – 210
Frequency	2	3	11	15	24	37	11

a) How many performances of the musical were there?

b) Estimate the mean number of people at each performance.
Give your answer to the nearest whole person.

4 A restaurant records how much some diners spend on food, f, during one evening.
The data is recorded, in pounds, in this table:

Amount (£)	$10 \leq f < 25$	$25 \leq f < 40$	$40 \leq f < 55$	$55 \leq f < 70$	$70 \leq f < 85$	$85 \leq f < 100$
Frequency	6	8	11	22	24	17

a) Estimate the mean amount spent in the restaurant.
Give your answer to the nearest £0.01.

b) Can you know exactly what the mean amount spent is? Explain your answer.

Investigate — Discrete and Continuous Data

Discrete data is data that can only take certain values, e.g. the number of dresses a shop sells each day — the shop can only sell whole numbers of dresses.

Continuous data can take any value in a given range: e.g. the time taken to complete a marathon — this could be rounded to the nearest second, but the actual time could be any number.

a) Decide whether the following data sets are discrete or continuous:

  i) The weights of some chickens on a farm.

  ii) The lengths of scarves some people in a knitting group have made.

  iii) The number of pets the children in a class have.

  iv) The number of rooms in some people's houses.

  v) The amount of pocket money a group of children gets.

b) Suggest some ways you could group the data in data sets **i)** – **v)**.
For each one, think about how wide the groups should be, and what the maximum and minimum values in the data set are likely to be.

c) Think of some more examples of discrete and continuous data.
For each one, construct a suitable grouped frequency table, making sure the maximum and minimum values are sensible.

Glossary

3D Shapes

Solid shapes with length, width and height.

Addition

Finding the sum when two or more numbers are combined.

Adjacent (trigonometry)

The side (that is not the hypotenuse) next to a particular angle in a right-angled triangle.

Allied Angles

Angles within a pair of parallel lines that add up to 180°.

Alternate Angles

Equal angles within a pair of parallel lines.

Angle Bisector

A straight line that cuts an angle exactly in half.

Approximation

A number that is not exact because it has been rounded or estimated.

Area

The space inside a 2D shape.

Arithmetic Sequence

A number sequence where the terms increase or decrease by the same amount each time.

Average

A measure of the most typical value in a set of data. Mean, median and mode are types of average.

Bar Chart

A chart where the height of the bars shows the frequency of each category.

Bar-line Chart

A chart where the height of the lines shows the frequency of each category.

Base

In a power, this is the number or letter which is multiplied by itself.

Bearing

The direction of one point from another, measured clockwise from north and given as three figures.

Biased

Where something, e.g. a dice or a spinner, is more likely to land on one or more of its sides than others.

BODMAS

An acronym to describe the order that operations should be done in a calculation containing multiple operations.

Brackets

Symbols, such as ( ), [ ] or { }, used to group things together.

Cancelling Down

Dividing all the parts of a fraction or ratio by the same number to reduce it to a simpler form.

Centre of Enlargement

The point where an enlargement is measured from.

Centre of Rotation

The point an object turns about in a rotation.

Circumference

The distance around the outside of a circle (its perimeter).

Coefficient

A number placed in front of a variable.

Common Denominator

Fractions have a common denominator when their denominators are the same.

Common Factor

A number that divides exactly into two or more different numbers.

Common Multiple

A number that appears in the times table of two or more different numbers.

Complement of a Set

All elements that are not in the set but are in the universal set.

Composite Shape

A shape made up of two or more simple shapes.

Compound Interest

A type of interest where each amount of interest is calculated using the new total, so it changes each time.

Congruence Condition

One of the three conditions that need to be satisfied for two triangles to be called congruent.

Congruent

The same shape and size. Congruent shapes have all sides and angles the same.

Constant

A number (or a letter representing a fixed number) in an equation or expression.

Construction

A drawing of a line, angle or shape using a ruler, protractor and compass.

Continuous Data

Data that is measured rather than counted. Continuous data can take any value.

Conversion Factor

The number you multiply or divide by to convert between different units.

Coordinates

A pair of numbers (x, y) that describe the position of a point on a grid or set of axes, e.g. (2, 3).

Correlation

The relationship between two variables, usually shown by the points on a scatter graph. Correlation can be either positive or negative.

Corresponding Angles

Equal angles around a pair of parallel lines.

Cosine

(Shortened to 'cos') One of three trigonometric functions. The cosine of an angle is equal to the length of the adjacent side divided by the hypotenuse.

Cross-Section

The shape you get when you cut through a 3D shape, parallel to the end surface.

Cube (power)

A number or letter raised to the power of 3.

Cube (shape)

A 3D shape with 6 identical square faces.

Cube Root

The inverse of raising a number to the power of 3.

Cuboid

A 3D shape with 3 pairs of matching rectangular faces.

Decimal

A number where tenths, hundredths and thousandths, etc. are written after a decimal point.

Decimal Place

The position of a digit to the right of the decimal point.

Decimal Point

A dot placed to the right of the units column in a decimal number.

Denominator

The bottom number of a fraction.

Density

A measure of mass per unit volume. The density tells you how heavy a material is.

Derive

Use known facts to come up with other ones. For example, deriving properties of shapes from angle laws.

Diameter

The length across a circle, going through the centre.

Direct Proportion

When the ratio between two things stays the same. If you increase one thing, the other increases at the same rate.

Distance

How far an object has travelled.

Division

The act of sharing a number into equal parts.

Dual Bar Chart

A type of bar chart where two sets of data are plotted for each category.

Edge

Part of a 3D shape, where two faces meet.

Element

A single value or item in a set.

Empty Set

A set with no elements in it, shown by empty brackets {}.

Enlargement

Changing an object's size but keeping the shape the same.

Equation

An algebraic statement made up of two expressions separated by an equals sign. E.g. $y = 2x + 3$.

Equidistant

The same distance away.

Equilateral Triangle

A regular triangle, with three equal sides and three equal angles of 60°.

Estimate

A less accurate value of a number, often the result of a calculation where rounded numbers have been used instead of the actual values.

Event

An outcome (or multiple outcomes) for which a probability can be found.

Expand

Multiply out brackets to remove them from an expression.

Expected Frequency

How many times you'd expect an event to happen during a certain number of trials.

Experimental Probability

An estimate of how likely something is to happen based on the results of an experiment. It's also called a relative frequency.

Expression

A collection of terms made up of numbers and letters, separated by + or − signs.

Exterior Angle

The angle between a side of a polygon, and the line extended from a neighbouring side.

Face

A surface of a 3D shape.

Factor

A number that divides exactly into another number.

Factorise

Rewrite an expression by putting in brackets with a factor on the outside.

Fair

Where something, e.g. a dice or a spinner, is equally likely to land on all of its sides.

Finite

Something that has a limit to how big it is — it doesn't go on forever.

Formula

A rule written using algebra which can be used to work out a value.

Fraction

A part of a whole, written as one number on top of another.

Frequency

How many items are in a category.

Frequency Bar Chart

A type of bar graph, used to show continuous data.

Frequency Polygon

A type of line graph, used to show continuous data.

Frequency Table

A table showing how many times each value in a set of data occurs.

Geometric Sequence

A number sequence where each term is found by multiplying the previous term by the same number.

Gradient

The steepness of a line — a measure of how much it slopes.

Highest Common Factor (HCF)

The highest number that can be divided exactly into a set of numbers.

Horizontal

A flat line with a gradient of zero.

Hypotenuse

The longest side of a right-angled triangle.

Imperial Units

A non-metric set of units for measuring, including inches, feet, yards, ounces, pounds, stones, pints and gallons.

Improper Fraction

A fraction where the numerator is greater than the denominator. These are also called top-heavy fractions.

Inequality

A way of comparing the values of numbers. < means less than, > means greater than, ≤ means less than or equal to and ≥ means greater than or equal to.

Infinite

Something that goes on forever.

Integer

A whole number, positive or negative (including zero).

Interior Angle

An angle within a polygon.

Intersecting Lines

Lines that cross at a point.

Intersection of Two Sets

The elements that are in both sets.

Inverse

The opposite operation. E.g. subtraction is the inverse of addition.

Inverse Proportion

If two things are in inverse proportion, one increases as the other decreases.

Irrational Number

A number that cannot be written as a fraction.

Isosceles Triangle

A triangle with two equal sides and two equal angles.

Key

An instruction for reading a diagram or graph.

Kite

A quadrilateral with two pairs of equal sides and one pair of equal angles.

Like Terms

Terms that contain the same variables (raised to the same powers).

Line of Best Fit

A line drawn on a scatter graph which passes as close to as many of the plotted points as possible, and shows the correlation of the variables.

Line of Symmetry

A mirror line where you can fold a shape so that both halves match up exactly.

Line Segment

A straight line between two points.

Linear

An equation or expression which contains an x term, but no higher powers of x.

Locus

A set of points that satisfy a particular condition.

Lowest Common Multiple (LCM)

The smallest number that's in the times tables of a group of numbers.

Map

An accurate drawing showing large distances on a smaller scale.

Mean

The average of a set of data, found by adding up all of the values and dividing by the number of values.

Median

The middle value when you put a set of data in size order.

Metric Units

A standard set of units for measuring, including mm, cm, m, km, g, kg, tonnes, ml and litres.

Mirror Line

The line that a shape or object is reflected in.

Mixed Number

A number made up of a whole number part and a fraction part.

Mode (or Modal Value)

The most common value in a set of data.

Modelling

Using an equation or a graph to represent a real-life situation.

Multiple

A value in a number's times table.

Multiplication

The act of multiplying numbers together.

Multiplier

A number that other numbers in a calculation are multiplied by.

Negative

Any number less than zero.

Net

A hollow 3D shape folded out flat.

nth Term

An expression that allows you to work out the value of a term in a given position, n, of a sequence.

Numerator

The top number of a fraction.

Operation

Something you do to one or more numbers, such as add, subtract, multiply or divide.

Opposite (trigonometry)

The side opposite a particular angle in a right-angled triangle.

Order of Rotational Symmetry

The number of positions, in one full turn, you can rotate a shape into so that it looks the same.

Origin

The point with coordinates (0, 0) on a graph. It's where the axes cross.

Outcome

A possible result of a probability trial.

Outlier

A value in a set of data that is much higher or much lower than the rest of the data.

Parallel Lines

Lines that are always the same distance apart and never meet.

Parallelogram

A quadrilateral with two pairs of equal parallel sides and two pairs of equal angles.

Percentage

'Per cent' means 'out of 100'. Percentage shows an amount as a number out of 100.

Percentage Change

The amount a value increases or decreases by, given as a percentage of the original value.

Perimeter

The total distance around the outside of a shape.

Perpendicular Lines

Two lines which cross at right angles.

Perpendicular Bisector

A straight line that cuts another line in half and is at right angles to it.

Pi

The number 3.14159265..., written using the Greek letter π.

Pictogram

A type of chart where frequency is represented by symbols or pictures.

Pie Chart

A chart where the angles of each sector are proportional to the frequency of each category.

Polygon

An enclosed shape whose sides are all straight.

Positive

Any number greater than zero.

Power

A way of showing that a number or letter (the base) is being multiplied by itself a certain number of times. The power tells you how many of the base to multiply together.

Power of 10

10 raised to the power of any whole number.

Prime Factor

A factor of a number that is a prime number.

Prime Number

A number that has no factors except itself and 1.

Prism

A 3D shape with the same cross-section all the way through.

Probability

How likely it is that something will happen.

Product

The result when two things are multiplied together.

Proof

Using known facts to show that something must be true.

Proportion

A part of a whole. Proportions can be written as fractions, decimals or percentages.

Pythagoras' Theorem

A formula linking the lengths of the sides of a right-angled triangle. Pythagoras' theorem states that $a^2 + b^2 = h^2$, where h is the hypotenuse and a and b are the shorter sides.

Quadratic

An equation or expression which contains an x^2 term, but no higher powers of x.

Quadrilateral

A four-sided shape.

Radius

The distance from the centre to the edge of a circle.

Range

The difference between the highest value and the lowest value in a set of data.

Ratio

The amount of one thing compared to another, written e.g. 2:1.

Rational Number

Any number that can be written as a fraction.

Rearrange

To make a different letter the subject of a formula.

Reciprocal

The reciprocal of a number is 1 divided by it. For a fraction, the reciprocal is found by swapping the numerator and the denominator.

Rectangle

A quadrilateral with two pairs of equal sides and four right angles (90°).

Recurring Decimal

A decimal that has a pattern of digits that repeats forever.

Reflection

A transformation where a shape is flipped in a mirror line. OR a mirror image of another shape, with every point the same distance from the mirror line as in the original shape.

Regular Polygon

A polygon with sides of equal length and angles that are all equal.

Relative Frequency

Another term for an experimental probability. It's an estimate of how likely something is to happen based on the results of an experiment.

Rhombus

A quadrilateral with four equal sides (opposite sides are parallel) and two pairs of equal angles.

Right Angle

An angle of 90°.

Right-angled Triangle

A triangle with one angle of 90°.

Root

The inverse of a power.

Rotation

Turning an object, either clockwise or anticlockwise, through a given angle at a given point.

Rounding

Approximating a number to another number which is easier to work with (e.g. has fewer decimal places or is a multiple of 10, 100 etc.)

Rounding Error

The difference between a rounded number and the actual value of the number.

S

Sample Space Diagram

A table showing all the possible outcomes from a combination of two or more trials.

Scale

The numbers on a map or plan that show how actual distances will be represented on the map.

Scale Factor

The amount each length increases by in an enlargement.

Scalene Triangle

A triangle with all three sides and angles different.

Scatter Graph

A graph showing two things plotted against each other. The plotted points are never joined with a line, but the graph may show a line of best fit.

Sector

A wedge-shaped area cut right from the centre of a circle.

Sequence

A pattern of numbers or shapes that follow a certain rule.

Set

A collection of items or numbers, shown using curly brackets {}.

Significant Figures

The first non-zero digits in a number.

Similar

When two objects have the same shape but different sizes.

Similarity Condition

One of the three conditions that need to be satisfied for two triangles to be called similar.

Simple Interest

A type of interest where the same percentage of the original amount is added on at regular intervals.

Simplify

Make something simpler, e.g. by dividing by common factors or collecting like terms.

Simultaneous Equations

Two equations with two unknowns that are both true for certain values of the variables.

Sine

(Shortened to 'sin') One of three trigonometric functions. The sine of an angle is equal to the length of the opposite side divided by the hypotenuse.

Speed

How fast an object is travelling.

Square

A regular quadrilateral, with four equal sides and four right angles (90°).

Square (power)

A number or letter raised to the power of 2.

Square Root

The inverse of raising a number to the power of 2.

Standard Form

A method of writing numbers as multiples of powers of 10 — it's useful for very large or very small numbers.

Straight Line Graph

A graph where all the coordinates lie on a straight line. The coordinates fit equations of the form $y = mx + c$.

Subject

The letter on its own on the left-hand side of a formula or equation.

Subtraction

Finding the difference between two numbers.

Surface Area

The total area of all the faces of a 3D shape added together.

Symmetry

A shape has (line) symmetry if you can draw on a mirror line where one side of the shape is the exact reflection of the other.

Tangent

(Shortened to 'tan') One of three trigonometric functions. The tangent of an angle is equal to the length of the opposite side divided by the adjacent.

Term (of an expression)

Each of the 'bits' in an expression, separated by plus or minus signs is called a term. A term can be numbers, letters or both.

Term (of a sequence)

A number or shape in a sequence.

Terminating Decimal

A decimal that has a finite number of decimal places.

Time

How long something takes.

Transformation

Changing the size, orientation or position of an object.

Translation

Changing the position of an object by sliding it horizontally and vertically.

Trapezium

A quadrilateral with one pair of parallel sides.

Trial

An action in a probability experiment that will end in an outcome — for example, tossing a coin or picking out a card.

Triangle

A three-sided shape.

Trigonometric functions

The three main functions (sine, cosine and tangent) that are used to work out side lengths and angles in right-angled triangles.

Union of Two Sets

The elements that are in either set.

Unique Factorisation Property

Every whole number can be made from its own unique set of prime numbers multiplied together.

Universal Set

The group of things from which the elements in a set are selected.

Variable

An unknown quantity, usually shown by a letter, that can take different values.

Vector

Mathematical notation for describing how far a shape moves left or right and up or down.

Venn Diagram

A way of displaying sets, using a circle to represent each set.

Vertex

The corner of a 2D or 3D shape.

Vertical

A line going straight up and down.

Vertically Opposite Angles

Opposite angles around the point where two lines intersect. Vertically opposite angles are equal.

Volume

The amount of space that a 3D shape occupies.

x-axis

The horizontal axis of a graph.

y-axis

The vertical axis of a graph.

y-intercept

The point at which a graph crosses the y-axis.

Index

M3NN31